Fundamentals of
PHYSICS

Fifth Edition

Selected Chapters

Halliday / Resnick / Walker

WILEY
Custom Services

ISBN 0-471-37551-9

FIFTH EDITION

FUNDAMENTALS OF
PHYSICS

VOLUME 2

DAVID HALLIDAY
University of Pittsburgh

ROBERT RESNICK
Rensselaer Polytechnic Institute

JEARL WALKER
Cleveland State University

JOHN WILEY & SONS, INC.

New York • Chichester • Brisbane • Toronto • Singapore

ACQUISITIONS EDITOR Stuart Johnson
DEVELOPMENTAL EDITOR Rachel Nelson
SENIOR PRODUCTION SUPERVISOR Cathy Ronda
PRODUCTION ASSISTANT Raymond Alvarez
MARKETING MANAGER Catherine Faduska
ASSISTANT MARKETING MANAGER Ethan Goodman
DESIGNER Dawn L. Stanley
MANUFACTURING MANAGER Mark Cirillo
PHOTO EDITOR Hilary Newman
COVER PHOTO William Warren/Westlight
ILLUSTRATION EDITOR Edward Starr
ILLUSTRATION Radiant/Precision Graphics

This book was set in Times Roman by Progressive Information Technologies, and printed and bound by Von Hofmann Press. The cover was printed by Phoenix Color Corp.

ISBN 0-471-15663-9

Printed in the United States of America

10 9 8 7 6 5

Hello There!

You are about to begin your first college level physics course. You may have heard from friends and fellow students that physics is a difficult course, especially if you don't plan to go on to a career in the hard sciences. But that doesn't mean it has to be difficult for you. The key to success in this course is to have a good understanding of each chapter before moving on to the next. When learned a little bit at a time, physics is straightforward and simple. Here are some ideas that can make this text and this class work for you:

- Read through the **Sample Problems** and solutions carefully. These problems are similar to many of the end-of-chapter exercises, so reading them will help you solve homework problems. In addition, they offer a look at how an experienced physicist would approach solving the problem.

- Try to answer the **Checkpoint** questions as you read through the chapter. Most of these can be answered by thinking through the problem, but it helps if you have some scratch paper and a pencil nearby to work out some of the harder questions. Hold the answer page at the back of the book with your thumb (or a tab or bookmark) so you can refer to it easily. The end-of-chapter **Questions** are very similar— you can use them to quiz yourself after you've read the whole chapter.

- Use the **Review & Summary** sections at the end of each chapter as the first place to look for formulas you might neeed to solve homework problems. These sections are also helpful in making study sheets for exams.

- The biggest tip I can give you is pretty obvious. Do your homework! Understanding the homework problems is the best way to master the material and do well in the course. Doing a lot of homework problems is also the best way to review for exams. And by all means, consult your classmates whenever you are stuck. Working in groups will make your studying more effective.

The study of basic physics is required for degrees in Engineering, Physics, Biology, Chemistry, Medicine, and many other sciences because the fundamentals of physics are the framework on which every other science is built. Therefore, a solid grasp of basic physical principles will help you understand upper-level science courses and make your study of these courses easier.

I took introductory physics because it was a prerequisite for my B.S. in Mechanical Engineering. Even though engineering and pure physics are worlds apart, I find myself using this book as a reference almost every day. I urge you to keep it after you have finished your course. The knowledge you will gain from this book and your introductory physics course is the foundation for all other sciences. This is the primary reason to take this class seriously and be successful in it.

Best of luck!

Josh Kane

Josh Kane

Preface

For four editions, *Fundamentals of Physics* has been successful in preparing physics students for careers in science and engineering. The first three editions were coauthored by the highly regarded team of David Halliday and Robert Resnick, who developed a groundbreaking text replete with conceptual structure and applications. In the fourth edition, the insights provided by new coauthor, Jearl Walker, took the text into the 1990s and met the challenge of guiding students through a time of tremendous advances and a ferment of activity in the science of physics. Now, in the fifth edition, we have expanded on the conventional strengths of the earlier editions and enhanced the applications that help students forge a bridge between concepts and reasoning. We not only *tell* students how physics works, we *show* them, and we give them the opportunity to show us what they have learned by testing their understanding of the concepts and applying them to real-world scenarios. Concept checkpoints, problem solving tactics, sample problems, electronic computations, exercises and problems—all of these skill-building signposts have been developed to help students establish a connection between conceptual theories and application. The students reading this text today are the scientists and engineers of tomorrow. It is our hope that the fifth edition of *Fundamentals of Physics* will help prepare these students for future endeavors by contributing to the enhancement of physics education.

CHANGES IN THE FIFTH EDITION

Although we have retained the basic framework of the fourth edition of *Fundamentals of Physics,* we have made extensive changes in portions of the book. Each chapter and element has been scrutinized to ensure clarity, currency, and accuracy, reflecting the needs of today's science and engineering students.

Content Changes

Mindful that textbooks have grown large and that they tend to increase in length from edition to edition, we have reduced the length of the fifth edition by combining several chapters and pruning their contents. In doing so, six chapters have been rewritten completely, while the remaining chapters have been carefully edited and revised, often extensively, to enhance their clarity, incorporating ideas and suggestions from dozens of reviewers.

- *Chapters 7 and 8 on energy* (and sections of later chapters dealing with energy) have been rewritten to provide a more careful treatment of energy, work, and the work–kinetic energy theorem. As the same time, the text material and problems at the end of each chapter still allow the instructor to present the more traditional treatment of these subjects.

- *Temperature, heat, and the first law of thermodynamics* have been condensed from two chapters to one chapter (*Chapter 19*).

- *Chapter 21 on entropy* now includes a statistical mechanical presentation of entropy that is tied to the traditional thermodynamical presentation.

- *Chapters on Faraday's law and inductance* have been combined into one new chapter (*Chapter 31*).

- *Treatment of Maxwell's equations* has been streamlined and moved up earlier into the chapter on magnetism and matter (*Chapter 32*).

- *Coverage of electromagnetic oscillations and alternating currents* has been combined into one chapter (*Chapter 33*).

- *Chapters 39, 40, and 41 on quantum mechanics* have been rewritten to modernize the subject. They now include experimental and theoretical results of the last few years. In addition, quantum physics and special relativity are introduced in some of the early chapters in short sections that can be covered quickly. These early sections lay some of the groundwork for the "modern physics" topics that appear later in the extended version of the text and add an element of suspense about the subject.

New Pedagogy

In the interest of addressing the needs of science and engineering students, we have added a number of new pedagogical features intended to help students forge a bridge between concepts and reasoning and to marry theory with practice. These new features are designed to help students test their understanding of the material. They were also developed to help students prepare to apply the information to exam questions and real-world scenarios.

- To provide opportunities for students to check their understanding of the physics concepts they have just read, we have placed **Checkpoint** questions within the chapter presentations. Nearly 300 Checkpoints have been added to help guide the student away from common errors and misconceptions. All of the Checkpoints require decision making and reasoning on the part of the student (rather than computations requiring calculators) and focus on the key points of the physics that students need to understand in order to tackle the exercises and problems at the end of each chapter. Answers to all of the Checkpoints are found in the back of the book, sometimes with extra guidance to the student.

- Continuing our focus on the key points of the physics, we have included additional **Checkpoint-type questions** in the Questions section at the end of each chapter. These new questions require decision making and reasoning on the part of the student; they ask the student to organize the physics concepts rather than just plug numbers into equations. Answers to the odd-numbered questions are now provided in the back of the book.

- To encourage the use of computer math packages and graphing calculators, we have added an **Electronic Computation problem section** to the Exercises and Problems sections of many of the chapters.

These new features are just a few of the pedagogical elements available to enhance the student's study of physics. A number of tried-and-true features of the previous edition have been retained and refined in the fifth edition, as described below.

CHAPTER FEATURES

The pedagogical elements that have been retained from previous editions have been carefully planned and crafted to motivate students and guide their reasoning process.

- *Puzzlers* Each chapter opens with an intriguing photograph and a ''puzzler'' that is designed to motivate the student to read the chapter. The answer to each puzzler is provided within the chapter, but it is not identified as such to ensure that the student reads the entire chapter.

- *Sample Problems* Throughout each chapter, sample problems provide a bridge from the concepts of the chapter to the exercises and problems at the end of the chapter. Many of the nearly 400 sample problems featured in the text have been replaced with new ones that more sharply focus on the common difficulties students experience in solving the exercises and problems. We have been especially mindful of the mathematical difficulties students face. The sample problems also provide

an opportunity for the student to see how a physicist thinks through a problem.

- *Problem Solving Tactics* To help further bridge concepts and applications and to add focus to the key physics concepts, we have refined and expanded the number of problem solving tactics that are placed within the chapters, particularly in the earlier chapters. These tactics provide guidance to the students about how to organize the physics concepts, how to tackle mathematical requirements in the exercises and problems, and how to prepare for exams.

- *Illustrations* Because the illustrations in a physics textbook are so important to an understanding of the concepts, we have altered nearly 30 percent of the illustrations to improve their clarity. We have also removed some of the less effective illustrations and added many new ones.

- *Review & Summary* A review and summary section is found at the end of each chapter, providing a quick review of the key definitions and physics concepts *without* being a replacement for reading the chapter.

- *Questions* Approximately 700 thought-provoking questions emphasizing the conceptual aspects of physics appear at the ends of the chapters. Many of these questions relate back to the checkpoints found throughout the chapters, requiring decision making and reasoning on the part of the student. Answers to the odd-numbered questions are provided in the back of the book.

- *Exercises & Problems* There are approximately 3400 end-of-chapter exercises and problems in the text, arranged in order of difficulty, starting with the exercises (labeled ''E''), followed by the problems (labeled ''P''). Particularly challenging problems are identified with an asterisk (*). Those exercises and problems that have been retained from previous editions have been edited for greater clarity; many have been replaced. Answers to the odd-numbered exercises and problems are provided in the back of the book.

VERSIONS OF THE TEXT

The fifth edition of *Fundamentals of Physics* is available in a number of different versions, to accommodate the individual needs of instructors and students alike. The Regular Edition consists of Chapters 1 through 38 (ISBN 0-471-10558-9). The Extended Edition contains seven additional chapters on quantum physics and cosmology (Chapters 1–45) (ISBN 0-471-10559-7). Both editions are available as single, hardcover books, or in the alternative versions listed on page ix:

- Volume 1—Chapters 1–21 (Mechanics/Thermodynamics), cloth, 0-471-15662-0
- Volume 2—Chapters 22–45 (E&M and Modern Physics), cloth, 0-471-15663-9
- Part 1—Chapters 1–12, paperback, 0-471-14561-0
- Part 2—Chapters 13–21, paperback, 0-471-14854-7
- Part 3—Chapters 22–33, paperback, 0-471-14855-5
- Part 4—Chapters 34–38, paperback, 0-471-14856-3
- Part 5—Chapters 39–45, paperback, 0-471-15719-8

The Extended edition of the text is also available on CD ROM.

SUPPLEMENTS

The fifth edition of *Fundamentals of Physics* is supplemented by a comprehensive ancillary package carefully developed to help teachers teach and students learn.

Instructor's Supplements

- *Instructor's Manual* by J. RICHARD CHRISTMAN, U.S. Coast Guard Academy. This manual contains lecture notes outlining the most important topics of each chapter, as well as demonstration experiments, and laboratory and computer exercises; film and video sources are also included. Separate sections contain articles that have appeared recently in the *American Journal of Physics* and *The Physics Teacher*.
- *Instructor's Solutions Manual* by JERRY J. SHI, Pasadena City College. This manual provides worked-out solutions for all the exercises and problems found at the end of each chapter within the text. *This supplement is available only to instructors.*
- *Solutions Disk.* An electronic version of the Instructor's Solutions Manual, for instructors only, available in TeX for Macintosh and Windows™.
- *Test Bank* by J. RICHARD CHRISTMAN, U.S. Coast Guard Academy. More than 2200 multiple-choice questions are included in the Test Bank for *Fundamentals of Physics*.

- *Computerized Test Bank.* IBM and Macintosh versions of the entire Test Bank are available with full editing features to help you customize tests.
- *Animated Illustrations.* Approximately 85 text illustrations are animated for enhanced lecture demonstrations.
- *Transparencies.* More than 200 four-color illustrations from the text are provided in a form suitable for projection in the classroom.

Student's Supplements

- *A Student's Companion* by J. RICHARD CHRISTMAN, U.S. Coast Guard Academy. Much more than a traditional study guide, this student manual is designed to be used in close conjunction with the text. The Student's Companion is divided into four parts, each of which corresponds to a major section of the text, beginning with an overview "chapter." These overviews are designed to help students understand how the important topics are integrated and how the text is organized. For each chapter of the text, the corresponding Companion chapter offers: Basic Concepts, Problem Solving, Notes, Mathematical Skills, and Computer Projects and Notes.
- *Solutions Manual* by J. RICHARD CHRISTMAN, U.S. Coast Guard Academy and EDWARD DERRINGH, Wentworth Institute. This manual provides students with complete worked-out solutions to 30 percent of the exercises and problems found at the end of each chapter within the text.
- **Interactive Learningware** by JAMES TANNER, Georgia Institute of Technology, with the assistance of GARY LEWIS, Kennesaw State College. This software contains 200 problems from the end-of-chapter exercises and problems, presented in an interactive format, providing detailed feedback for the student. Problems from Chapter 1 to 21 are included in Part 1, from Chapters 22 to 38 in Part 2. The accompanying workbooks allow the student to keep a record of the worked-out problems. The Learningware is available in IBM 3.5″ and Macintosh formats.
- **CD Physics.** The entire Extended Version of the text (Chapters 1–45) is available on CD ROM, along with the student solutions manual, study guide, animated illustrations, and Interactive Learningware.

Acknowledgments

A textbook contains far more contributions to the elucidation of a subject than those made by the authors alone. J. Richard Christman, of the U.S. Coast Guard Academy, has once again created many fine supplements for us; his knowledge of our book and his recommendations to students and faculty are invaluable. James Tanner, of Georgia Institute of Technology, and Gary Lewis, of Kennesaw State College, have provided us with innovative software, closely tied to the text's exercises and problems. J. Richard Christman, of the U.S. Coast Guard Academy, and Glen Terrell, of the University of Texas at Arlington, contributed problems to the Electronic Computation sections of the text. Jerry Shi, of Pasadena City College, performed the Herculean task of working out solutions for every one of the Exercises and Problems in the text. We thank John Merrill, of Brigham Young University, and Edward Derringh, of the Wentworth Institute of Technology for their many contributions in the past. We also thank George W. Hukle of Oxnard, California, for his check of the answers at the back of the book.

At John Wiley, publishers, we have been fortunate to receive strong coordination and support from our former editor, Cliff Mills. Cliff guided our efforts and encouraged us along the way. When Cliff moved on to other responsibilities at Wiley, we were ably guided to completion by his successor, Stuart Johnson. Rachel Nelson has coordinated the developmental editing and multilayered preproduction process. Catherine Faduska, our senior marketing manager, and Ethan Goodman, assistant marketing manager, have been tireless in their efforts on behalf of this edition. Jennifer Bruer has built a fine supporting package of ancillary materials. Monica Stipanov and Julia Salsbury managed the review and administrative duties admirably.

We thank Lucille Buonocore, our able production manager, and Cathy Ronda, our production editor, for pulling all the pieces together and guiding us through the complex production process. We also thank Dawn Stanley, for her design; Brenda Griffing, for her copy editing; Edward Starr, for managing the line art program; Lilian Brady, for her proofreading; and all other members of the production team.

Stella Kupferburg and her team of photo researchers, particularly Hilary Newman and Pat Cadley, were inspired in their search for unusual and interesting photographs that communicate physics principles beautifully. We thank Boris Starosta and Irene Nunes for their careful development of a full-color line art program, for which they scrutinized and suggested revisions of every piece. We also owe a debt of gratitude for the line art to the late John Balbalis, whose careful hand and understanding of physics can still be seen in every diagram.

We especially thank Edward Millman for his developmental work on the manuscript. With us, he has read every word, asking many questions from the point of view of a student. Many of his questions and suggested changes have added to the clarity of this volume. Irene Nunes added a final, valuable developmental check in the last stages of the book.

We owe a particular debt of gratitude to the numerous students who used the fourth edition of *Fundamentals of Physics* and took the time to fill out the response cards and return them to us. As the ultimate consumers of this text, students are extremely important to us. By sharing their opinions with us, your students help us ensure that we are providing the best possible product and the most value for their textbook dollars. We encourage the users of this book to contact us with their thoughts and concerns so that we can continue to improve this text in the years to come. In particular, we owe a special debt of gratitude to the students who participated in a final focus group at Union College in Schenecdaty, New York: Matthew Glogowski, Josh Kane, Lauren Papa, Phil Tavernier, Suzanne Weldon, and Rebecca Willis.

Finally, our external reviewers have been outstanding and we acknowledge here our debt to each member of that team:

MARIS A. ABOLINS
Michigan State University

BARBARA ANDERECK
Ohio Wesleyan University

ALBERT BARTLETT
University of Colorado

MICHAEL E. BROWNE
University of Idaho

TIMOTHY J. BURNS
Leeward Community College

JOSEPH BUSCHI
Manhattan College

PHILIP A. CASABELLA
Rensselaer Polytechnic Institute

RANDALL CATON
Christopher Newport College

J. RICHARD CHRISTMAN
U.S. Coast Guard Academy

ROGER CLAPP
University of South Florida

W. R. CONKIE
Queen's University

PETER CROOKER
University of Hawaii at Manoa

WILLIAM P. CRUMMETT
Montana College of Mineral Science and Technology

EUGENE DUNNAM
University of Florida

ROBERT ENDORF
University of Cincinnati

F. PAUL ESPOSITO
University of Cincinnati

JERRY FINKELSTEIN
San Jose State University

ALEXANDER FIRESTONE
Iowa State University

ALEXANDER GARDNER
Howard University

ANDREW L. GARDNER
Brigham Young University

JOHN GIENIEC
Central Missouri State University

JOHN B. GRUBER
San Jose State University

ANN HANKS
American River College

SAMUEL HARRIS
Purdue University

EMILY HAUGHT
Georgia Institute of Technology

LAURENT HODGES
Iowa State University

JOHN HUBISZ
North Carolina State University

JOEY HUSTON
Michigan State University

DARRELL HUWE
Ohio University

CLAUDE KACSER
University of Maryland

LEONARD KLEINMAN
University of Texas at Austin

EARL KOLLER
Stevens Institute of Technology

ARTHUR Z. KOVACS
Rochester Institute of Technology

KENNETH KRANE
Oregon State University

SOL KRASNER
University of Illinois at Chicago

PETER LOLY
University of Manitoba

ROBERT R. MARCHINI
Memphis State University

DAVID MARKOWITZ
University of Connecticut

HOWARD C. MCALLISTER
University of Hawaii at Manoa

W. SCOTT MCCULLOUGH
Oklahoma State University

JAMES H. MCGUIRE
Tulane University

DAVID M. MCKINSTRY
Eastern Washington University

JOE P. MEYER
Georgia Institute of Technology

ROY MIDDLETON
University of Pennsylvania

IRVIN A. MILLER
Drexel University

EUGENE MOSCA
United States Naval Academy

MICHAEL O'SHEA
Kansas State University

PATRICK PAPIN
San Diego State University

GEORGE PARKER
North Carolina State University

ROBERT PELCOVITS
Brown University

OREN P. QUIST
South Dakota State University

JONATHAN REICHART
SUNY—Buffalo

MANUEL SCHWARTZ
University of Louisville

DARRELL SEELEY
Milwaukee School of Engineering

BRUCE ARNE SHERWOOD
Carnegie Mellon University

JOHN SPANGLER
St. Norbert College

ROSS L. SPENCER
Brigham Young University

HAROLD STOKES
Brigham Young University

JAY D. STRIEB
Villanova University

DAVID TOOT
Alfred University

J. S. TURNER
University of Texas at Austin

T. S. VENKATARAMAN
Drexel University

GIANFRANCO VIDALI
Syracuse University

FRED WANG
Prairie View A&M

ROBERT C. WEBB
Texas A&M University

GEORGE WILLIAMS
University of Utah

DAVID WOLFE
University of New Mexico

We hope that our words here reveal at least some of the wonder of physics, the fundamental clockwork of the universe. And, hopefully, those words might also reveal some of our awe of that clockwork.

DAVID HALLIDAY
6563 NE Windermere Road
Seattle, WA 98105

ROBERT RESNICK
Rensselaer Polytechnic Institute
Troy, NY 12181

JEARL WALKER
Cleveland State University
Cleveland, OH 44115

HOW TO USE THIS BOOK:

You are about to begin what could be one the most exciting course that you will undertake in college. It offers you the opportunity to learn what makes our world "tick" and to gain insight into the role physics plays in our everyday lives. This knowledge will not come without some effort, however, and this book has been carefully designed and written with an awareness of the kinds of difficulties and challenges you may face. Therefore, before you begin, we have provided a visual overview of some of the key features of the book that will aid in your studies.

Chapter Opening Puzzlers

Each chapter opens with an intriguing example of physics in action. By presenting high-interest applications of each chapters concepts, the puzzlers are intended to peak your interest and motivate you to read the chapter.

In 1977, Kitty O'Neil set a dragster record by reaching 392.54 mi/h in a sizzling time of 3.72 s. In 1958, Eli Beeding Jr. rode a rocket sled from a standstill to a speed of 72.5 mi/h in an elapsed time of 0.04 s (less than an eye blink). How can we compare these two rides to see which was more exciting (or more frightening)—by final speeds, by elapsed times, or by some other quantity?

SAMPLE PROBLEM 2-6

(a) When Kitty O'Neil set the dragster records for the greatest speed and least elapsed time, she reached 392.54 mi/h in 3.72 s. What was her average acceleration?

SOLUTION: From Eq. 2-7, O'Neil's average acceleration was

$$\bar{a} = \frac{\Delta v}{\Delta t} = \frac{392.54 \text{ mi/h} - 0}{3.72 \text{ s} - 0}$$

$$= +106 \frac{\text{mi}}{\text{h} \cdot \text{s}}, \qquad \text{(Answer)}$$

where the motion is taken to be in the positive *x* direction. In

Answers to Puzzlers

All chapter-opening puzzlers are answered later in the chapter, either in text discussion or in a sample problem.

If the car
r, the bob
oninertial

CHECKPOINT **1:** In the figure, two perpendicular forces **F**₁ and **F**₂ are combined in six different ways. Which ways may be used to correctly determine the net force $\Sigma\mathbf{F}$?

w wish to
accelera-
the stan-
use) the
been as-

ictionless
at by trial
accelera-
lefinition,
ody has a

body by

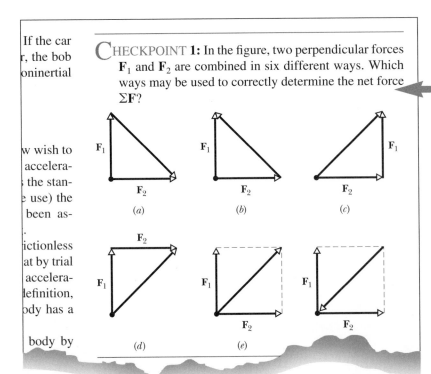

Checkpoints
Checkpoints appear throughout the text, focusing on the key points of physics you will need to tackle the exercises and problems found at the end of each chapter. These checkpoints help guide you away from common errors and misconceptions.

Checkpoint Questions
Checkpoint-type questions at the end of each chapter ask you to organize the physics concepts rather than plug numbers into equations. Answers to the odd-numbered questions are provided in the back of the book.

ey puck in

$\mathbf{v} = -2t\mathbf{i}$

ponents of
ion vector
nd and t is
−2 and 3?
cal projec-
t identical
n the same
nal speeds

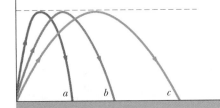

(c)

peed (a) a

4.9**j** (x is
). Has the

9. Figure 4-25 shows three paths for a kicked football. Ignoring the effects of air on the flight, rank the paths according to (a) time of flight, (b) initial vertical velocity component, (c) initial horizontal velocity component, and (d) initial speed. Place the greatest first in each part.

FIGURE 4-25 Question 9.

10. Figure 4-26 shows the velocity and acceleration of a particle at a particular instant in three situations. In which situation, and at that instant, is (a) the speed increasing, (b) the speed decreasing, (c) the speed not changing, (d) $\mathbf{v}\cdot\mathbf{a}$ positive, (e) $\mathbf{v}\cdot\mathbf{a}$ negative, and (f) $\mathbf{v}\cdot\mathbf{a} = 0$?

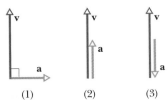

FIGURE 4-26 Question 10.

Sample Problems

The sample problems offer you the opportunity to work through the physics concepts just presented. Often built around real-world applications, they are closely coordinated with the end-of-chapter Questions, Exercises, and Problems.

d the
(This
ed in
e two

ation
bject
, Fig.

long
ction.
e +**j**

SAMPLE PROBLEM 4-1

The position vector for a particle is initially

$$\mathbf{r}_1 = -3\mathbf{i} + 2\mathbf{j} + 5\mathbf{k}$$

and then later is

$$\mathbf{r}_2 = 9\mathbf{i} + 2\mathbf{j} + 8\mathbf{k}$$

(see Fig. 4-2). What is the displacement from $\mathbf{r}_1$ to $\mathbf{r}_2$?

SOLUTION: Recall from Chapter 3 that we add (or subtract) two vectors in unit-vector notation by combining the components, axis by axis. So Eq. 4-2 becomes

$$\mathbf{\Delta r} = (9\mathbf{i} + 2\mathbf{j} + 8\mathbf{k}) - (-3\mathbf{i} + 2\mathbf{j} + 5\mathbf{k})$$
$$= 12\mathbf{i} + 3\mathbf{k}. \qquad \text{(Answer)}$$

The displacement vector is parallel to the xz plane, because it lacks any y component, a fact that is easier to pick out in the numerical result than in Fig. 4-2.

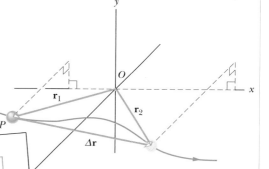

Sample Problem 4-1. The displacement $\mathbf{\Delta r} =$
d of $\mathbf{r}_1$ to the head of $\mathbf{r}_2$.

PROBLEM SOLVING TACTICS

TACTIC 1: *Reading Force Problems*
Read the problem statement several times until you have a good mental picture of what the situation is, what data are given, and what is requested. In Sample Problem 5-1, for example, you should tell yourself: "Someone is pushing a sled. Its speed changes, so acceleration is involved. The motion is along a straight line. A force is given in one part and asked for in the other, and so the situation looks like Newton's second law applied to one-dimensional motion."

If you know what the problem is about but don't know what to do next, put the problem aside and reread the text. If you are hazy about Newton's second law, reread that section. Study the sample problems. The one-dimensional-motion parts of Sample Problem 5-1 and the constant acceleration parts of Sample Problem 5-1 and the constant acceleration should send you back to Chapter 2 and especially to Table 2-1, which displays all the equations you are likely to need.

TACTIC 2: *Draw Two Types of Figures*
You may need two figures. One is a rough sketch of the actual real-world situation. When you draw the forces on it, place the tail of each force vector either on the boundary of or within the body feeling that force. The other figure is a free-body diagram in which the forces on a *single* body are drawn, with the body represented with a dot or a sketch. Place the tail of each force vector on the dot or sketch.

TACTIC 3: *What* em?

Problem Solving Tactics

Careful attention has been paid to helping you develop your problem-solving skills. Problem-solving tactics are closely related to the sample problems and can be found throughout the text, though most fall within the first half. The tactics are designed to help you work through assigned homework problems and prepare for exams. Collectively, they represent the stock in trade of experienced problem solvers and practicing scientists and engineers.

REVIEW & SUMMARY

Review and Summary
Review & Summary sections at the end of each chapter review the most important concepts and equations.

Conservative Forces

A force is a **conservative force** if the net work it does on a particle moving along a closed path from an initial point and then back to that point is zero. Or, equivalently, it is conservative if its work on a particle moving between two points does not depend on the path taken by the particle. The gravitational force (weight) and the spring force are conservative forces; the kinetic frictional force is a **nonconservative force**.

Potential Energy

A **potential energy** is energy that is associated with the configuration of a system in which a conservative force acts. When the conservative force does work W on a particle within the system, the change ΔU in the potential energy of the system is

$$\Delta U = -W. \tag{8-1}$$

If the particle moves from point x_i to point x_f, the change in the potential energy of the system is

$$\Delta U = -\int_{x_i}^{x_f} F(x)\, dx. \tag{8-6}$$

Gravitational Potential Energy

The potential energy associated with a system consisting of the Earth and a nearby particle is the **gravitational potential energy.** If the particle moves from height y_i to height y_f, the change in the gravitational potential energy of the particle–Earth system is

$$\Delta U = mg(y_f - y_i) = mg\,\Delta y. \tag{8-7}$$

If the **reference position** of the particle is set as $y_i = 0$ and the corresponding gravitational potential energy of the system is set as $U_i = 0$, then the gravitational potential energy U when the particle is at any position y is

$$U = mgy. \tag{8-9}$$

in which the subscripts refer to different instants during an transfer process. This conservation can also be written as

$$\Delta E = \Delta K + \Delta U = 0.$$

Potential Energy Curves

If we know the **potential energy function** $U(x)$ for a sy which a force F acts on a particle, we can find the force

$$F(x) = -\frac{dU(x)}{dx}.$$

If $U(x)$ is given on a graph, then at any value of x, the for the negative of the slope of the curve there and the kinetic of the particle is given by

$$K(x) = E - U(x),$$

where E is the mechanical energy of the system. A **turnin** is a point x where the particle reverses its motion (there, The particle is in **equilibrium** at points where the slope $U(x)$ curve is zero (there, $F(x) = 0$).

Work by Nonconservative Forces

If a nonconservative applied force F does work on particle part of a system having a potential energy, then the wor done on the system by F is equal to the change ΔE in the m ical energy of the system:

$$W_{app} = \Delta K + \Delta U = \Delta E. \tag{8-24}$$

If a kinetic frictional force $\mathbf{f}_k$ does work on an obj change ΔE in the total mechanical energy of the object system containing it is given by

$$\Delta E = -f_k d,$$

in which d is the displacement of the object during the wo

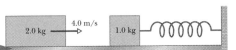

FIGURE 10-44   Problem 56.

57P. Two 22.7 kg ice sleds are placed a short distance apart, one directly behind the other, as shown in Fig. 10-45. A 3.63 kg cat, standing on one sled, jumps across to the other and immediately back to the first. Both jumps are made at a speed of 3.05 m/s relative to the ice. Find the final speeds of the two sleds.

FIGURE 10-45   Problem 57.

58P. The bumper of a 1200 kg car is designed so that it can just absorb all the energy when the car runs head-on into a solid wall at 5.00 km/h. The car is involved in a collision in which it runs at 70.0 km/h into the rear of a 900 kg car moving at 60.0 km/h in the same direction. The 900 kg car is accelerated to 70.0 km/h as a result of the collision. (a) What is the speed of the 1200 kg car immediately after impact? (b) What is the ratio of the kinetic energy absorbed in the collision to that which can be absorbed by the bumper of the 1200 kg car?

59P. A railroad freight car weighing 32 tons and traveling at 5.0

Exercises and Problems
A hallmark of this text, nearly 3400 end-of-chapter exercises and problems are arranged in order of difficulty, starting with the exercises (labeled "E"), followed by the problems (labeled "P"). Particularly difficult problems are identified with an asterisk (*). Answers to all the odd-numbered exercises and problems are provided in the back of the book. New electronic computation problems, which require the use of math packages and graphing calculators, have been added to many of the chapters.

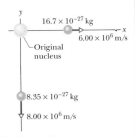

FIGURE 10-46   Exercise 62.

63E. In a game of pool, the cue ball strikes anothe at rest. After the collision, the cue ball moves at 3.5 line making an angle of 22.0° with its original dir tion, and the second ball has a speed of 2.00 m/s angle between the direction of motion of the secon original direction of motion of the cue ball and (b speed of the cue ball. (c) Is kinetic energy conserve

64E. Two vehicles A and B are traveling west and tively, toward the same intersection, where they co together. Before the collision, A (total weight 2700 with a speed of 40 mi/h and B (total weight 3600 lt of 60 mi/h. Find the magnitude and direction of the v (interlocked) vehicles immediately after the collisi

65E. In a game of billiards, the cue ball is given a V and strikes the pack of 15 stationary balls. All engage in nume_____ and ball–cushion co time la_____ _____ame accident) all

Brief Contents

Contents

CHAPTER 36

INTERFERENCE *901*

*What produces the blue-green of a
Morpho's wing?*

CHAPTER 37

DIFFRACTION *929*

*Why do the colors in a pointillism painting change
with viewing distance?*

CHAPTER 38

RELATIVITY *958*

*Why is special relativity so important in modern
navigation?*

CHAPTER 39

PHOTONS AND MATTER WAVES *985*

*How can a particle such as an electron
be a wave?*

CHAPTER 40

MORE ABOUT MATTER WAVES *1007*

How can you corral an electron?

CHAPTER 41

ALL ABOUT ATOMS *1028*

What is so different about light from a laser?

CHAPTER 42

CONDUCTION OF ELECTRICITY IN SOLIDS *1052*

Why are "spacesuits" the dress code at the Fab 11 factory in New Mexico?

36
Interference

At first glance, the top surface of the <u>Morpho</u> butterfly's wing is simply a beautiful blue-green. But there is something strange about the color, for it almost glimmers, unlike the colors of most objects. And if you change your perspective, or if the wing moves, the tint of the color changes. The wing is said to be iridescent, and the blue-green we see hides the wing's "true" dull brown color that appears on the bottom surface. What, then, is so different about the top surface that gives us this arresting display?

36-1 INTERFERENCE

Sunlight, as the rainbow shows us, is a composite of all the colors of the visible spectrum. The colors reveal themselves in the rainbow because the incident wavelengths are bent through different angles as they pass through raindrops that produce the bow. However, soap bubbles and oil slicks can also show striking colors, produced not by refraction but by constructive and destructive **interference** of light. The interfering waves combine either to enhance or to suppress certain colors in the spectrum of the incident sunlight. Interference of light waves is thus a superposition phenomenon like those we discussed in Chapter 17.

This selective enhancement or suppression of wavelengths has many applications. When light encounters an ordinary glass surface, for example, about 4% of the incident energy is reflected, thus weakening the transmitted beam by that amount. This unwanted loss of light can be a real problem in optical systems with many components. A thin, transparent "interference film," deposited on the glass surface, can reduce the amount of reflected light (and thus enhance the transmitted light) by destructive interference. The bluish cast of a camera lens reveals the presence of such a coating. Interference coatings can also be used to enhance—rather than reduce—the ability of a surface to reflect light.

To understand interference, we must go beyond the restrictions of geometrical optics and employ the full power of wave optics. In fact, as you will see, the existence of interference phenomena is perhaps our most convincing evidence that light is a wave—because interference cannot be explained other than with waves.

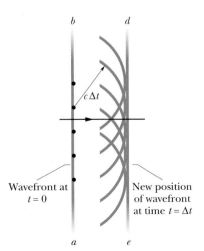

FIGURE 36-1 The propagation of a plane wave in vacuum, as portrayed by Huygens' principle.

36-2 LIGHT AS A WAVE

The first person to advance a convincing wave theory for light was Dutch physicist Christian Huygens, in 1678. While much less comprehensive than the later electromagnetic theory of Maxwell, Huygens' theory was simpler mathematically and remains useful today. Its great advantages are that it accounts for the laws of reflection and refraction in terms of waves and gives physical meaning to the index of refraction.

Huygens' wave theory is based on a geometrical construction that allows us to tell where a given wavefront will be at any time in the future if we know its present position. This construction is based on **Huygens' principle,** which is:

> All points on a wavefront serve as point sources of spherical secondary wavelets. After a time t, the new position of the wavefront will be that of a surface tangent to these secondary wavelets.

Here is a simple example. At the left in Fig. 36-1, the present location of a wavefront of a plane wave traveling to the right in vacuum is represented by plane ab, perpendicular to the page. Where will the wavefront be at time Δt later? We let several points on plane ab (the dots) serve as sources of spherical secondary wavelets that are emitted at $t = 0$. At time Δt, the radius of all these spherical wavelets will have grown to $c\,\Delta t$, where c is the speed of light in vacuum. We draw plane de tangent to these wavelets at time Δt. This plane represents the wavefront of the plane wave at time Δt; it is parallel to plane ab and a perpendicular distance $c\,\Delta t$ from it.

The Law of Refraction

We now use Huygens' principle to derive the law of refraction, Eq. 34-44 (Snell's law). Figure 36-2 shows three stages in the refraction of several wavefronts at a plane interface between air (medium 1) and glass (medium 2). We arbitrarily choose the wavefronts in the incident beam to be separated by λ_1, the wavelength in medium 1. Let the speed of light in air be v_1 and that in glass be v_2. We assume that $v_2 < v_1$, which happens to be true.

Angle θ_1 in Fig. 36-2a is the angle between the wavefront and the interface; this is the same as the angle between the *normal* to the wavefront (that is, the incident ray) and the *normal* to the interface; thus θ_1 is the angle of incidence. As the wave moves into the glass (Fig. 36-2b), the time ($= \lambda_1/v_1$) for a Huygens wavelet to expand from

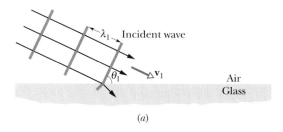

(a)

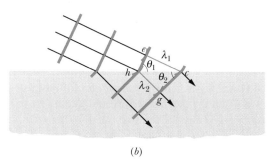

(b)

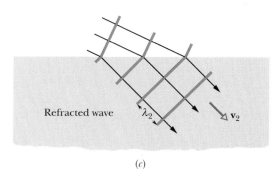

(c)

FIGURE 36-2 The refraction of a plane wave at an air–glass interface, as portrayed by Huygens' principle. The wavelength in glass is smaller than that in air. For simplicity, the reflected wave is not shown.

point e to include point c will equal the time ($= \lambda_2/v_2$) for a wavelet in the glass to expand at the reduced speed v_2 from h to include g. By equating these times, we obtain the relation

$$\frac{\lambda_1}{\lambda_2} = \frac{v_1}{v_2}, \qquad (36\text{-}1)$$

which shows that the wavelengths of light in two media are proportional to the speeds of light in those media.

By Huygens' principle, the refracted wavefront must be tangent to an arc of radius λ_2 centered on h, say at point g. The refracted wavefront must also be tangent to an arc of radius λ_1 centered on e, say at c. Then the refracted wavefront must be oriented as shown. Note that θ_2, the angle between the refracted wavefront and the interface, is actually the angle of refraction.

For the right triangles hce and hcg in Fig. 36-2b we

may write

$$\sin \theta_1 = \frac{\lambda_1}{hc} \qquad \text{(for triangle } hce\text{)}$$

and

$$\sin \theta_2 = \frac{\lambda_2}{hc} \qquad \text{(for triangle } hcg\text{)}.$$

Dividing the first of these two equations by the second and using Eq. 36-1, we find

$$\frac{\sin \theta_1}{\sin \theta_2} = \frac{\lambda_1}{\lambda_2} = \frac{v_1}{v_2}. \qquad (36\text{-}2)$$

We can define an **index of refraction** for each medium as the ratio of the speed of light in vacuum to the speed of light v in the medium. Thus

$$n = \frac{c}{v} \qquad \text{(index of refraction)}. \qquad (36\text{-}3)$$

In particular, for our two media, we have

$$n_1 = \frac{c}{v_1} \quad \text{and} \quad n_2 = \frac{c}{v_2}. \qquad (36\text{-}4)$$

If we combine Eqs. 36-2 and 36-4 we find

$$\frac{\sin \theta_1}{\sin \theta_2} = \frac{c/n_1}{c/n_2} = \frac{n_2}{n_1} \qquad (36\text{-}5)$$

or

$$n_1 \sin \theta_1 = n_2 \sin \theta_2 \qquad \begin{array}{l}\text{(law of}\\ \text{refraction),}\end{array} \qquad (36\text{-}6)$$

as introduced in Chapter 34.

CHECKPOINT **1:** The figure shows a monochromatic ray of light traveling across parallel interfaces, from an original material a, through layers of material b and c, and then back into material a. Rank the materials according to the speed of light in them, greatest first.

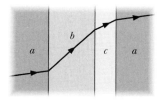

Wavelength and Index of Refraction

We have now seen that the wavelength of light changes when the speed of the light changes, as happens when light crosses an interface from one medium into another. Further, the speed of light in any medium depends on the index of refraction of the medium, according to Eq. 36-3. Thus the wavelength of light in any medium depends on the index of refraction of the medium. Let a certain monochromatic light have wavelength λ and speed c in vacuum and wavelength λ_n and speed v in a medium with an index of refraction n. Then we can rewrite Eq. 36-1 as

$$\lambda_n = \lambda \frac{v}{c}. \tag{36-7}$$

Using Eq. 36-3 to substitute $1/n$ for v/c then yields

$$\lambda_n = \frac{\lambda}{n}. \tag{36-8}$$

This equation relates the wavelength of light in any medium to its wavelength in vacuum. It tells us that the larger the index of refraction of a medium, the smaller the wavelength of light in that medium.

This fact is important in certain situations involving the interference of light waves. For example, in Fig. 36-3, the *waves of the rays* (that is, the waves represented by the rays) have identical wavelengths λ and are initially in phase in air ($n \approx 1$). One of the waves travels through medium 1 of index of refraction n_1 and length L. The other travels through medium 2 of index of refraction n_2 and the same length L. Because the wavelength of the light differs in the two media, the two waves may no longer be in phase when they leave these media.

> The phase difference between two light waves can change if the waves travel through different materials having different indices of refraction.

As we shall discuss soon, this change in the phase difference can determine the interference of the light waves if they reach some common point. To find their new phase difference in terms of wavelengths, we first count the number N_1 of wavelengths there are in the length L of medium 1. From Eq. 36-8, the wavelength in medium 1 is $\lambda_{n1} = \lambda/n_1$. So

$$N_1 = \frac{L}{\lambda_{n1}} = \frac{Ln_1}{\lambda}. \tag{36-9}$$

Similarly, we count the number N_2 of wavelengths there are in the length L of medium 2, where the wavelength is

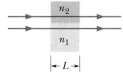

FIGURE 36-3 Two light rays travel through two media having different indices of refraction.

$\lambda_{n2} = \lambda/n_2$:

$$N_2 = \frac{L}{\lambda_{n2}} = \frac{Ln_2}{\lambda}. \tag{36-10}$$

To find the new phase difference between the waves, we subtract the smaller of N_1 and N_2 from the larger. Assuming $n_2 > n_1$, we would obtain

$$N_2 - N_1 = \frac{Ln_2}{\lambda} - \frac{Ln_1}{\lambda} = \frac{L}{\lambda}(n_2 - n_1). \tag{36-11}$$

Suppose Eq. 36-11 tells us that the waves now have a phase difference of 45.6 wavelengths. That is equivalent to taking the initially in-phase waves and shifting one of them by 45.6 wavelengths. However, a shift of an integer number of wavelengths (such as 45) would put the waves back in phase. So it is only the decimal fraction (here, 0.6) that is important. A phase difference of 45.6 wavelengths is equivalent to a phase difference of 0.6 wavelength.

A phase difference of 0.5 wavelength puts the waves exactly out of phase. If the waves were to reach some common point, they would then undergo fully destructive interference, producing darkness at that point. With a phase difference of 0.0 or 1.0 wavelength, they would, instead, undergo fully constructive interference, resulting in brightness at the common point. Our phase difference of 0.6 wavelength is an intermediate situation, but closer to destructive interference, and the waves would produce a dimly illuminated crossing point.

We can also express phase difference in terms of radians and degrees, as we have done already. A phase difference of one wavelength is equivalent to phase differences of 2π rad and 360°.

SAMPLE PROBLEM 36-1

In Fig. 36-3, the two light waves that are represented by the rays have wavelength 550.0 nm before entering media 1 and 2. Medium 1 is now just air, and medium 2 is a transparent plastic layer of index of refraction 1.600 and thickness 2.600 μm.

(a) What is the phase difference of the emerging waves, in wavelengths?

SOLUTION: From Eq. 36-11, with $n_1 = 1.000$, $n_2 = 1.600$, $L = 2.600$ μm, and $\lambda = 550.0$ nm, we have

$$N_2 - N_1 = \frac{L}{\lambda}(n_2 - n_1)$$

$$= \frac{2.600 \times 10^{-6} \text{ m}}{5.500 \times 10^{-7} \text{ m}}(1.600 - 1.000)$$

$$= 2.84, \tag{Answer}$$

which is equivalent to a phase difference of 0.84 wavelength.

(b) If the rays of the waves were angled slightly so that the waves reached the same point on a distant viewing screen, what type of interference would the waves produce at that point?

SOLUTION: The effective phase difference of 0.84 wavelength is an intermediate situation, but closer to fully constructive interference (1.0) than to fully destructive interference (0.5).

(c) What is the phase difference in radians and in degrees?

SOLUTION: In radians,

$$(0.84)(2\pi \text{ rad}) = 5.3 \text{ rad}. \qquad \text{(Answer)}$$

In degrees,

$$(0.84)(360°) = 302° \approx 300°. \qquad \text{(Answer)}$$

CHECKPOINT 2: The light waves of the rays in Fig. 36-3 have the same wavelength and are initially in phase. (a) If 7.60 wavelengths fit within the length of the top layer and 5.50 wavelengths fit within that of the bottom layer, which layer has the greater index of refraction? (b) If the rays are angled slightly so that they meet at the same point on a distant screen, will the interference there result in brightness, bright intermediate illumination, dark intermediate illumination, or darkness?

36-3 DIFFRACTION

In the next section we shall discuss the experiment that first proved that light is a wave. To prepare for that discussion, we must introduce the idea of **diffraction** of waves, a phenomenon that we explore much more fully in Chapter 37. Its essence is this: if a wave encounters a barrier that has an opening of dimensions similar to the wavelength, the part of the wave that passes through the opening will flare out —will *diffract*—into the region beyond the barrier. The flaring out is consistent with the spreading of the wavelets in the Huygens construction of Fig. 36-1. Diffraction occurs for waves of all types, not just light waves; Fig. 36-4 shows the diffraction of water waves traveling across the surface of water in a shallow tank.

Figure 36-5*a* shows the situation schematically for an incident plane wave of wavelength λ encountering a slit that has width $a = 6.0\lambda$ and extends into and out of the page. The wave flares out on the far side of the slit. Figures 36-5*b* (with $a = 3.0\lambda$) and 36-5*c* ($a = 1.5\lambda$) illustrate the main feature of diffraction: the narrower the slit, the greater the diffraction.

Diffraction limits geometrical optics, in which we represent an electromagnetic wave with a ray. If we actu-

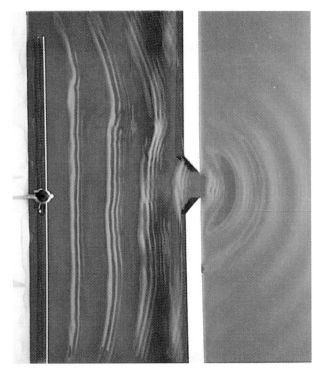

FIGURE 36-4 The diffraction of water waves in a ripple tank. Waves moving from left to right flare out through an opening in a barrier along the water surface.

ally try to form a ray by sending light through a narrow slit, or through a series of narrow slits, diffraction will always defeat our effort because it always causes the light to spread. Indeed, the narrower we make the slits (in the hope of producing a narrower beam), the greater the spreading is. Thus, geometrical optics holds only when slits or other apertures that might be located in the path of light do not have dimensions comparable to or smaller than the wavelength of the light.

36-4 YOUNG'S INTERFERENCE EXPERIMENT

In 1801 Thomas Young experimentally proved that light is a wave, contrary to what most other scientists then thought. He did so by demonstrating that light undergoes interference, as do water waves, sound waves, and waves of all other types. In addition, he was able to measure the average wavelength of sunlight; his value, 570 nm, is impressively close to the modern accepted value of 555 nm. We shall here examine Young's historic experiment as an example of the interference of light waves.

Figure 36-6 gives the basic arrangement of Young's experiment. Light from a distant monochromatic source illuminates slit S_0 in screen A. The emerging light then

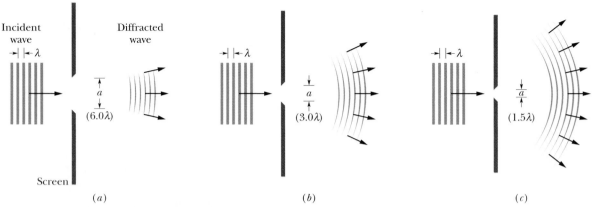

FIGURE 36-5 Diffraction represented schematically. For a given wavelength λ, the diffraction is more pronounced the smaller the slit width a. The figures show the cases for (a) slit width $a = 6.0\lambda$, (b) slit width $a = 3.0\lambda$, and (c) slit width $a = 1.5\lambda$. In all three cases, the screen and the length of the slit extend well into and out of the page, perpendicular to it.

spreads via diffraction to illuminate two slits S_1 and S_2 in screen B. Diffraction of the light by the two slits sends overlapping circular waves into the region beyond screen B, where the waves from one slit interfere with the waves from the other slit.

In the "snapshot" of Fig. 36-6, points at which the interference is fully constructive (interference maxima) are

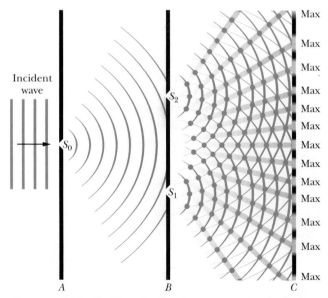

FIGURE 36-6 In Young's interference experiment, incident monochromatic light is diffracted by slit S_0, which then acts as a point source of light that emits semicircular wavefronts. As that light reaches screen B, it is diffracted by slits S_1 and S_2, which then act as two point sources of light. The light waves traveling from slits S_1 and S_2 overlap and undergo interference, forming an interference pattern of maxima and minima on viewing screen C. This figure is a cross section; the screens, slits, and interference pattern extend into and out of the page.

marked with dots. We cannot see such points except where a viewing screen C intercepts the light. On the screen, points of interference maxima form visible bright rows—called *bright bands, bright fringes,* or (loosely speaking) *maxima*—that extend across the screen (into and out of the page in Fig. 36-6). Dark regions—called *dark bands, dark fringes,* or (loosely speaking) *minima*—result from fully destructive interference and are visible between adjacent pairs of bright fringes. (*Maxima* and *minima* more properly refer to the center of a band.) The pattern of bright and dark fringes on the screen is called an **interference pattern.** Figure 36-7 is a photograph of the interference pattern; the photograph has been rotated by 90° to save space.

Locating the Fringes

Waves produce fringes in a *Young's double-slit interference experiment,* as it is called, but what exactly determines the locations of the fringes? To answer, we shall use the arrangement in Fig. 36-8a. There, a plane wave of monochromatic light is incident on two slits S_1 and S_2 in screen B; the light diffracts through the slits and produces an interference pattern on screen C. We draw a central axis from the point halfway between the slits to screen C as a

FIGURE 36-7 A photograph of an interference pattern produced by the arrangement shown in Fig. 36-6. (The photograph is a front view of part of screen C and has been rotated clockwise by 90°.) The alternating maxima and minima are called *interference fringes* (because they resemble the decorative fringe sometimes used on clothing and drapery).

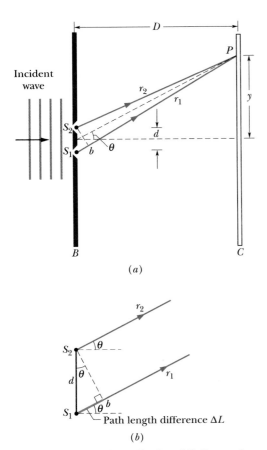

(a)

(b)

FIGURE 36-8 (a) Waves from slits S_1 and S_2 (into and out of the page) combine at P, an arbitrary point on screen C at distance y from the central axis. The angle θ serves as a convenient locator for P. (b) For $D \gg d$, we can approximate rays r_1 and r_2 as being parallel, at angle θ to the central axis.

reference. We then pick, for discussion, an arbitrary point P on the screen, at angle θ to the central axis. This point intercepts the wave of ray r_1 from the bottom slit and the wave of ray r_2 from the top slit.

These waves are in phase when they pass through the two slits because there they are just portions of the same incident wave. But once they have passed the slits, the two waves must travel different distances to reach P. We saw a similar situation in Section 18-4 with sound waves and concluded that

---

The phase difference between two waves can change if the waves travel paths of different lengths.

The change in phase difference is due to the *path length difference* ΔL in the paths taken by the waves. Consider two waves initially exactly in phase, traveling along paths with a path length difference ΔL, and then passing through

some common point. When ΔL is zero or an integer number of wavelengths, the waves arrive at the common point exactly in phase and they interfere fully constructively there. If that is true for the waves of rays r_1 and r_2 in Fig. 36-8, then point P is part of a bright fringe. When, instead, ΔL is an odd multiple of half a wavelength, the waves arrive at the common point exactly out of phase and they interfere fully destructively there. If that is true for the waves of rays r_1 and r_2, then point P is part of a dark fringe. (And, of course, we can have intermediate situations of interference and thus intermediate illumination at P.) Thus:

What appears at each point on the viewing screen in a Young's interference experiment is determined by the path length difference ΔL of the rays reaching that point.

We can specify where each bright or dark fringe is located on the screen by giving the angle θ from the central axis to that fringe. To find θ, we must relate it to ΔL. We start with Fig. 36-8a by finding a point b along ray r_1 such that the path length from b to P equals the path length from S_2 to P. Then the path length difference ΔL between the two rays is the distance from S_1 to b.

The relation between this S_1-to-b distance and θ is complicated, but we can simplify it considerably if we arrange for the distance D from the slits to the screen to be much greater than the slit separation d. Then we can approximate rays r_1 and r_2 as being parallel to each other and at angle θ to the central axis (Fig. 36-8b). We can also approximate the triangle formed by points S_1, S_2, and b as being a right triangle, and the angle inside that triangle at S_2 as being θ. Then, for that triangle, $\sin \theta = \Delta L/d$ and thus

$$\Delta L = d \sin \theta \quad \text{(path length difference)}. \quad (36\text{-}12)$$

For a bright fringe, we saw that ΔL must be zero or an integer number of wavelengths. Using Eq. 36-12, we can write this requirement as

$$\Delta L = d \sin \theta = (\text{integer})(\lambda), \quad (36\text{-}13)$$

or as

$$d \sin \theta = m\lambda, \quad \text{for } m = 0, 1, 2, \ldots$$
$$\text{(maxima—bright fringes)}. \quad (36\text{-}14)$$

For a dark fringe, ΔL must be an odd multiple of half a wavelength. Again using Eq. 36-12, we can write this requirement as

$$\Delta L = d \sin \theta = (\text{odd number})(\tfrac{1}{2}\lambda), \quad (36\text{-}15)$$

or as

$$d \sin \theta = (m + \tfrac{1}{2})\lambda, \qquad \text{for } m = 0, 1, 2, \ldots$$
$$\text{(minima—dark fringes)}. \quad (36\text{-}16)$$

With Eqs. 36-14 and 36-16, we can find the angle θ to any fringe and thus locate that fringe; further, we can use the values of m to label the fringes. For $m = 0$, Eq. 36-14 tells us that a bright fringe is at $\theta = 0$, that is, on the central axis. This *central maximum* is the point at which waves arriving from the two slits have a path length difference $\Delta L = 0$, hence zero phase difference.

For, say, $m = 2$, Eq. 36-14 tells us that *bright* fringes are at

$$\theta = \sin^{-1}\left(\frac{2\lambda}{d}\right)$$

above and below the central axis. Waves from the two slits arrive at these two fringes with $\Delta L = 2\lambda$ and with a phase difference of two wavelengths. These fringes are said to be the *second-order fringes* (meaning $m = 2$) or the *second side maxima* (the second maxima to the side of the central maximum), or they are described as being the second fringes from the central maximum.

For $m = 1$, Eq. 36-16 tells us that *dark* fringes are at

$$\theta = \sin^{-1}\left(\frac{1.5\lambda}{d}\right)$$

above and below the central axis. Waves from the two slits arrive at these two fringes with $\Delta L = 1.5\lambda$ and with a phase difference, in wavelengths, of 1.5. These fringes are called the *second dark fringes* or *second minima* because they are the second dark fringes from the central axis. (The first dark fringes, or first minima, are at locations for which $m = 0$ in Eq. 36-16.)

Equations 36-14 and 36-16 are derived for the situation of $D \gg d$. However, they also apply if we place a converging lens between the slits and the viewing screen and then move the viewing screen to the focal point of the lens. (The screen is then said to be in the *focal plane* of the lens; that is, it is in the plane perpendicular to the central axis at the focal point.) The rays that now arrive at any point on the screen must have been exactly parallel (rather than approximately) when they left the slits—they are like the initially parallel rays in Fig. 35-13a that are directed to a point by a lens.

CHECKPOINT 3: In Fig. 36-8a, what are ΔL (as a multiple of the wavelength) and the phase difference (in wavelengths) for the two rays if point P is (a) a third side maximum and (b) a third minimum?

SAMPLE PROBLEM 36-2

What is the distance on screen C in Fig. 36-8a between adjacent maxima near the center of the interference pattern? The wavelength λ of the light is 546 nm, the slit separation d is 0.12 mm, and the slit–screen separation D is 55 cm. Assume that the angle θ in Fig. 36-8 is small enough to permit use of the approximations $\sin \theta \approx \tan \theta \approx \theta$, in which θ is expressed in radian measure.

SOLUTION: From Fig. 36-8 we see that, for some value of m (a low value, to ensure that the corresponding maximum will be near the center of the pattern as required),

$$\tan \theta \approx \theta = \frac{y_m}{D},$$

where y_m is the distance to the mth maximum. From Eq. 36-14 we have, for the same value of m,

$$\sin \theta \approx \theta = \frac{m\lambda}{d}.$$

If we equate these two expressions for θ and solve for y_m, we find

$$y_m = \frac{m\lambda D}{d}. \quad (36\text{-}17)$$

For the adjacent maximum that is farther out, we have

$$y_{m+1} = \frac{(m+1)\lambda D}{d}. \quad (36\text{-}18)$$

We find the distance between adjacent maxima by subtracting Eq. 37-17 from Eq. 36-18:

$$\Delta y = y_{m+1} - y_m = \frac{\lambda D}{d}$$
$$= \frac{(546 \times 10^{-9}\text{ m})(55 \times 10^{-2}\text{ m})}{0.12 \times 10^{-3}\text{ m}}$$
$$= 2.50 \times 10^{-3}\text{ m} \approx 2.5\text{ mm}. \qquad \text{(Answer)}$$

As long as d and θ in Fig. 36-8a are small, the separation of the interference fringes is independent of m; that is, the fringes are evenly spaced.

36-5 COHERENCE

For the interference pattern to appear on viewing screen C in Fig. 36-6, the light waves reaching any point P on the screen must have a phase difference that does not vary in time. That is the case in Fig. 36-6, because the waves passing through slits S_1 and S_2 are portions of the single light wave that illuminates the slits. Because the phase difference remains constant, the light from slits S_1 and S_2 is said to be completely **coherent.**

Direct sunlight is partially coherent; that is, sunlight waves intercepted at two points have a constant phase difference only if the points are very close. If you look closely at your fingernail in bright sunlight, you can see a faint interference pattern called *speckle* that causes the nail to appear covered with specks. You see this effect because light waves scattering from very close points on the nail are sufficiently coherent to interfere with one another at your eye. The slits in a double-slit experiment, however, are not close enough, and in direct sunlight, the light at the slits is **incoherent.** To get coherent light, we have to send the sunlight through a single slit; because that single slit is small, the light that passes through it is coherent. In addition, the smallness of the slit causes the light to spread sufficiently via diffraction to illuminate both slits in the double-slit experiment with that coherent light.

If we replace the double slits with two similar but independent monochromatic light sources, such as two fine incandescent wires, the phase difference between the waves emitted by the sources varies rapidly and randomly. This occurs because the light is emitted by vast numbers of atoms in the wires, acting randomly and independently for extremely short times (of the order of nanoseconds). As a result, at any given point on the viewing screen, the interference between the waves from the two sources varies rapidly and randomly between fully constructive and fully destructive. The eye (and most common optical detectors) cannot follow such changes, and no interference pattern can be seen. The fringes disappear, and the screen is seen as being uniformly illuminated. Such light is said to be completely incoherent.

A *laser* differs from common light sources in that its atoms emit light in a cooperative manner, thereby making the light coherent. Moreover, the light is almost monochromatic, is emitted in a thin beam with little spreading, and can be focused to a width that almost matches the wavelength of the light.

36-6 INTENSITY IN DOUBLE-SLIT INTERFERENCE

Equations 36-14 and 36-16 tell us how to locate the maxima and minima of the double-slit interference pattern on screen C of Fig. 36-8 as a function of the angle θ in that figure. Here we wish to derive an expression for the intensity I of the fringes as a function of θ.

The light leaving the slits is in phase. However, let us assume that the electric field components of the light waves arriving at point P in Fig. 36-8 from the two slits are not in phase and vary with time as

$$E_1 = E_0 \sin \omega t \tag{36-19}$$

and
$$E_2 = E_0 \sin (\omega t + \phi), \tag{36-20}$$

where ω is the angular frequency of the waves and ϕ is the phase constant of wave E_2. Note that the two waves have the same amplitude E_0 and a phase difference of ϕ. Because that phase difference does not vary, the waves are coherent. We shall show that these two waves will combine at P to produce an illumination of intensity I given by

$$I = 4I_0 \cos^2 \tfrac{1}{2}\phi, \tag{36-21}$$

and that

$$\phi = \frac{2\pi d}{\lambda} \sin \theta. \tag{36-22}$$

In Eq. 36-21, I_0 is the intensity of the light that arrives on the screen from one slit when the other slit is temporarily covered. We assume that the slits are so narrow in comparison to the wavelength that this single-slit intensity is essentially uniform over the region of the screen in which we wish to examine the fringes.

Equations 36-21 and 36-22, which together tell us how the intensity I of the fringe pattern varies with the angle θ in Fig. 36-8, necessarily contain information about the location of the maxima and minima. Let us see if we can extract it.

Study of Eq. 36-21 shows that intensity maxima will occur when

$$\tfrac{1}{2}\phi = m\pi, \quad \text{for } m = 0, 1, 2, \ldots . \tag{36-23}$$

If we put this result into Eq. 36-22, we find

$$2m\pi = \frac{2\pi d}{\lambda} \sin \theta, \quad \text{for } m = 0, 1, 2, \ldots$$

or
$$d \sin \theta = m\lambda, \quad \text{for } m = 0, 1, 2, \ldots \atop \text{(maxima)}, \tag{36-24}$$

which is exactly Eq. 36-14, the expression that we derived earlier for the locations of the maxima.

The minima in the fringe pattern occur when

$$\tfrac{1}{2}\phi = (m + \tfrac{1}{2})\pi, \quad \text{for } m = 0, 1, 2, \ldots .$$

If we combine this relation with Eq. 36-22 we are led at once to

$$d \sin \theta = (m + \tfrac{1}{2})\lambda \quad \text{for } m = 0, 1, 2, \ldots \atop \text{(minima)}, \tag{36-25}$$

FIGURE 36-9 A plot of Eq. 36-21, showing the intensity of a double-slit interference pattern as a function of the phase difference between the waves from the two slits. I_0 is the (uniform) intensity that would appear on the screen if one slit were covered. The average intensity of the fringe pattern is $2I_0$, and the *maximum* intensity (for coherent light) is $4I_0$.

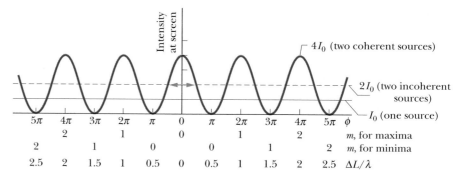

which is just Eq. 36-16, the expression derived earlier for the locations of the fringe minima.

Figure 36-9, which is a plot of Eq. 36-21, shows the intensity pattern for double-slit interference as a function of the phase difference ϕ at the screen. The horizontal solid line is I_0, the (uniform) intensity on the screen when one of the slits is covered up. Note in Eq. 36-21 and the graph that the intensity I (which is always positive) varies from zero at the fringe minima to $4I_0$ at the fringe maxima.

If the waves from the two sources (slits) were *incoherent,* so that no enduring phase relation existed between them, there would be no fringe pattern and the intensity would have the uniform value $2I_0$ for all points on the screen; the horizontal dashed line in Fig. 36-9 shows this uniform value.

Interference cannot create or destroy energy but merely redistributes it over the screen. Thus the *average* intensity on the screen must be the same $2I_0$ regardless of whether the sources are coherent. This follows at once from Eq. 36-21; if we substitute $\frac{1}{2}$, the average value of the cosine-squared function, this equation reduces to $\bar{I} = 2I_0$.

Proof of Eqs. 36-21 and 36-22

We shall combine the electric field components E_1 and E_2, given by Eqs. 36-19 and 36-20, respectively, by the method of phasors discussed in Section 17-10. In Fig. 36-10a, the waves with components E_1 and E_2 are represented by phasors of magnitude E_0 that rotate around the origin at angular speed ω. The values of E_1 and E_2 at any time are the projections of the corresponding phasors onto the vertical axis. Figure 36-10a shows the phasors and their projections at an arbitrary time t. Consistent with Eqs. 36-19 and 36-20, the phasor for E_1 has a rotation angle ωt and the phasor for E_2 has a rotation angle $\omega t + \phi$.

To combine the field components E_1 and E_2 on a phasor diagram, we add them vectorially, as shown in Fig. 36-10b. The magnitude of the vector sum is the amplitude E of the resultant wave, and that wave has a certain phase constant β. To find the amplitude E in Fig. 36-10b, we first

note that the two angles marked β are equal because they are opposite equal-length sides of a triangle. From the theorem (for triangles) that an exterior angle (ϕ) is equal to the sum of the two opposite interior angles ($\beta + \beta$), we see that $\beta = \frac{1}{2}\phi$. Thus we have

$$E = 2(E_0 \cos \beta) = 2E_0 \cos \tfrac{1}{2}\phi. \qquad (36\text{-}26)$$

If we square each side of this relation we obtain

$$E^2 = 4E_0^2 \cos^2 \tfrac{1}{2}\phi. \qquad (36\text{-}27)$$

From Eq. 34-24, we know that the intensity of an electromagnetic wave is proportional to the square of its amplitude. So the waves we are combining in Fig. 36-10b, whose amplitudes are E_0, have an intensity I_0 that is proportional to E_0^2. And the resultant wave, with amplitude E, has an intensity I that is proportional to E^2. Thus,

$$\frac{I}{I_0} = \frac{E^2}{E_0^2}.$$

Substituting Eq. 36-27 into this and rearranging then yield

$$I = 4I_0 \cos^2 \tfrac{1}{2}\phi,$$

which is Eq. 36-21, which we set out to prove.

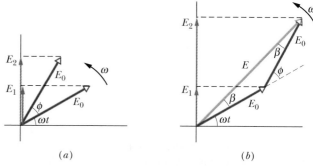

(a)   (b)

FIGURE 36-10 (a) Phasors representing the electric field components of the waves given by Eqs. 36-19 and 36-20. They both have magnitude E_0 and rotate with angular speed ω. (b) Vector addition of the two phasors gives the phasor representing the resultant wave, with magnitude E and phase constant β.

It remains to prove Eq. 36-22, which relates the phase difference ϕ between the waves arriving at any point P on the screen of Fig. 36-8 to the angle θ that serves as a locator of that point.

The phase difference ϕ in Eq. 36-20 is associated with the path difference $S_1 b$ in Fig. 36-8. If $S_1 b$ is $\frac{1}{2}\lambda$, then ϕ is π; if $S_1 b$ is λ, then ϕ is 2π, and so on. This suggests

$$\begin{pmatrix} \text{phase} \\ \text{difference} \end{pmatrix} = \frac{2\pi}{\lambda} \begin{pmatrix} \text{path length} \\ \text{difference} \end{pmatrix}. \quad (36\text{-}28)$$

The path difference $S_1 b$ in Fig. 36-8b is just $d \sin \theta$, so Eq. 36-28 becomes

$$\phi = \frac{2\pi d}{\lambda} \sin \theta,$$

which is just Eq. 36-22, the other equation that we set out to prove.

Combining More than Two Waves

In a more general case, we might want to find the resultant of more than two sinusoidally varying waves. The general procedure is this:

1. Construct a series of phasors representing the functions to be added. Draw them end to end, maintaining the proper phase relations between adjacent phasors.

2. Construct the vector sum of this array. The length of this vector sum gives the amplitude of the resultant phasor. The angle between the vector sum and the first phasor is the phase of the resultant with respect to this first phasor. The projection of this vector-sum phasor on the vertical axis gives the time variation of the resultant wave.

SAMPLE PROBLEM 36-3

Find the resultant wave $E(t)$ of the following waves:

$$E_1 = E_0 \sin \omega t,$$

$$E_2 = E_0 \sin(\omega t + 60°),$$

$$E_3 = E_0 \sin(\omega t - 30°).$$

SOLUTION: The resultant wave is

$$E(t) = E_1(t) + E_2(t) + E_3(t).$$

In using the method of phasors to find this sum, we are free to evaluate the phasors at any time t. To simplify the problem we choose $t = 0$, for which the phasors representing the three waves are shown in Fig. 36-11. We now treat the addition of the phasors as we would any other addition of vectors. The sum of the horizontal components of E_1, E_2, and E_3 is

$$\sum E_h = E_0 \cos 0 + E_0 \cos 60° + E_0 \cos(-30°)$$

$$= E_0 + 0.500 E_0 + 0.866 E_0 = 2.37 E_0.$$

The sum of the vertical components, which is the value of E at $t = 0$, is

$$\sum E_v = E_0 \sin 0 + E_0 \sin 60° + E_0 \sin(-30°)$$

$$= 0 + 0.866 E_0 - 0.500 E_0 = 0.366 E_0.$$

The resultant wave $E(t)$ has an amplitude E_R of

$$E_R = \sqrt{(2.37 E_0)^2 + (0.366 E_0)^2} = 2.4 E_0,$$

and a phase angle β relative to phasor E_1 of

$$\beta = \tan^{-1}\left(\frac{0.366 E_0}{2.37 E_0}\right) = 8.8°.$$

We can now write, for the resultant wave $E(t)$,

$$E = E_R \sin(\omega t + \beta)$$

$$= 2.4 E_0 \sin(\omega t + 8.8°). \quad \text{(Answer)}$$

Be careful to interpret the angle β correctly in Fig. 36-11: it is the constant angle between E_R and E_1 as the four phasors rotate as a single unit around the origin. The angle between E_R and the horizontal axis does not remain equal to β.

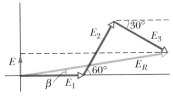

FIGURE 36-11 Sample Problem 36-3. Three phasors E_1, E_2, and E_3, shown at time $t = 0$, combine to give resultant phasor E_R.

CHECKPOINT **4:** Each of four pairs of light waves arrives at a certain point on a screen. The waves have the same wavelength. At the arrival point, their amplitudes and phase differences are (a) $2E_0$, $6E_0$, and π rad; (b) $3E_0$, $5E_0$, and π rad; (c) $9E_0$, $7E_0$, and 3π rad; (d) $2E_0$, $2E_0$, and 0 rad. Rank the four pairs according to the intensity of the light at those points, greatest first. (*Hint:* Draw phasors.)

36-7 INTERFERENCE FROM THIN FILMS

The colors we see when sunlight illuminates a soap bubble or an oil slick are caused by the interference of light waves reflected from the front and back surfaces of a thin transparent film. The thickness of the soap or oil film is typically of the order of magnitude of the wavelength of the (visible) light involved. (We shall not consider greater thicknesses, which spoil the coherence of the light needed to produce colors by interference; we shall discuss lesser thicknesses shortly.)

Figure 36-12 shows a thin transparent film of uniform thickness L and index of refraction n_2, illuminated by bright light of wavelength λ from a distant point source. For now, we assume that air lies on both sides of the film and thus that $n_1 = n_3$ in Fig. 36-12. For simplicity, we also assume that the light rays are almost perpendicular to the film ($\theta \approx 0$). We are interested in whether the film is bright or dark to an observer viewing it almost perpendicularly. (Since the film is brightly illuminated, how could it possibly be dark? You will see.)

The incident light, represented by ray i, intercepts the front (left) surface of the film at point a and undergoes both reflection and refraction there. The reflected ray r_1 is intercepted by the observer's eye. The refracted light crosses the film to point b on the back surface, where it undergoes both reflection and refraction. The light reflected at b crosses back through the film to point c, where it undergoes both reflection and refraction. The light refracted at c, represented by ray r_2, is intercepted by the observer's eye.

If the light waves of rays r_1 and r_2 are exactly in phase at the eye, they produce an interference maximum, and region ac on the film is bright to the observer. If they are exactly out of phase, they produce an interference minimum, and region ac is dark to the observer, *even though it is illuminated*. And if there is some intermediate phase difference, there are intermediate interference and intermediate brightness.

So the key to what the observer sees is the phase difference between the waves of rays r_1 and r_2. Both rays are

derived from the same ray i, but the path involved in producing r_2 involves light traveling twice across the film (a to b, and then b to c), whereas the path involved in producing r_1 involves no travel through the film. Because θ is about zero, we approximate the path length difference between the waves of r_1 and r_2 as $2L$. However, to find the phase difference between the waves, we cannot just find the number of wavelengths λ that is equivalent to a path length difference of $2L$. This simple approach is impossible for two reasons: (1) the path length difference occurs in a medium other than air, and (2) reflections are involved, which can change the phase.

The phase difference between two waves can change if one or both are reflected.

Before we continue our discussion of interference from thin films, we must discuss changes in phase that are caused by reflections.

Reflection Phase Shifts

Refraction at an interface never causes a phase change. But reflection can, depending on the indices of refraction on the two sides of the interface. Figure 36-13 shows what happens when reflection causes a phase change, using pulses on a denser string (along which pulse travel is relatively slow) and a lighter string (along which pulse travel is relatively fast).

When a pulse traveling slowly along the denser string in Fig. 36-13a reaches the interface with the lighter string, the pulse is partially transmitted and partially reflected, with no change in orientation. For light, this situation corresponds to the incident wave traveling in the medium of greater index of refraction n (recall that greater n means slower speed). In that case, the wave that is reflected at the interface does not undergo a change in phase; that is, the *reflection phase shift* is zero.

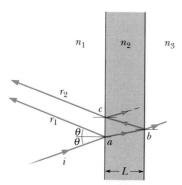

FIGURE 36-12 Light waves, represented with ray i, are incident on a thin film of thickness L and index of refraction n_2. Rays r_1 and r_2 represent light waves reflected by the front and back surfaces of the film. (All three rays are actually nearly perpendicular to the film.) The interference of the waves of r_1 and r_2 with each other depends on their phase difference. The index of refraction n_1 of the medium at the left can differ from the index of refraction n_3 of the medium at the right, but for now we assume that both media are air, with $n_1 = n_3 = 1.0$, which is less than n_2.

FIGURE 36-13 Phase changes when a pulse is reflected at the interface between two stretched strings of different linear densities. The wave speed is greater in the lighter string. (*a*) The incident pulse is in the denser string. (*b*) The incident pulse is in the lighter string. Only here is there a phase change.

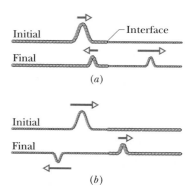

When a pulse traveling more quickly along the lighter string in Fig. 36-13b reaches the interface with the denser string, the transmitted pulse has the same orientation as the incident pulse, but the reflected pulse is inverted. For a sinusoidal wave, such an inversion involves a phase change of π rad, or half a wavelength. For light, this situation corresponds to the incident wave traveling in the medium of lesser index of refraction (with greater speed). In that case, the wave that is reflected at the interface undergoes a phase shift of π rad, or half a wavelength. We can summarize these results for light in terms of the index of refraction of the medium off which (or from which) the light reflects:

Reflection	Reflection phase shift
Off lower index	0
Off higher index	0.5 wavelength

This might be remembered as "higher means half."

Equations for Thin-Film Interference

In this chapter we have now seen three ways in which the phase difference between two waves can change:

1. by reflection
2. by the waves traveling along paths of different lengths
3. by the waves traveling through media of different indices of refraction

When light reflects from a thin film, producing the waves of rays r_1 and r_2 in Fig. 36-12, all three ways are involved. Let us consider them one by one.

We first reexamine the two reflections in Fig. 36-12. At point a on the front interface, the incident wave (in air) reflects from the medium having the higher of the two indices of refraction, so the wave of reflected ray r_1 has its phase shifted by 0.5 wavelength. At point b on the back interface, the incident wave reflects from the medium (air) having the lower of the two indices of refraction, so the wave reflected there is not shifted in phase by the reflection, and thus neither is the portion of it that exits the film as ray r_2. We can organize this information with the first line in Table 36-1. It tells us that, so far, as a result of the reflection phase shifts, the waves of r_1 and r_2 have a phase difference of 0.5 wavelength and thus are exactly out of phase.

Now we must consider the path length difference $2L$ that occurs because the wave of ray r_2 crosses the film twice. (This difference $2L$ is shown on the second line in Table 36-1.) If the waves of r_1 and r_2 are to be exactly in phase so that they produce fully constructive interference,

TABLE 36-1 AN ORGANIZING TABLE FOR THIN-FILM INTERFERENCE IN AIR[a]

	r_1	r_2
Reflection phase shifts	0.5 wavelength	0
Path length difference	$2L$	
Index in which path length difference occurs	n_2	
In phase[a]:	$2L = \dfrac{\text{odd number}}{2} \times \dfrac{\lambda}{n_2}$	
Out of phase[a]:	$2L = \text{integer} \times \dfrac{\lambda}{n_2}$	

[a]Valid for $n_2 > n_1$ and $n_2 > n_3$.

the path length $2L$ must cause an additional phase difference of 0.5, 1.5, 2.5, . . . wavelengths. Only then will the net phase difference be an integer number of wavelengths. Thus, for a bright film, we must have

$$2L = \frac{\text{odd number}}{2} \times \text{wavelength}$$
$$\text{(in-phase waves).} \quad (36\text{-}29)$$

The wavelength we need here is the wavelength λ_{n2} of the light in the medium containing path length $2L$, that is, in the medium with index of refraction n_2. So, we can rewrite Eq. 36-29 as

$$2L = \frac{\text{odd number}}{2} \times \lambda_{n2} \quad \text{(in-phase waves).} \quad (36\text{-}30)$$

If, instead, the waves are to be exactly out of phase so that there is fully destructive interference, the path length $2L$ must cause either no additional phase difference or a phase difference of 1, 2, 3, . . . wavelengths. Only then will the net phase difference be an odd number of half-wavelengths. So, for a dark film, we must have

$$2L = \text{integer} \times \text{wavelength}, \quad (36\text{-}31)$$

where, again, the wavelength is the wavelength λ_{n2} in the medium containing $2L$. So, this time we have

$$2L = \text{integer} \times \lambda_{n2} \quad \text{(out-of-phase waves).} \quad (36\text{-}32)$$

Now recalling that the wave of ray r_2 traveled through a medium of index of refraction n_2 whereas the wave of ray r_1 did not, we can use Eq. 36-8 ($\lambda_n = \lambda/n$) to write the wavelength of the wave inside the film as

$$\lambda_{n2} = \frac{\lambda}{n_2}, \quad (36\text{-}33)$$

where λ is the wavelength of the incident light in vacuum (and approximately also in air). Substituting Eq. 36-33 into

Eq. 36-30 and replacing "odd number/2" with $(m + \frac{1}{2})$ give us

$$2L = (m + \tfrac{1}{2})\frac{\lambda}{n_2}, \quad \text{for } m = 0, 1, 2, \ldots$$
$$\text{(maxima—bright film in air).} \quad (36\text{-}34)$$

Similarly, with m replacing "integer," Eq. 36-32 yields

$$2L = m\frac{\lambda}{n_2}, \quad \text{for } m = 0, 1, 2, \ldots$$
$$\text{(minima—dark film in air).} \quad (36\text{-}35)$$

For a given film thickness L, Eqs. 36-34 and 36-35 tell us the wavelengths of light for which the film appears bright and dark, respectively, one wavelength for each value of m. Intermediate wavelengths give intermediate brightnesses. For a given wavelength λ, Eqs. 36-34 and 36-35 tell us the thicknesses of the films that appear bright and dark in that light, respectively, one thickness for each value of m. Intermediate thicknesses give intermediate brightnesses.

A special situation arises when a film is so thin that L is much less than λ, say, $L < 0.1\lambda$. Then the path length difference $2L$ can be neglected, and the phase difference between r_1 and r_2 is due *only* to reflection phase shifts. If the film of Fig. 36-12, where the reflections cause a phase difference of 0.5 wavelength, has thickness $L < 0.1\lambda$, then r_1 and r_2 are exactly out of phase, and thus the film is dark, regardless of the wavelength and even the intensity of the light that illuminates it. This special situation corresponds to $m = 0$ in Eq. 36-35. We shall count any $L < 0.1\lambda$ as being the least thickness that makes the film of Fig. 36-12 dark. The next greater thickness that makes the film dark is that corresponding to $m = 1$.

Figure 36-14 shows a vertical soap film whose thickness increases from top to bottom because the weight of the film has caused it to slump. Bright white light illuminates the film. However, the top portion is so thin that it is dark. In the (somewhat thicker) middle we see fringes, or bands, whose color depends primarily on the wavelength at which reflected light undergoes fully constructive interference for a particular thickness. Toward the (thickest) bottom of the film the fringes become progressively narrower and the colors begin to overlap and fade.

FIGURE 36-14 The reflection of light from a soapy water film spanning a vertical loop. The top portion is so thin that the light reflected there undergoes destructive interference, making that portion dark. Colored interference fringes, or bands, decorate the rest of the film but are marred by circulation of liquid within the film as the liquid is gradually pulled downward by gravitation.

PROBLEM SOLVING TACTICS

TACTIC 1: *Thin-Film Equations*

Some students believe that Eq. 36-34 gives the maxima and Eq. 36-35 gives the minima for *all* thin-film situations. This is not true. These relations were derived only for the situation in which $n_2 > n_1$ and $n_2 > n_3$ in Fig. 36-12.

The appropriate equations for other relative values of the indices of refraction can be derived by following the reasoning of this section and constructing new versions of Table 36-1. In each case you will end up with Eqs. 36-34 and 36-35, but sometimes Eq. 36-34 will give the minima and Eq. 36-35 will give the maxima—the opposite of what we found here. Which equation gives which depends on whether the reflections at the two interfaces give the same reflection phase shift.

$\mathbb{C}$HECKPOINT 5: The figure shows four situations in which light reflects perpendicularly from a thin film (as in Fig. 36-12), with the indices of refraction as given. (a) For which situations does reflection cause a zero phase difference for the two reflected rays? (b) For which situations will the film be dark if the path length difference $2L$ causes a phase difference of 0.5 wavelength?

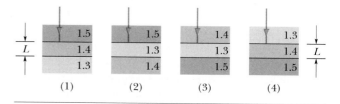

SAMPLE PROBLEM 36-4

White light, with a uniform intensity across the visible wavelength range of 400–690 nm, is perpendicularly incident on a water film, of index of refraction $n_2 = 1.33$ and thickness $L = 320$ nm, that is suspended in air. At what wavelength λ is the light reflected by the film brightest to an observer?

SOLUTION: This situation is like that of Fig. 36-12, for which Eq. 36-34 gives the interference maxima. Solving for λ and inserting the given data, we obtain

$$\lambda = \frac{2n_2L}{m + \frac{1}{2}} = \frac{(2)(1.33)(320\ \text{nm})}{m + \frac{1}{2}} = \frac{851\ \text{nm}}{m + \frac{1}{2}}.$$

For $m = 0$, this gives us $\lambda = 1700$ nm, which is in the infrared region. For $m = 1$, we find $\lambda = 567$ nm, which is yellow-green light, near the middle of the visible spectrum. For $m = 2$, $\lambda = 340$ nm, which is in the ultraviolet region. So the wavelength at which the light seen by the observer is brightest is

$$\lambda = 567\ \text{nm}. \qquad \text{(Answer)}$$

Solving for L and inserting the given data, we obtain

$$L = \frac{\lambda}{4n_2} = \frac{550\ \text{nm}}{(4)(1.38)} = 99.6\ \text{nm}. \qquad \text{(Answer)}$$

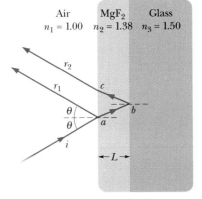

FIGURE 36-15 Sample Problem 36-5. Unwanted reflections from glass can be suppressed (at a chosen wavelength) by coating the glass with a thin transparent film of magnesium fluoride of a properly chosen thickness.

SAMPLE PROBLEM 36-5

A glass lens is coated on one side with a thin film of magnesium fluoride (MgF$_2$) to reduce reflection from the lens surface (Fig. 36-15). The index of refraction of MgF$_2$ is 1.38; that of the glass is 1.50. What is the least coating thickness that eliminates (via interference) the reflections at the middle of the visible spectrum ($\lambda = 550$ nm)? Assume that the light is approximately perpendicular to the lens surface.

SOLUTION: Figure 36-15 differs from Fig. 36-12 in that now $n_3 > n_2 > n_1$. This means there is now a reflection phase shift of 0.5 wavelength associated with the reflections at *both* front and back interfaces of the thin film. Constructing a table like Table 36-1, we fill in 0.5 and 0.5 for the first line. For the second and third lines, the path length difference is still $2L$ and it still occurs in a medium (here MgF$_2$) having index of refraction n_2.

The reflections alone tend to put the waves of r_1 and r_2 in phase. For these rays to be out of phase so that the reflections from the lens are eliminated, the path length difference $2L$ within the film must be

$$2L = \frac{\text{odd number}}{2} \times \text{wavelength}$$

$$= (m + \tfrac{1}{2})\lambda_{n2}, \qquad \text{for } m = 0, 1, 2, \ldots.$$

Substituting λ/n_2 for λ_{n2} yields

$$2L = (m + \tfrac{1}{2})\frac{\lambda}{n_2}, \qquad \text{for } m = 0, 1, 2, \ldots.$$

We want the least thickness for the coating, that is, the smallest L. Thus we choose $m = 0$, the smallest value of m.

SAMPLE PROBLEM 36-6

Figure 36-16a shows a transparent plastic block with a thin wedge of the plastic removed at the right. A broad beam of red light, with wavelength $\lambda = 632.8$ nm, is directed directly downward through the top of the block (at an incidence angle of 0°). Some of the light is reflected back up from the top and bottom surfaces of the wedge, which acts as a thin film (of air) with a thickness that varies uniformly and gradually from L_L at the left-hand end to L_R at the right-hand end. An observer

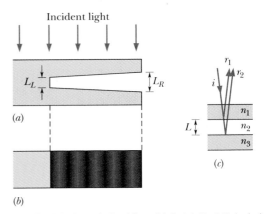

FIGURE 36-16 Sample Problem 36-6. (a) Red light is incident on a thin air-filled wedge in the side of a transparent plastic block. The thickness of the wedge is L_L at the left end and L_R at the right end. (b) The view from above the block: an interference pattern of six dark fringes and five bright red fringes lies over the region of the wedge. (c) A representation of the incident ray i, reflected rays r_1 and r_2, and thickness L of the wedge anywhere along the length of the wedge.

looking down on the block sees an interference pattern consisting of six dark fringes and five bright red fringes along the wedge. What is the change in thickness $\Delta L (= L_R - L_L)$ along the wedge?

SOLUTION: This thin-film problem differs from preceding problems because the thickness of the film varies. It is that variation that produces the observed variation between dark and bright fringes along the wedge. Because the observer sees more dark fringes than bright fringes, we can assume that a dark fringe is produced at both the left and right ends of the film. Thus the interference pattern is that shown in Fig. 36-16b, which we can use to determine the change in thickness ΔL of the wedge.

We can represent the reflection of light by the top and bottom surfaces of the wedge anywhere along its length with Fig. 36-16c, at a place where we assume that the wedge has thickness L. From what we know about phase shifts by reflection, we see that the reflection phase shift for ray r_1 is zero and that for ray r_2 is 0.5 wavelength. Constructing a table like Table 36-1, we fill in 0 and 0.5 for the first line. For the second and third lines, the path length difference is still $2L$ and it still occurs in a medium (here air) with index of refraction n_2. Thus, for fully destructive interference we find that

$$2L = \text{integer} \times \frac{\lambda}{n_2} = m \frac{\lambda}{n_2}. \qquad (36\text{-}36)$$

We can apply this equation at any point along the wedge where a dark fringe is observed. The least value of the integer m is associated with the least thickness of the wedge where a dark fringe is observed. And progressively greater values of m are associated with progressively greater thicknesses of the wedge where a dark fringe is observed.

A dark fringe happens to be observed at the left end of the wedge, where the thickness is least. Applying Eq. 36-36 to that end, substituting L_L for L, and then solving for L_L, we have

$$L_L = \frac{m_L \lambda}{2n_2}, \qquad (36\text{-}37)$$

where m_L is the integer associated with the dark fringe at the left end and n_2 is the index of refraction of the material inside the wedge (air).

We can also apply Eq. 36-36 to the right end of the wedge, where another dark fringe is seen. There the thickness is L_R, and the integer associated with L_R and this dark fringe is $m_L + 5$ (because the fringe is the fifth one from the fringe at the left-hand end). Substituting L_R for L and $m_L + 5$ for m into Eq. 36-36 and solving for L_R yield

$$L_R = \frac{(m_L + 5)\lambda}{2n_2}. \qquad (36\text{-}38)$$

Subtracting Eq. 36-37 from Eq. 36-38 then gives us the change in thickness ΔL of the wedge:

$$\Delta L = L_R - L_L = \frac{(m_L + 5)\lambda}{2n_2} - \frac{m_L \lambda}{2n_2} = \frac{5}{2} \frac{\lambda}{n_2}.$$

Substituting 632.8×10^{-9} m for λ and 1.00 for n_2 into this equation, we find

$$\Delta L = \frac{5}{2} \frac{632.8 \times 10^{-9} \text{ m}}{1.00}$$
$$= 1.58 \times 10^{-6} \text{ m}. \qquad \text{(Answer)}$$

SAMPLE PROBLEM 36-7

The iridescence seen in the top surface of *Morpho* butterfly wings is due to constructive interference of the light reflected by thin terraces of transparent cuticle-like material. The terraces extend outward, parallel to the wings, from a central structure that is approximately perpendicular to the wing. Cross sections of the central structure and terraces are shown in the electron micrograph of Fig. 36-17a. The terraces have index of refraction $n = 1.53$ and thickness $D_t = 63.5$ nm; they are separated (by air) by $D_a = 127$ nm. If the incident light is perpendicular to the terraces (see Fig. 36-17b, where the angle of the incident light is exaggerated), at what wavelength of visible light do the reflections from the terraces have an interference maximum?

SOLUTION: Let us first consider rays r_1 and r_2 in Fig. 36-17b, which involve reflections at points a and b. This situation is just like that of Fig. 36-12, and so Eq. 36-34 gives the interference maxima. Solving Eq. 36-34 for λ gives us

$$\lambda = \frac{2n_2 L}{m + \frac{1}{2}}.$$

Substituting $D_t (= 63.5$ nm) for L and $n (= 1.53)$ for n_2, we have

$$\lambda = \frac{2nD_t}{m + \frac{1}{2}} = \frac{(2)(1.53)(63.5 \text{ nm})}{m + \frac{1}{2}} = \frac{194 \text{ nm}}{m + \frac{1}{2}}.$$

For $m = 0$, we find an interference maximum at $\lambda = 388$ nm, which is in the ultraviolet region. For all larger values of m, λ is even smaller, farther into the ultraviolet. So rays r_1 and r_2 do not produce the bright blue-green color of the *Morpho*.

Let us next consider rays r_1 and r_3 in Fig. 36-17b. The wave producing the latter passes through a terrace and then through air to the next terrace, where it reflects at point d. Then it travels upward, resulting in ray r_3. The path length difference between the waves leading to rays r_1 and r_3 is $2D_t + 2D_a$. This situation differs considerably from that of Fig. 36-12, and Eq. 36-34 does not apply. To find a new equation for interference maxima for this new situation, we first consider the reflections involved and then count the wavelengths along path length difference $2D_t + 2D_a$.

The reflections at points a and d both introduce a phase change of half a wavelength. So the reflections alone tend to put the waves of rays r_1 and r_3 in phase. Thus for these waves actually to end up in phase, the number of wavelengths along the path length difference $2D_t + 2D_a$ must be an integer. The wavelength within the terrace is $\lambda_n = \lambda/n$. So the number of

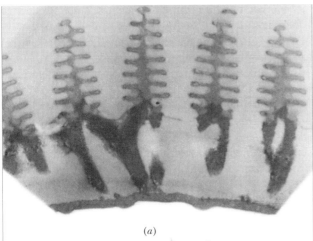

(a)

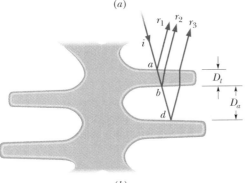

(b)

FIGURE 36-17 Sample Problem 36-7. (*a*) An electron micrograph shows the cross section of terrace structures of cuticle material that stick up from the top surface of a *Morpho* wing. (*b*) Light waves reflecting at points *a* and *b* on a terrace, represented by rays r_1 and r_2, interfere at the eye of an observer. The wave of ray r_1 also interferes with the wave that reflects at point *d* and is represented by ray r_3.

wavelengths in length $2D_t$ is

$$N_t = \frac{2D_t}{\lambda_n} = \frac{2D_t n}{\lambda}.$$

Similarly, the number of wavelengths in length $2D_a$ is

$$N_a = \frac{2D_a}{\lambda}.$$

For the waves of rays r_1 and r_3 to be in phase, we need $N_t + N_a$ to be equal to an integer *m*. Thus for an interference maximum,

$$\frac{2D_t n}{\lambda} + \frac{2D_a}{\lambda} = m, \qquad \text{for } m = 1, 2, 3, \ldots .$$

Solving for λ and substituting the given data, we obtain

$$\lambda = \frac{(2)(63.5 \text{ nm})(1.53) + (2)(127 \text{ nm})}{m} = \frac{448 \text{ nm}}{m}.$$

For $m = 1$, we find

$$\lambda = 448 \text{ nm}. \qquad \text{(Answer)}$$

This wavelength corresponds to the bright blue-green color of the top surface of a *Morpho* wing. Further, when the

incident light is not exactly perpendicular to the terraces but travels along a slanted path, the paths taken by the waves represented by r_1 and r_3 change, and so does the wavelength of maximum interference. Thus as the wing moves in your view, the wavelength at which the wing is brightest changes slightly, producing iridescence of the wing.

36-8 MICHELSON'S INTERFEROMETER

An **interferometer** is a device that can be used to measure lengths or changes in length with great accuracy by means of interference fringes. We describe the form originally devised and built by A. A. Michelson in 1881. Consider light that leaves point *P* on extended source *S* (Fig. 36-18) and encounters a *beam splitter M*. This is a mirror with the following property: it transmits half the incident light, reflecting the rest. In the figure we have assumed, for convenience, that this mirror possesses negligible thickness. At *M* the light thus divides into two waves. One proceeds by transmission toward mirror M_1; the other proceeds by reflection toward M_2. The waves are reflected at each of these mirrors and are sent back along their directions of incidence, each wave eventually entering the telescope *T*. What the observer sees is a pattern of curved or approximately straight interference fringes; the latter resemble the stripes on a zebra.

The path length difference for the two waves when they recombine is $2d_2 - 2d_1$, and anything that changes this path difference will cause a change in the phase between these two waves at the eye. As an example, if mirror M_2 is moved by a distance $\frac{1}{2}\lambda$, the path length difference is changed by λ and the fringe pattern is shifted by one fringe (as if each dark stripe on a zebra had moved to where the

FIGURE 36-18 Michelson's interferometer, showing the path of light originating at point *P* of an extended source *S*. Mirror *M* splits the light into two beams, which reflect from mirrors M_1 and M_2 back to *M* and then to telescope *T*. In the telescope an observer sees a pattern of interference fringes.

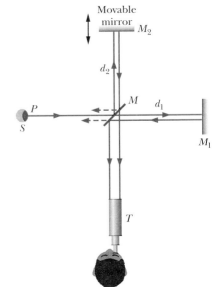

adjacent dark stripe had been). Similarly, moving mirror M_2 by $\frac{1}{4}\lambda$ causes a shift by half a fringe (each zebra stripe shifts by one stripe width).

A shift in the fringe pattern can also be caused by the insertion of a thin transparent material into the optical path of one of the mirrors, say, M_1. If the material has thickness L and index of refraction n, then the number of wavelengths along the light's doubled-back path through the material is

$$N_m = \frac{2L}{\lambda_n} = \frac{2Ln}{\lambda}. \qquad (36\text{-}39)$$

The number of wavelengths in the same thickness $2L$ of air before the insertion of the material is

$$N_a = \frac{2L}{\lambda}. \qquad (36\text{-}40)$$

So when the material is inserted, the light returned by mirror M_1 undergoes a phase change (in terms of wavelengths) of

$$N_m - N_a = \frac{2Ln}{\lambda} - \frac{2L}{\lambda} = \frac{2L}{\lambda}(n-1). \qquad (36\text{-}41)$$

For each phase change of one wavelength, the fringe pattern is shifted by one fringe. Thus by counting the number of fringes through which the material causes the pattern to shift, and substituting that number for $N_m - N_a$ in Eq. 36-41, you can determine the thickness L of the material in terms of λ.

By such techniques the lengths of objects can be expressed in terms of the wavelengths of light. In Michelson's day, the standard of length—the meter—was chosen by international agreement to be the distance between two fine scratches on a certain metal bar preserved at Sèvres, near Paris. Michelson was able to show, using his interferometer, that the standard meter was equivalent to 1,553,163.5 wavelengths of a certain monochromatic red light emitted from a light source containing cadmium. For this careful measurement, Michelson received the 1907 Nobel prize in physics. His work laid the foundation for the eventual abandonment (in 1961) of the meter bar as a standard of length and for the redefinition of the meter in terms of the wavelength of light. By 1983, as we have seen, even this wavelength standard was not precise enough to meet the growing requirements of science and technology, and it was replaced with a new standard based on a defined value for the speed of light.

REVIEW & SUMMARY

Huygens' Principle

The three-dimensional transmission of waves, including light, may often be predicted by *Huygens' principle*, which states that all points on a wavefront serve as point sources of spherical secondary wavelets. After a time t, the new position of the wavefront will be that of a surface tangent to these secondary wavelets.

The law of refraction can be derived from Huygens' principle by assuming that the index of refraction of any medium is $n = c/v$, in which v is the speed of light in the medium and c is the speed of light in vacuum.

Wavelength and Index of Refraction

The wavelength λ_n of light in a medium depends on the index of refraction n of the medium:

$$\lambda_n = \frac{\lambda}{n}, \qquad (36\text{-}8)$$

in which λ is the wavelength of the light in vacuum. Because of this dependency, the phase difference between two waves can change if they pass through different materials with different indices of refraction.

Geometrical Optics and Diffraction

Attempts to isolate a ray by forcing light through a narrow slit fail because of **diffraction,** the flaring out of the light into the geometrical shadow of the slit. If such slits are present, the approxi-

mations of geometrical optics (Chapters 34 and 35) fail, and the full treatment of wave optics must be used.

Young's Experiment

In **Young's interference experiment,** light passing through a single slit falls on two slits in a screen. The light leaving these slits flares out (by diffraction), and interference occurs in the region beyond the screen. A fringe pattern, due to the interference, forms on a viewing screen.

The light intensity at any point on the viewing screen depends in part on the difference in the path lengths from the slits to that point. If this difference is an integer number of wavelengths, the waves interfere constructively and an intensity maximum results. If it is an odd number of half-wavelengths, there is destructive interference and an intensity minimum occurs. The conditions for maximum and minimum intensity are

$$d \sin \theta = m\lambda, \qquad \text{for } m = 0, 1, 2, \ldots$$
$$\text{(maxima—bright fringes),} \qquad (36\text{-}14)$$

$$d \sin \theta = (m + \tfrac{1}{2})\lambda, \qquad \text{for } m = 0, 1, 2, \ldots$$
$$\text{(minima—dark fringes),} \qquad (36\text{-}16)$$

where θ is the angle the light path makes with a central axis and d is the slit separation.

Coherence

If two overlapping light waves are to interfere perceptibly, the phase difference between them must remain constant with time; that is, the waves must be **coherent.** When two coherent waves overlap, the resulting intensity may be found by using phasors.

Intensity in Two-Slit Interference

In Young's interference experiment, two waves, each with intensity I_0, yield a resultant wave of intensity I at the viewing screen:

$$I = 4I_0 \cos^2(\tfrac{1}{2}\phi), \qquad \text{where } \phi = \frac{2\pi d}{\lambda} \sin \theta.$$

$$(36\text{-}21, 36\text{-}22)$$

Equations 36-14 and 36-16, which identify the positions of the fringe maxima and minima, are contained within this relation.

Thin-Film Interference

When light is incident on a thin transparent film, the light waves reflected from the front and back surfaces interfere. For near-normal incidence the wavelength conditions for maximum and minimum intensity of the light reflected from a *film in air* are

$$2L = (m + \tfrac{1}{2}) \frac{\lambda}{n_2}, \qquad \text{for } m = 0, 1, 2 \dots$$

$$\text{(maxima—bright film in air)}, \qquad (36\text{-}34)$$

$$2L = m \frac{\lambda}{n_2}, \qquad \text{for } m = 0, 1, 2 \dots$$

$$\text{(minima—dark film in air)}, \qquad (36\text{-}35)$$

where n_2 is the index of refraction of the film, L is its thickness, and λ is the wavelength of the light in air.

If the light incident at an interface between media with different indices of refraction is in the medium with the smaller index of refraction, the reflection causes a phase change of π rad, or half a wavelength, in the reflected wave. Otherwise, there is no phase change due to the reflection. Refraction at an interface does not cause a phase shift.

The Michelson Interferometer

In *Michelson's interferometer* a light wave is split into two beams, which, after traversing paths of different lengths, are recombined so that they interfere and form a fringe pattern. Varying the path length of one of the beams allows distances to be accurately expressed in terms of wavelengths of light, by counting the number of fringes through which the fringe pattern shifts.

QUESTIONS

1. In Fig. 36-19, three pulses of light—a, b, and c—of the same wavelength are sent through layers of plastic whose indices of refraction are given. Rank the pulses according to their travel time through the plastic, greatest first.

FIGURE 36-19
Question 1.

2. Light travels along the length of a 1500 nm long nanostructure. When a peak of the wave is at one end of the nanostructure, is there a peak or a valley at the other end if the wavelength is (a) 500 nm and (b) 1000 nm?

3. Figure 36-20 shows two rays of light, of wavelength 600 nm, that reflect from glass surfaces separated by 150 nm. The rays are initially in phase. (a) What is the path length difference of the rays? (b) When they have cleared the reflection region, are the rays exactly in phase, exactly out of phase, or in some intermediate state?

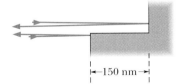

FIGURE 36-20
Question 3.

4. Figure 36-21 shows two light rays that are initially exactly in phase and reflect from several glass surfaces. Neglect the slight slant in the path of the light in the second arrangement. (a) What is the path length difference of the rays? In wavelengths λ, (b) what should that path length difference equal if the rays are to be exactly out of phase when they emerge, and (c) what is the smallest value of d that will allow that final phase difference?

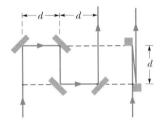

FIGURE 36-21
Question 4.

5. Figure 36-22 shows three situations in which two rays of sunlight penetrate slightly into and then scatter out of lunar soil. Assume that the rays are initially in phase. In which situation are the associated waves most likely to end up in phase? (Just as the Moon becomes full, its brightness suddenly peaks, becoming 25% greater than its brightness on the nights before and after, because at full Moon we intercept light waves that are scattered by lunar soil back toward the Sun and undergo constructive interference at our eyes.)

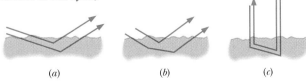

(a) $\qquad\qquad$ (b) $\qquad\qquad$ (c)

FIGURE 36-22 Question 5.

6. Is there an interference maximum, a minimum, an intermediate state closer to a maximum, or an intermediate state closer to a minimum at point P in Fig. 36-8 if the path length difference of the two rays is (a) 2.2λ, (b) 3.5λ, (c) 1.8λ, and (d) 1.0λ? For each situation, give the value of m associated with the maximum or minimum involved.

7. (a) If you move from one bright fringe in a two-slit interference pattern to the next one farther out, (a) does the path length difference ΔL increase or decrease and (b) by how much does it change, in wavelengths λ?

8. Does the spacing between fringes in a two-slit interference pattern increase, decrease, or stay the same if (a) the slit separation is increased, (b) the color of the light is switched from red to blue, and (c) the whole apparatus is submerged in cooking sherry? (d) If the slits are illuminated with white light, then at any side maximum, does the blue component or the red component peak closer to the central maximum?

9. In Fig. 36-23, a thin, transparent plastic layer has been placed over the lower slit in a double-slit experiment. Does this cause the central maximum (the fringe where waves arrive with a phase difference of zero wavelengths) to move up or down the screen? (*Hint:* Is the wavelength in the plastic greater than or less than that in air?)

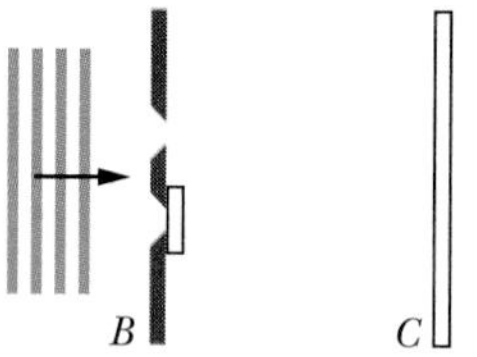

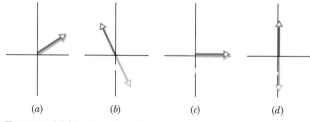

FIGURE 36-23 Question 9.

10. Figure 36-24 shows, at different times, the phasors representing the two light waves arriving at four different points on the viewing screen in a double-slit interference experiment. Assuming all eight phasors have the same length, rank the points according to the intensity of the light there, greatest first.

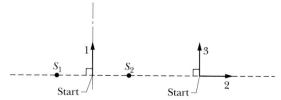

(a)   (b)   (c)   (d)

FIGURE 36-24 Question 10.

11. Figure 36-25 shows two sources S_1 and S_2 that emit radio waves of wavelength λ in all directions. The sources are exactly in phase and are separated by a distance equal to 1.5λ. The vertical broken line is the perpendicular bisector of the distance be-

FIGURE 36-25 Question 11.

tween the sources. (a) If we start at the indicated start point and travel along path 1, does the interference produce a maximum all along the path, a minimum all along the path, or alternating maxima and minima? Repeat for (b) path 2 and (c) path 3.

12. Whole milk is a liquid suspension of fat and other particles. If you hold a spoon partially filled with milk in bright sunlight, you will see fleeting points of color near the perimeter of the milk. What causes them?

13. Figure 36-26 shows two rays of light encountering interfaces, where they reflect and refract. Which of the resulting waves are shifted in phase at the interface?

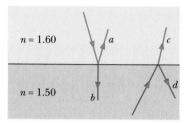

FIGURE 36-26 Question 13.

14. Suppose that the equation $2L = (m + \frac{1}{2})\lambda/n_2$ gives the maxima for interference by a certain thin film. (a) For a given film thickness, does $m = 2$ correspond to the maximum due to the second longest wavelength, the second shortest wavelength, the third longest wavelength, or the third shortest wavelength? (b) For a given wavelength, what value of m corresponds to the third least thickness giving a maximum?

15. Figure 36-27a shows the cross section of a vertical thin film whose width increases downward owing to its weight. Figure 36-27b is a face-on view of the film, showing four bright interference fringes that result when the film is illuminated with a perpendicular beam of red light. Points in the cross section corresponding to the bright fringes are labeled. In terms of the wavelength of the light inside the film, what is the difference in film thickness between (a) points a and b and (b) points b and d?

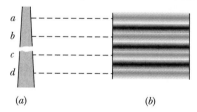

(a)   (b)

FIGURE 36-27 Question 15.

16. Figure 36-28 shows the transmission of light through a thin film in air by a perpendicular beam (tilted in the figure for clarity). (a) Did ray r_3 undergo a phase shift due to reflection? (b) In wavelengths, what is the reflection phase shift for ray r_4? (c) If the film thickness is L, what is the path length difference between rays r_3 and r_4?

Incident light r_4 r_3

FIGURE 36-28 Question 16.

17. Sunlight illuminates a thin film of oil that floats on water, which has a greater index of refraction than the oil. The edge of the film has thickness $L < 0.1\lambda$. Is the edge dark (like the corresponding thin region of the soap film in Fig. 36-14) or bright?

18. The eyes of some animals contain reflectors that send light to receptors where the light is absorbed. In the scallop, the reflector consists of many thin transparent layers alternating between high and low indices of refraction. With the proper layer thicknesses, the combined reflections from the interfaces end up in phase with one another, thereby giving a much brighter reflection than a single biological surface or layer could give. Figure 36-29 shows such an arrangement of alternating layers, along with the reflec-

tions due to a single perpendicularly incident ray i. In terms of the indices of refraction n_1 and n_2 and the wavelength λ of visible light, should the thicknesses be (a) $L_1 = \lambda/4n_1$ and $L_2 = \lambda/4n_2$ or (b) $L_1 = \lambda/2n_1$ and $L_2 = \lambda/2n_2$?

19. Figure 36-30 shows four situations in which light of wavelength λ is incident perpendicularly on a very thin layer. The indicated indices of refraction are $n_1 = 1.33$ and $n_2 = 1.50$. In each situation the thin layer has thickness $L < 0.1\lambda$. In which situations will the light reflected by the thin layer be approximately eliminated by interference?

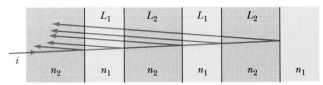

FIGURE 36-29 Question 18.

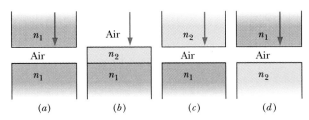

FIGURE 36-30 Question 19.

EXERCISES & PROBLEMS

SECTION 36-2 Light as a Wave

1E. The wavelength of yellow sodium light in air is 589 nm. (a) What is its frequency? (b) What is its wavelength in glass whose index of refraction is 1.52? (c) From the results of (a) and (b) find its speed in this glass.

2E. How much faster, in meters per second, does light travel in sapphire than in diamond? See Table 34-1.

3E. Derive the law of reflection using Huygens' principle.

4E. The speed of yellow light (from a sodium lamp) in a certain liquid is measured to be 1.92×10^8 m/s. What is the index of refraction of this liquid for the light?

5E. What is the speed in fused quartz of light of wavelength 550 nm? (See Fig. 34-19.)

6E. When an electron moves through a medium at a speed exceeding the speed of light in that medium, the electron radiates electromagnetic energy (the *Cerenkov effect*). What minimum speed must an electron have in a liquid of refractive index 1.54 in order to radiate?

7E. A laser beam travels along the axis of a straight section of pipeline, 1 mi long. The pipe normally contains air at standard temperature and pressure (see Table 34-1), but it may also be evacuated. In which case would the travel time for the beam be greater, and by how much?

8P. One end of a stick is pushed through water at speed v, which is greater than the speed u of water waves. Applying Huygens' construction to the water waves produced by the stick, show that a conical wavefront is set up and that its half-angle θ (see Fig. 18-22) is given by

$$\sin\theta = u/v.$$

This is familiar as the bow wave of a ship and the shock wave caused by an object moving through air with a speed exceeding that of sound.

9P. Ocean waves moving at a speed of 4.0 m/s are approaching a beach at an angle of 30° to the normal, as shown in Fig. 36-31. Suppose the water depth changes abruptly at a certain distance from the beach and the wave speed there drops to 3.0 m/s. Close to the beach, what is the angle θ between the direction of wave motion and the normal? (Assume the same law of refraction as for light.) Explain why most waves come in normal to a shore even though at large distances they approach at a variety of angles.

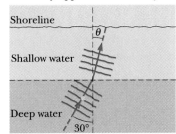

FIGURE 36-31
Problem 9.

10P. In Fig. 36-32, light travels from point A to point B, through two regions having indices of refraction n_1 and n_2. Show that the path that requires the least travel time from A to B is the path for which θ_1 and θ_2 in the figure satisfy Eq. 36-6.

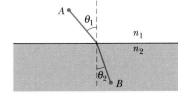

FIGURE 36-32
Problem 10.

11P. In Fig. 36-33, two pulses of light are sent through layers of plastic with the indices of refraction indicated and with thicknesses of either L or $2L$ as shown. (a) Which pulse travels through the plastic in less time? (b) In terms of L/c, what is the difference in the traversal times of the pulses?

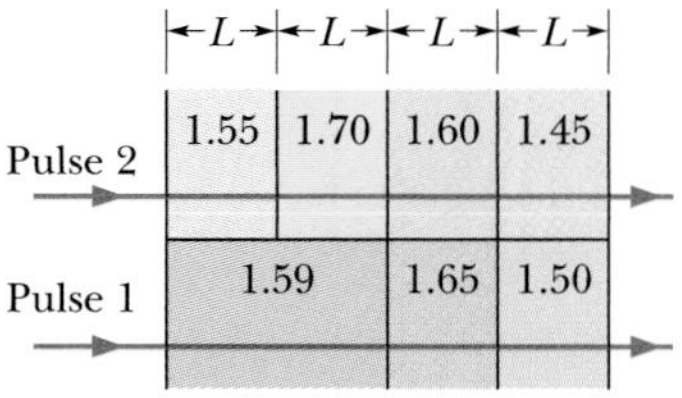

1.55	1.70	1.60	1.45

Pulse 2

1.59	1.65	1.50

Pulse 1

FIGURE 36-33
Problem 11.

12P. In Fig. 36-3, assume two waves of light in air, of wavelength 400 nm, are initially in phase. One travels through a glass layer of index of refraction $n_1 = 1.60$ and thickness L. The other travels through an equally thick plastic layer of index of refraction $n_2 = 1.50$. (a) What is the (least) value of L if the waves are to end up with a phase difference of 5.65 rad? (b) If the waves arrive at some common point after emerging, what type of interference do they undergo?

13P. Suppose the two waves in Fig. 36-3 have wavelength 500 nm in air. In wavelengths, what is their phase difference after traversing media 1 and 2 if (a) $n_1 = 1.50$, $n_2 = 1.60$, and $L = 8.50$ μm; (b) $n_1 = 1.62$, $n_2 = 1.72$, and $L = 8.50$ μm; and (c) $n_1 = 1.59$, $n_2 = 1.79$, and $L = 3.25$ μm? (d) Suppose that in each of these three situations the waves arrive at a common point after emerging. Rank the situations according to the brightness the waves produce at the common point.

14P. In Fig. 36-3, assume the two light waves, of wavelength 620 nm in air, are initially out of phase by π rad. The indices of refraction of the media are $n_1 = 1.45$ and $n_2 = 1.65$. (a) What is the least thickness L that will put the waves exactly in phase once they pass through the two media? (b) What is the next greater L that will do this?

15P. Two waves of light in air, of wavelength 600.0 nm, are initially in phase. They then travel through plastic layers as shown in Fig. 36-34, with $L_1 = 4.00$ μm, $L_2 = 3.50$ μm, $n_1 = 1.40$, and $n_2 = 1.60$. (a) In wavelengths, what is their phase difference after they both have emerged from the layers? (b) If the waves later arrive at some common point, what type of interference do they undergo?

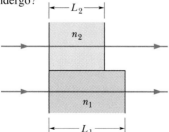

FIGURE 36-34   Problem 15.

SECTION 36-4   Young's Interference Experiment

16E. Monochromatic green light, of wavelength 550 nm, illuminates two parallel narrow slits 7.70 μm apart. Calculate the angular deviation (θ in Fig. 36-8) of the third-order (for $m = 3$) bright fringe (a) in radians and (b) in degrees.

17E. What is the phase difference between the waves from the two slits arriving at the mth dark fringe in a Young's double-slit experiment?

18E. If the slit separation d in Young's experiment is doubled, how must the distance D of the viewing screen be changed to maintain the same fringe spacing?

19E. Suppose Young's experiment is performed with blue-green light of wavelength 500 nm. The slits are 1.20 mm apart, and the viewing screen is 5.40 m from the slits. How far apart are the bright fringes?

20E. Find the slit separation of a double-slit arrangement that will produce interference fringes 0.018 rad apart on a distant screen. Assume sodium light ($\lambda = 589$ nm).

21E. A double-slit arrangement produces interference fringes for sodium light ($\lambda = 589$ nm) that have an angular separation of 3.50×10^{-3} rad. For what wavelength would the angular separation be 10.0% greater?

22E. In a double-slit arrangement the slits are separated by a distance equal to 100 times the wavelength of the light passing through the slits. (a) What is the angular separation in radians between the central maximum and an adjacent maximum? (b) What is the distance between these maxima on a screen 50.0 cm from the slits?

23E. In a double-slit experiment (Fig. 36-8), $\lambda = 546$ nm, $d = 0.10$ mm, and $D = 20$ cm. On a viewing screen, what is the distance between the fifth maximum and the seventh minimum from the central maximum?

24E. A double-slit arrangement produces interference fringes for sodium light ($\lambda = 589$ nm) that are 0.20° apart. What is the angular fringe separation if the entire arrangement is immersed in water ($n = 1.33$)?

25E. Two radio-frequency point sources separated by 2.0 m are radiating in phase with $\lambda = 0.50$ m. A detector moves in a circular path around the two sources in a plane containing them. Without written calculation, find how many maxima it detects.

26E. Source A and B emit long-range radio waves of wavelength 400 m, with the phase of the emission from A ahead of that from source B by 90°. The distance r_A from A to a detector is greater than the corresponding distance r_B by 100 m. What is the phase difference at the detector?

27P. In a double-slit experiment the distance between slits is 5.0 mm and the slits are 1.0 m from the screen. Two interference patterns can be seen on the screen: one due to light with wavelength 480 nm, and the other due to light with wavelength 600 nm. What is the separation on the screen between the third-order ($m = 3$) bright fringes of the two different patterns?

28P. If the distance between the first and tenth minima of a double-slit pattern is 18 mm and the slits are separated by 0.15 mm with the screen 50 cm from the slits, what is the wavelength of the light used?

29P. In Fig. 36-35, A and B are identical radiators of waves that are in phase and of the same wavelength λ. The radiators are separated by distance $d = 3.00\lambda$. Find the greatest distance from A, along the x axis, for which fully destructive interference occurs. Express this distance in wavelengths.

FIGURE 36-35 Problems 29 and 39.

30P. Laser light of wavelength 632.8 nm passes through a double-slit arrangement at the front of a lecture room, reflects off a mirror 20.0 m away at the back of the room, and then produces an interference pattern on a screen at the front of the room. The distance between adjacent bright fringes is 10.0 cm. (a) What is the slit separation? (b) What happens to the pattern when the lecturer places a thin cellophane sheet over one slit, thereby increasing by 2.50 the number of wavelengths along the path that includes the cellophane?

31P. Sodium light ($\lambda = 589$ nm) illuminates two slits separated by $d = 2.0$ mm. The slit–screen distance D is 40 mm. What percentage error is made by using Eq. 36-14 to locate the $m = 10$ bright fringe on the screen rather than using the exact path length difference?

32P. Two point sources, S_1 and S_2 in Fig. 36-36, emit waves in phase and at the same frequency. Show that all curves (such as that given) over which the phase difference for rays r_1 and r_2 is a constant are hyperbolas. (*Hint:* A constant phase difference implies a constant difference in length between r_1 and r_2.)

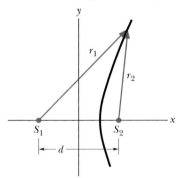

FIGURE 36-36 Problem 32.

33P. A thin flake of mica ($n = 1.58$) is used to cover one slit of a double-slit arrangement. The central point on the screen is now occupied by what had been the seventh bright side fringe ($m = 7$) before the mica was used. If $\lambda = 550$ nm, what is the thickness of the mica? (*Hint:* Consider the wavelength within the mica.)

34P. One slit of a double-slit arrangement is covered by a thin glass plate of refractive index 1.4, and the other by a thin glass plate of refractive index 1.7. The point on the screen at which the central maximum fell before the glass plates were inserted is now occupied by what had been the $m = 5$ bright fringe. Assuming that $\lambda = 480$ nm and that the plates have the same thickness t, find t.

SECTION 36-6 Intensity in Double-Slit Interference

35E. Find the sum y of the following quantities:

$$y_1 = 10 \sin \omega t \quad \text{and} \quad y_2 = 8.0 \sin(\omega t + 30°).$$

36E. Two waves of the same frequency have amplitudes 1.00 and 2.00. They interfere at a point where their phase difference is 60.0°. What is the resultant amplitude?

37E. Light of wavelength 600 nm is incident normally on two parallel narrow slits separated by 0.60 mm. Sketch the intensity pattern observed on a distant screen as a function of angle θ for the range of values $0 \le \theta \le 0.0040$ rad.

38E. Add the following quantities using the phasor method:

$$y_1 = 10 \sin \omega t$$
$$y_2 = 15 \sin(\omega t + 30°)$$
$$y_3 = 5.0 \sin(\omega t - 45°)$$

39P. A and B in Fig. 36-35 are point sources of electromagnetic waves of wavelength 1.00 m. They are in phase and separated by $d = 4.00$ m, and they emit at the same power. (a) If a detector is moved to the right along the x axis from point A, at what distances from A are the first three interference maxima detected? (b) Is the intensity of the nearest minimum exactly zero? (*Hint:* Does the intensity of a wave from a point source remain constant with an increase in distance from the source?)

40P. The double horizontal arrow in Fig. 36-9 marks the points on the intensity curve where the intensity of the central fringe is half the maximum intensity. Show that the angular separation $\Delta\theta$ between the corresponding points on the screen is

$$\Delta\theta = \frac{\lambda}{2d}$$

if θ in Fig. 36-8 is small enough so that $\sin \theta \approx \theta$.

41P*. Suppose that one of the slits of a double-slit arrangement is wider than the other, so that the amplitude of the light reaching the central part of the screen from one slit, acting alone, is twice that from the other slit, acting alone. Derive an expression for the light intensity I at the screen in terms of θ, corresponding to Eqs. 36-21 and 36-22.

SECTION 36-7 Interference from Thin Films

42E. In Fig. 36-37, light wave W_1 reflects once from a reflecting surface while light wave W_2 reflects twice from that surface and once from a reflecting sliver at distance L from the mirror. The waves are initially in phase and have a wavelength of 620 nm. Neglect the slight tilt of the rays. (a) For what least value of L are the reflected waves exactly out of phase? (b) How far must the sliver be moved to put the waves exactly out of phase again?

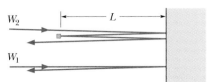

FIGURE 36-37
Exercise 42.

43E. Suppose the light waves of Exercise 42 are initially exactly out of phase. Find an expression for the values of L in terms of the wavelength λ for the situations in which the reflected waves are exactly in phase.

44E. Bright light of wavelength 585 nm is incident perpendicularly on a soap film ($n = 1.33$) of thickness 1.21 μm, suspended in air. Is the light reflected by the two surfaces of the film closer to interfering fully destructively or fully constructively?

45E. Light of wavelength 624 nm is incident perpendicularly on a soap film (with $n = 1.33$) suspended in air. What are the smallest two thicknesses of the film for which the reflections from the film undergo fully constructive interference?

46E. A lens with index of refraction greater than 1.30 is coated with a thin transparent film of index of refraction 1.30 to eliminate by interference the reflection of red light at wavelength 680 nm that is incident perpendicularly on the lens. What minimum film thickness is needed?

47E. A camera lens with index of refraction greater than 1.30 is coated with a thin transparent film of index of refraction 1.25 to eliminate by interference the reflection of light at wavelength λ that is incident perpendicularly on the lens. In terms of λ, what minimum film thickness is needed?

48E. A thin film suspended in air is 0.410 μm thick and illuminated with white light that is incident perpendicularly on its surface. The index of refraction of the film is 1.50. At what wavelengths will visible light reflected from the two surfaces of the film undergo fully constructive interference?

49E. The rhinestones in costume jewelry are glass with index of refraction 1.50. To make them more reflective, they are often coated with a layer of silicon monoxide of index of refraction 2.00. What is the minimum coating thickness needed to ensure that light of wavelength 560 nm and of perpendicular incidence will be reflected from the two surfaces of the coating with fully constructive interference?

50E. We wish to coat flat glass ($n = 1.50$) with a transparent material ($n = 1.25$) so that reflection of light at wavelength 600 nm is eliminated by interference. What minimum thickness can the coating have to do this?

51P. In Fig. 36-38, light of wavelength 600 nm is incident perpendicularly on five sections of a transparent structure suspended in air. The structure has index of refraction 1.50. The thickness of each section is given in terms of $L = 4.00$ μm. For which sections will the light that is reflected from the top and bottom surfaces of that section undergo fully constructive interference?

52P. In Fig. 36-39, light is incident perpendicularly on four thin layers of thickness L. The indices of refraction of the thin layers and of the media above and below these layers are given. Let λ represent the wavelength of the light in air, and n_2 represent the index of refraction of the thin layer in each situation. Consider only the transmission of light that undergoes no reflection or two reflections, as in Fig. 36-39a. For which of the situations does the expression

$$\lambda = \frac{2Ln_2}{m}, \qquad \text{for } m = 0, 1, 2, \ldots,$$

give the wavelengths of the transmitted light that undergoes fully constructive interference?

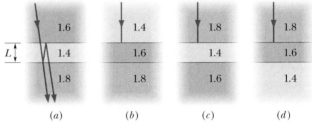

(a) (b) (c) (d)

FIGURE 36-39 Problems 52, 53, and 56.

53P. A disabled tanker leaks kerosene ($n = 1.20$) into the Persian Gulf, creating a large slick on top of the water ($n = 1.30$). (a) If you are looking straight down from an airplane, while the Sun is overhead, at a region of the slick where its thickness is 460 nm, for which wavelength(s) of visible light is the reflection brightest because of constructive interference? (b) If you are scuba diving directly under this same region of the slick, for which wavelength(s) of visible light is the transmitted intensity strongest? (*Hint:* Use Fig. 36-39a with appropriate indices of refraction.)

54P. A plane wave of monochromatic light is incident normally on a uniformly thin film of oil that covers a glass plate. The wavelength of the source can be varied continuously. Fully destructive interference of the reflected light is observed for wavelengths of 500 and 700 nm and for no wavelengths in between. If the index of refraction of the oil is 1.30 and that of the glass is 1.50, find the thickness of the oil film.

55P. The reflection of perpendicularly incident white light by a soap film in air has an interference maximum at 600 nm and a minimum at 450 nm, with no minimum in between. If $n = 1.33$ for the film, what is the film thickness, assumed uniform?

56P. A sheet of glass having an index of refraction of 1.40 is to be coated with a film of material having a refractive index of 1.55 such that green light with a wavelength of 525 nm is preferentially transmitted via constructive interference. (a) What is the minimum thickness of the film that will achieve the result? (*Hint:* Use Fig. 36-39a with appropriate indices of refraction.) (b) Why are other parts of the visible spectrum not also preferentially transmitted? (c) Will the transmission of any colors be sharply reduced? If so, which colors?

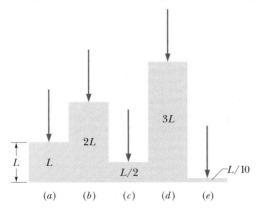

(a) (b) (c) (d) (e)

FIGURE 36-38 Problem 51.

57P. A plane monochromatic light wave in air is perpendicularly incident on a thin film of oil that covers a glass plate. The wavelength of the source may be varied continuously. Fully destructive interference of the reflected light is observed for wavelengths of 500 and 700 nm and for no wavelength in between. The index of refraction of glass is 1.50. Show that the index of refraction of the oil must be less than 1.50.

58P. A thin film of acetone ($n = 1.25$) coats a thick glass plate ($n = 1.50$). White light is incident normal to the film. In the reflections, fully destructive interference occurs at 600 nm and fully constructive interference at 700 nm. Calculate the thickness of the acetone film.

59P. Suppose that in Fig. 36-12 the light is not incident perpendicularly on the thin film but at an angle $\theta_i > 0$. Find an equation like Eqs. 36-34 and 36-35 that gives the interference maxima for the waves of rays r_1 and r_2. The wavelength is λ, the film thickness is L, and $n_2 > n_1 = n_3 = 1.0$.

60P. From a medium of index of refraction n_1, monochromatic light of wavelength λ is incident normally on a thin film of uniform thickness L (where $L > 0.1\lambda$) and index of refraction n_2. The light transmitted by the film travels into a medium with index of refraction n_3. Find expressions for the minimum film thickness (in terms of λ and the indices of refraction) for the following cases: (a) minimum light is reflected (hence maximum light is transmitted) with $n_1 < n_2 > n_3$; (b) minimum light is reflected (hence maximum light is transmitted) with $n_1 < n_2 < n_3$; and (c) maximum light is reflected (hence minimum light is transmitted) with $n_1 < n_2 < n_3$.

61P. In Sample Problem 36-5 assume that the coating eliminates the reflection of light of wavelength 550 nm at normal incidence. Calculate the factor by which reflection is diminished by the coating at 450 and 650 nm.

62P. In Fig. 36-40, a broad beam of light of wavelength 683 nm is sent directly downward through the top plate of a pair of glass plates. The plates are 120 mm long, touch at the left end, and are separated by a wire of diameter 0.048 mm at the right end. The air between the plates acts as a thin film. How many bright fringes will be seen by an observer looking down through the top plate?

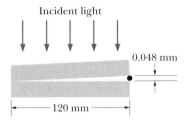

FIGURE 36-40 Problems 62 and 63.

63P. In Fig. 36-40, white light is sent directly downward through the top plate of a pair of glass plates. The plates touch at the left end and are separated by wire (of diameter 0.048 mm) at the right end; the air between the plates acts as a thin film. An observer looking down through the top plate sees bright and dark fringes due to that film. (a) Is a dark fringe or a bright fringe seen at the left end? (b) To the right of that end, fully destructive interference occurs at different locations for different wave-

lengths of the light. Does it occur first for the red end or the blue end of the visible spectrum?

64P. In Fig. 36-41a, a broad beam of light of wavelength 600 nm is sent directly downward through a glass plate ($n = 1.5$) that, with a plastic plate ($n = 1.2$), forms a thin wedge of air which acts as a thin film. An observer looking down through the top plate sees the fringe pattern shown in Fig. 36-41b, with dark fringes centered on ends A and B. (a) What is the thickness of the wedge at B? (b) How many dark fringes will the observer see if the air between the plates is replaced with water ($n = 1.33$)?

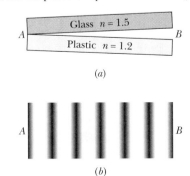

FIGURE 36-41 Problem 64.

65P. A broad beam of light of wavelength 630 nm is incident at 90° on a thin, wedge-shaped film with index of refraction 1.50. An observer intercepting the light transmitted by the film sees 10 bright and 9 dark fringes along the length of the film. By how much does the film thickness change over this length?

66P. Two glass plates are held together at one end to form a wedge of air that acts as a thin film. A broad beam of light of wavelength 480 nm is directed through the plates, perpendicular to the first plate. An observer intercepting light reflected from the plates sees on the plates an interference pattern that is due to the wedge of air. How much thicker is the wedge at the sixteenth bright fringe than it is at the sixth bright fringe, counting from where the plates touch?

67P. A broad beam of monochromatic light is directed perpendicularly through two glass plates that are held together at one end, creating a wedge of air between them. An observer intercepting light reflected from the wedge of air, which acts as a thin film, sees 4001 dark fringes along the length of the wedge. When the air between the plates is evacuated, only 4000 dark fringes are seen. Calculate the index of refraction of air from these data.

68P. Figure 36-42a shows a lens with radius of curvature R lying on a plane glass plate and illuminated from above by light with wavelength λ. Figure 36-42b shows that circular interference fringes (called *Newton's rings*) appear, associated with the variable thickness d of the air film between the lens and the plate. Find the radii r of the interference maxima assuming $r/R \ll 1$.

69P. In a Newton's rings experiment (see Problem 68), the radius of curvature R of the lens is 5.0 m and its diameter is 20 mm. (a) How many bright rings are produced? Assume that $\lambda = 589$ nm. (b) How many bright rings would be produced if the arrangement were immersed in water ($n = 1.33$)?

70P. A Newton's rings apparatus is to be used to determine the radius of curvature of a lens (see Fig. 36-42 and Problem 68). The radii of the nth and $(n + 20)$th bright rings are measured and found to be 0.162 and 0.368 cm, respectively, in light of wavelength 546 nm. Calculate the radius of curvature of the lower surface of the lens.

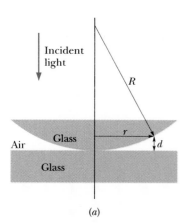

Incident light

R

Glass
Air
r
d
Glass

(a)

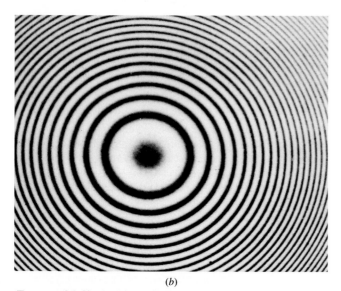

(b)

FIGURE 36-42   Problems 68 through 71.

71P. (a) Use the result of Problem 68 to show that, in a Newton's rings experiment, the difference in radius between adjacent bright rings (maxima) is given by

$$\Delta r = r_{m+1} - r_m \approx \tfrac{1}{2}\sqrt{\lambda R/m},$$

assuming $m \gg 1$. (b) Now show that the *area* between adjacent bright rings is given by

$$A = \pi\lambda R,$$

assuming $m \gg 1$. Note that this area is independent of m.

72P. In Fig. 36-43, a microwave transmitter at height a above the water level of a wide lake transmits microwaves of wavelength λ toward a receiver on the opposite shore, a distance x above the water level. The microwaves reflecting from the water

interfere with the microwaves arriving directly from the transmitter. Assuming that the lake width D is much larger than a and x, and that $\lambda \gtrsim a$, at what values of x is the signal at the receiver maximum? (*Hint:* Does the reflection cause a phase change?)

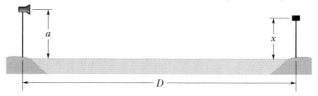

a

x

D

FIGURE 36-43   Problem 72.

SECTION 36-8   Michelson's Interferometer

73E. If mirror M_2 in a Michelson interferometer is moved through 0.233 mm, a shift of 792 fringes occurs. What is the wavelength of the light producing the fringe pattern?

74E. A thin film with index of refraction $n = 1.40$ is placed in one arm of a Michelson interferometer, perpendicular to the optical path. If this causes a shift of 7.0 fringes of the pattern produced by light of wavelength 589 nm, what is the film thickness?

75P. An airtight chamber 5.0 cm long with glass windows is placed in one arm of a Michelson interferometer as indicated in Fig. 36-44. Light of wavelength $\lambda = 500$ nm is used. When the air has been completely evacuated from the chamber, there has been a shift of 60 fringes. From these data, find the index of refraction of air at atmospheric pressure.

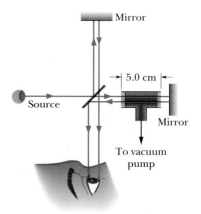

Mirror

5.0 cm

Source

Mirror

To vacuum pump

FIGURE 36-44   Problem 75.

76P. The element sodium can emit light at two wavelengths, $\lambda_1 = 589.10$ nm and $\lambda_2 = 589.59$ nm. If light from sodium is used in a Michelson interferometer, through what distance must one mirror be moved to cause the fringe pattern for one wavelength to shift 1.00 fringe more than the pattern for the other wavelength?

77P. Write an expression for the intensity observed in a Michelson interferometer (Fig. 36-18) as a function of the position of the movable mirror. Measure the position of the mirror from the point at which $d_1 = d_2$.

78P. By the late 1800s, most scientists believed that light (any electromagnetic wave) required a medium in which to travel, that it could not travel through vacuum. One reason for this belief was that any other type of wave known to the scientists requires a medium. For example, sound waves can travel through air, water, or ground but not through vacuum. Thus, reasoned the scientists, when light travels from the Sun or any other star to Earth, it cannot be traveling through vacuum; instead, it must be traveling through a medium that fills all of space and through which Earth slips. Presumably, light has a certain speed c through this medium, which was called *aether (or ether)*.

In 1887 Michelson and Edward Morely used a version of Michelson's interferometer to test for the effects of aether on the travel of light within the device. Specifically, the motion of the device through aether as Earth moves around the Sun should affect the interference pattern produced by the device. Scientists assumed that the Sun is approximately stationary in aether; hence the speed of the interferometer through aether should be Earth's speed v about the Sun.

Figure 36-45a shows the basic arrangement of mirrors in the 1887 experiment. The mirrors were mounted on a heavy slab that was suspended on a pool of mercury so that the slab could be rotated smoothly about a vertical axis. Michelson and Morely wanted to monitor the interference pattern as they rotated the slab, changing the orientation of the interferometer arms relative to the motion through aether. A fringe shift in the interference pattern during the rotation would clearly signal the presence of aether.

Figure 36-45b, an overhead view of the equipment, shows the path of the light. To improve the possibility of fringe shift, the light was reflected several times along the arms of the interferometer, instead of only once along each arm as indicated in the basic interferometer of Fig. 36-18. This repeated reflection increased the effective length of each arm to about 10 m. In spite of the added complexity, the interferometer of Figs. 36-45a and b functions just like the simpler interferometer of Fig. 36-18; so we can use Fig. 36-18 in our discussion here by merely taking the arm lengths d_1 and d_2 to be 10 m each.

Let us assume that there is aether through which light has speed c. Figure 36-45c shows a side view of the arm of length d_1 from the aether reference frame as the interferometer moves rightward through it with velocity **v**. (For simplicity, the beam splitter M of Fig. 36-18 is drawn parallel to the mirror M_1 at the far end of the arm.) Figure 36-45d shows the arm just as a particular portion of the light (represented by a dot) begins its travel along the arm. We shall follow this light to find the path length along the arm.

As the light moves at speed c rightward through aether and toward mirror M_1, that mirror moves rightward at speed v. Figure 36-45e shows the positions of M and M_1 when the light reaches M_1, reflecting there. The light now moves leftward through aether at speed c while M moves rightward. Figure 36-45f shows the positions of M and M_1 when the light has returned to M. (a) Show that the total time of travel for this light, from M to M_1 and then back to M, is

$$t_1 = \frac{2cd_1}{c^2 - v^2}$$

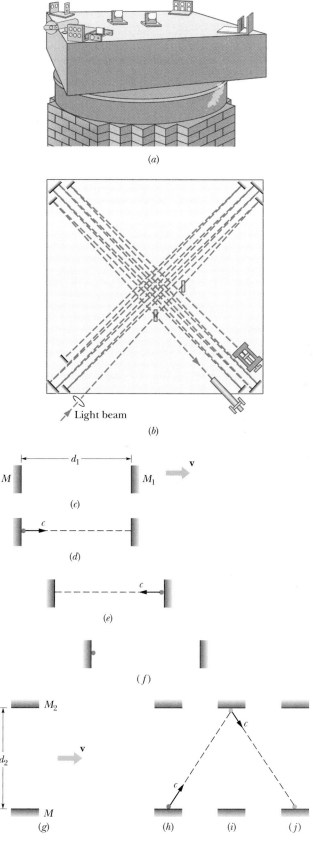

FIGURE 36-45 Problem 78.

928   CHAPTER 36   INTERFERENCE

and thus that the path length L_1 traveled by the light along this arm is

$$L_1 = ct_1 = \frac{2c^2 d_1}{c^2 - v^2}.$$

Figure 36-45g shows a view of the arm of length d_2; that arm also moves rightward with velocity $\mathbf{v}$ through the aether. For simplicity, the beam splitter M of Fig. 36-18 is now drawn parallel to the mirror M_2 at the far end of this arm. Figure 36-45h shows the arm just as a particular portion of the light (the dot) begins its travel along the arm. Because the arm moves rightward during the flight of the light, the path of the light is angled rightward toward the position that M_2 will have when the light reaches that mirror (Fig. 36-45i). The reflection of the light from M_2 sends the light angled rightward toward the position that M will have when the light returns to it (Fig. 36-45j). (b) Show that the total time of travel for the light, from M to M_2 and then back to M, is

$$t_2 = \frac{2d_2}{\sqrt{c^2 - v^2}}$$

and thus that the path length L_2 traveled by the light along this arm is

$$L_2 = ct_2 = \frac{2cd_2}{\sqrt{c^2 - v^2}}.$$

Substitute d for d_1 and d_2 in the expressions for L_1 and L_2. Then expand the two expressions by using the binomial expansion (given in Appendix E and explained in the Problem Solving Tactic on page 145); retain the first two terms in each expansion.

(c) Show that path length L_1 is greater than path length L_2 and that their difference ΔL is

$$\Delta L = \frac{dv^2}{c^2}.$$

(d) Next show that the phase difference between the light traveling along L_1 and that along L_2 is

$$\frac{\Delta L}{\lambda} = \frac{dv^2}{\lambda c^2},$$

where λ is the wavelength of the light. This phase difference determines the fringe pattern produced by the light arriving at the telescope in the interferometer.

Now rotate the interferometer by 90° so that the arm of length d_2 is along the direction of motion through the aether and the arm of length d_1 is perpendicular to that direction. (e) Show that the shift in the fringe pattern due to the rotation is

$$\text{shift} = \frac{2dv^2}{\lambda c^2}.$$

(f) Evaluate the shift, setting $c = 3.0 \times 10^8$ m/s, $d = 10$ m, and $\lambda = 500$ nm and using data about Earth given in Appendix C.

This expected fringe shift would have been easily observable. However, Michelson and Morely observed no fringe shift, which cast grave doubt on the existence of aether. In fact, the idea of aether soon disappeared. Moreover, the null result of Michelson and Morely led, at least indirectly, to Einstein's special theory of relativity.

37
Diffraction

Georges Seurat painted <u>Sunday Afternoon on the Island of La Grande Jatte</u> using not brush strokes in the usual sense, but rather a myriad of small colored dots, in a style of painting now known as pointillism. You can see the dots if you stand close enough to the painting, but as you move away from it, they eventually blend and cannot be distinguished. Moreover, the color that you see at any given place on the painting changes as you move away—which is why Seurat painted with the dots. What causes this change in color?

37-1 DIFFRACTION AND THE WAVE THEORY OF LIGHT

In Chapter 36 we defined diffraction rather loosely as the flaring of light as it emerges from a narrow slit. More than just flaring occurs, however, because the light produces an interference pattern called a **diffraction pattern.** For example, when monochromatic light from a distant source (or a laser) passes through a narrow slit and is then intercepted by a viewing screen, the light produces on the screen a diffraction pattern like that in Fig. 37-1. This pattern consists of a broad and intense (very bright) central maximum and a number of narrower and less intense maxima (called **secondary** or **side** maxima) to both sides. In between the maxima are minima.

Such a pattern would be totally unexpected in geometrical optics: if light traveled in straight lines as rays, then the slit would merely allow some of those rays through and they would form a sharp, bright rendition of the slit on the viewing screen. As in Chapter 36, we again must conclude that geometrical optics is only an approximation.

Diffraction of light is not limited to situations of light passing through a narrow opening (such as a slit or pinhole). It also occurs when light passes an edge, such as the edges of the razor blade in Fig. 37-2. Note the lines of maxima and minima that run approximately parallel to the edges, both on the inside of the blade and on the outside. As the light passes, say, the vertical edge at the left, it flares left and right and undergoes interference, producing the pattern along the left edge. The right-most portion of that pattern actually lies within what would have been the shadow of the blade if geometrical optics prevailed.

You encounter a common example of diffraction when you look at a clear blue sky and see tiny specks and hairlike structures floating in your view. These *floaters,* as they are called, are produced when light passes the edges of tiny bits of vitreous humor (the transparent material fill-

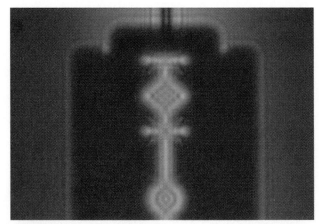

FIGURE 37-2 The diffraction pattern of a razor blade in monochromatic light. Note the lines of alternating maximum and minimum intensity.

ing most of the eyeball). These bits have broken off from the main section and now float in a water layer just in front of the retina where light is detected. What you are seeing when a floater is in your field of vision is the diffraction pattern produced by one of these floating bits. If you sight through a pinhole in an otherwise opaque sheet so as to make the light entering your eye approximately a plane wave, you might be able to distinguish individual maxima and minima in the patterns.

The Fresnel Bright Spot

Diffraction finds a ready explanation in the wave theory of light. However, this theory, originally advanced by Huygens and used 123 years later by Young to explain double-slit interference, was very slow in being adopted, largely because it ran counter to Newton's theory that light was a stream of particles.

Newton's view was the prevailing view in French scientific circles of the early nineteenth century, when Augustin Fresnel was a young military engineer. Fresnel, who believed in the wave theory of light, submitted a paper to the French Academy of Sciences describing his experiments and his wave-theory explanations of them.

In 1819, the Academy, dominated by the supporters of Newton and thinking to challenge the wave point of view, organized a prize competition for an essay on the subject of diffraction. Fresnel won. The Newtonians, however, were neither converted nor silenced. One of them, S. D. Poisson, pointed out the "strange result" that if Fresnel's theories were correct, then light waves should flare into the shadow region of a sphere as they pass the edge of the sphere, producing a bright spot at the center of the shadow. The prize committee arranged a test of the famous mathemati-

FIGURE 37-1 This diffraction pattern appeared on a viewing screen when light that had passed through a narrow horizontal slit reached the screen. The diffraction process causes light to flare out perpendicular to the long sides of the slit. The process also produces an interference pattern consisting of a broad central maximum, less intense and narrower secondary (or side) maxima, and minima.

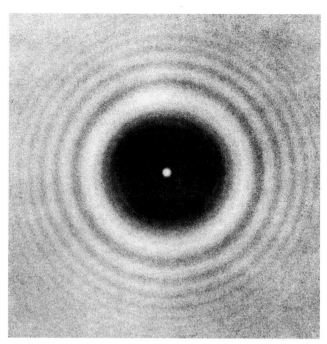

FIGURE 37-3 The diffraction pattern of a disk. Note the concentric diffraction rings and the Fresnel bright spot at the center of the pattern. This experiment is essentially identical to that arranged by the committee testing Fresnel's theories, because both the sphere they used and the disk used here have a cross section with a circular edge.

cian's prediction and discovered (see Fig. 37-3) that the predicted *Fresnel bright spot,* as we call it today, was indeed there! Nothing builds confidence in a theory so much as having one of its unexpected and counterintuitive predictions verified by experiment.

37-2 DIFFRACTION BY A SINGLE SLIT: LOCATING THE MINIMA

Let us now consider how plane waves of light of wavelength λ are diffracted by a single long narrow slit of width a in an otherwise opaque screen B, as shown in cross section in Fig. 37-4a. (In that figure, the slit's length extends into and out of the page.) When the diffracted light reaches viewing screen C, waves from different points within the slit undergo interference and produce a diffraction pattern of bright and dark fringes (interference maxima and minima) on the screen. To locate the fringes, we shall use a procedure somewhat similar to the one we used to locate the fringes in a two-slit interference pattern. However, diffraction is more mathematically challenging, and here we shall be able to find equations for only the dark fringes.

Before we do that, however, we can justify the central

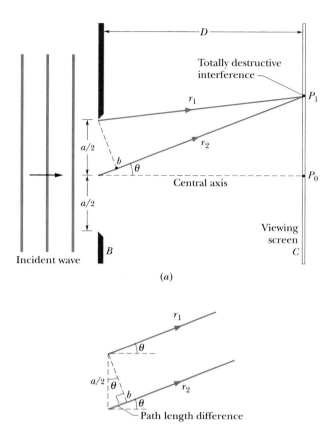

(a)

(b)

FIGURE 37-4 (a) Waves from the top points of two zones of width $a/2$ undergo totally destructive interference at point P_1 on viewing screen C. (b) For $D \gg a$, we can approximate rays r_1 and r_2 as being parallel, at angle θ to the central axis.

bright fringe seen in Fig. 37-1 by noting that the waves from all points in the slit travel about the same distance to reach the center of the pattern and thus are in phase there. As for the other bright fringes, we can say only that they are approximately halfway between adjacent dark fringes.

To find the dark fringes, we shall use a clever (and simplifying) strategy that involves pairing up all the rays coming through the slit and then finding what conditions cause the waves of the rays in each pair to cancel each other. Figure 37-4a shows how we apply this strategy to locate the first dark fringe, at point P_1. First, we mentally divide the slit into two *zones* of equal widths $a/2$. Then we extend to P_1 a light ray r_1 from the top point of the top zone and a light ray r_2 from the top point of the bottom zone. A central axis is drawn from the center of the slit to screen C, and P_1 is located at an angle θ to that axis.

The waves of the pair of rays r_1 and r_2 are in phase within the slit because they originate from the same wavefront passing through the slit. However, to produce the first dark fringe they must be out of phase by $\lambda/2$ when they reach P_1; this phase difference is due to their path length difference, with the wave of r_2 traveling a longer path to reach P_1 than the wave of r_1. To display this path length difference, we find a point b on ray r_2 such that the path length from b to P_1 matches the path length of ray r_1. Then the path length difference between the two rays is the distance from the center of the slit to b.

When viewing screen C is near screen B, as in Fig. 37-4a, the diffraction pattern on C is difficult to describe mathematically. However, we can simplify the mathematics considerably if we arrange for the screen separation D to be much larger than the slit width a. Then we can approximate rays r_1 and r_2 as being parallel, at angle θ to the central axis (Fig. 37-4b). We can also approximate the triangle formed by point b, the top point of the slit, and the center of the slit as being a right triangle, and one of the angles inside that triangle as being θ. The path length difference between rays r_1 and r_2 (which is still the distance from the center of the slit to point b) is then equal to $(a/2) \sin \theta$.

We can repeat this analysis for any other pair of rays originating at corresponding points in the two zones (say, at the midpoints of the zones) and extending to point P_1. Each such pair of rays has the same path length difference $(a/2) \sin \theta$. Setting this common path length difference equal to $\lambda/2$, we have

$$\frac{a}{2} \sin \theta = \frac{\lambda}{2},$$

which gives us

$$a \sin \theta = \lambda \quad \text{(first minimum)}. \quad (37\text{-}1)$$

Given slit width a and wavelength λ, Eq. 37-1 tells us the angle θ of the first dark fringe above and (by symmetry) below the central axis.

Note that if we begin with $a > \lambda$ and then narrow the slit while holding the wavelength constant, the angle for the first dark fringe increases; that is, the extent of the diffraction (the extent of the flaring) is *greater* for a *narrower* slit. For $a = \lambda$, the angle of the first dark fringes is 90°. Since these dark fringes mark the two edges of the central bright fringe, that bright fringe must cover the entire viewing screen.

We find the second dark fringes above and below the central axis as we found the first dark fringes, except that we now divide the slit into *four* zones of equal widths $a/4$, as shown in Fig. 37-5a. We then extend rays r_1, r_2, r_3, and r_4 from the top points of the zones to point P_2, the location of the second dark fringe above the central axis. To produce that fringe, the path length difference between r_1 and r_2, that between r_2 and r_3, and that between r_3 and r_4 must each be equal to $\lambda/2$.

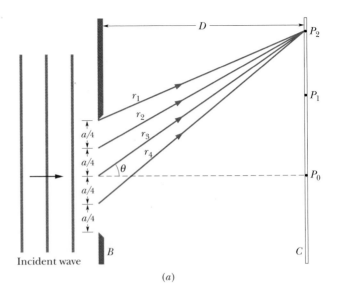

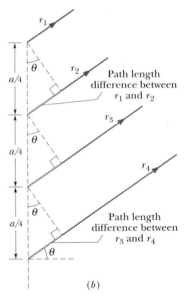

FIGURE 37-5 (a) Waves from the top points of four zones of width $a/4$ undergo totally destructive interference at point P_2. (b) For $D \gg a$, we can approximate rays r_1, r_2, r_3, and r_4 as being parallel, at angle θ to the central axis.

For $D \gg a$, we can approximate these four rays as being parallel, at angle θ to the central axis. To display their path length differences, we extend a perpendicular line through each adjacent pair of rays, as shown in Fig. 37-5b, to form a series of right triangles, each of which has a path length difference as one side. We see from the top triangle that the path length difference between r_1 and r_2 is $(a/4) \sin \theta$. Similarly, from the bottom triangle, the path length difference between r_3 and r_4 is also $(a/4) \sin \theta$. In fact, the path length difference between the members of any pair of rays that originate at corresponding points in two adjacent zones is $(a/4) \sin \theta$. Since in each such case the path length difference is equal to $\lambda/2$, we have

$$\frac{a}{4} \sin \theta = \frac{\lambda}{2},$$

which gives us

$$a \sin \theta = 2\lambda \quad \text{(second minimum)}. \quad (37\text{-}2)$$

We could now continue to locate dark fringes in the diffraction pattern by splitting up the slit into more zones of equal width. We would always choose an even number of zones so that the zones (and their waves) could be paired as we have been doing. We would find that the dark fringes can be located with the following general equation:

$$a \sin \theta = m\lambda, \quad \text{for } m = 1, 2, 3, \ldots$$
$$\text{(minima—dark fringes)}. \quad (37\text{-}3)$$

You can remember this result in the following way. Draw a triangle like the one in Fig. 37-4b, but for the full slit width a, and note that the path length difference between the top and bottom rays from the slit equals $a \sin \theta$. So, Equation 37-3 says:

In a single-slit diffraction experiment, dark fringes are produced where the path length differences ($a \sin \theta$) between the top and bottom rays are equal to λ, 2λ, 3λ, ...

This may seem to be wrong, because the waves of those two particular rays will be exactly in phase with each other. However, they each will still be part of a pair of waves that are exactly out of phase with each other; thus, *each* will be canceled by some other wave.

Equations 37-1, 37-2, and 37-3 are derived for the case of $D \gg a$. However, they also apply if we place a converging lens between the slit and the viewing screen and then move the screen in so that it coincides with the focal plane of the lens. The rays that now arrive at any point on the screen are *exactly* parallel (rather than approximately) when they leave the slit—they are like the initially parallel rays of Fig. 35-13a that are directed to a point by a lens.

CHECKPOINT 1: We produce a diffraction pattern on a viewing screen by using a long narrow slit illuminated by blue light. Does the pattern expand away from the bright center or contract toward it if we (a) switch to yellow light or (b) decrease the slit width?

SAMPLE PROBLEM 37-1
A slit of width a is illuminated by white light.

(a) For what value of a will the first minimum for red light of $\lambda = 650$ nm be at $\theta = 15°$?

SOLUTION: At the first minimum, $m = 1$ in Eq. 37-3. Solving for a, we then find

$$a = \frac{m\lambda}{\sin \theta} = \frac{(1)(650 \text{ nm})}{\sin 15°}$$
$$= 2511 \text{ nm} \approx 2.5 \ \mu\text{m}. \quad \text{(Answer)}$$

For the incident light to flare out that much ($\pm 15°$) the slit has to be very fine indeed, amounting to about four times the wavelength. Note that a fine human hair may be about 100 μm in diameter.

(b) What is the wavelength λ' of the light whose first side diffraction maximum is at 15°, thus coinciding with the first minimum for the red light?

SOLUTION: This maximum is about halfway between the first and second minima produced with wavelength λ'. We can find it without too much error by putting $m = 1.5$ in Eq. 37-3, obtaining

$$a \sin \theta = 1.5\lambda'.$$

Solving for λ' and substituting known data yield

$$\lambda' = \frac{a \sin \theta}{1.5} = \frac{(2511 \text{ nm})(\sin 15°)}{1.5}$$
$$= 430 \text{ nm}. \quad \text{(Answer)}$$

Light of this wavelength is violet. The first side maximum for light of wavelength 430 nm will always coincide with the first minimum for light of wavelength 650 nm, no matter what the slit width. If the slit is relatively narrow, the angle θ at which this overlap occurs will be relatively large, and conversely.

37-3 INTENSITY IN SINGLE-SLIT DIFFRACTION, QUALITATIVELY

In Section 37-2 we saw how to find the positions of the maxima and the minima in a single-slit diffraction pattern. Now we turn to a more general problem: find an expression for the intensity I of the pattern as a function of θ, the angular position of a point on a viewing screen.

To do this, we divide the slit of Fig. 37-4a into N zones of equal widths Δx so small that we can assume that each zone acts as a source of Huygens' wavelets. We wish to superimpose the wavelets arriving at an arbitrary point P on the viewing screen, at angle θ to the central axis, so that we can determine the amplitude E_θ of the resultant wave at P. The intensity of the light at P is then proportional to the square of the amplitude.

To find E_θ, we need the phase relationships among the arriving wavelets. The phase difference between wavelets from adjacent zones is given by

$$\frac{\text{phase}}{\text{difference}} = \left(\frac{2\pi}{\lambda}\right)\left(\frac{\text{path length}}{\text{difference}}\right).$$

For point P at angle θ, the path length difference between wavelets from adjacent zones is $\Delta x \sin\theta$. So the phase difference $\Delta\phi$ between wavelets from adjacent zones is

$$\Delta\phi = \left(\frac{2\pi}{\lambda}\right)(\Delta x \sin\theta). \qquad (37\text{-}4)$$

We assume that the wavelets arriving at P all have the same amplitude ΔE. To find the amplitude E_θ of the resultant wave at P, we add the amplitudes ΔE via phasors. To do this, we construct a diagram of N phasors, one corresponding to the wavelet from each zone in the slit.

For point P_0 at $\theta = 0$ on the central axis of Fig. 37-4a, Eq. 37-4 tells us that the phase difference $\Delta\phi$ between the wavelets is zero. That is, the wavelets all arrive in phase. Figure 37-6a is the corresponding phasor diagram; adjacent phasors represent wavelets from adjacent zones and are arranged head to tail. Because there is zero phase difference between the wavelets, there is zero angle between each pair of adjacent phasors. The amplitude E_θ of the net wave at P_0 is the vector sum of these phasors. This arrangement of the phasors turns out to be the one that gives the greatest value for the wave amplitude E_θ. We call this value E_m; that is, E_m is the value of E_θ for $\theta = 0$.

We next consider a point P that is at a small angle θ to the central axis. Equation 37-4 now tells us that the phase difference $\Delta\phi$ between wavelets from adjacent zones is no longer zero. Figure 37-6b shows the corresponding phasor diagram; as before, the phasors are arranged head to tail, but now there is an angle $\Delta\phi$ between adjacent phasors. The amplitude E_θ at this new point is still the vector sum of the phasors, but it is smaller than that in Fig. 37-6a, which means that the intensity of the light is less at this new point P than at P_0.

If we continue to increase θ, the angle $\Delta\phi$ between adjacent phasors increases, and eventually the chain of phasors curls completely around so that the head of the last phasor reaches the tail of the first phasor (Fig. 37-6c). The amplitude E_θ is now zero, which means that the intensity of the light is also zero. We have reached the first minimum, or dark fringe, in the diffraction pattern. The first and last phasors now have a phase difference of 2π rad, which means that the path length difference between the top and bottom rays through the slit equals one wavelength. Recall that this is the condition we determined for the first diffraction minimum.

As we continue to increase θ, the angle $\Delta\phi$ between adjacent phasors increases, the chain of phasors begins to wrap back on itself, and the resulting coil begins to shrink. Amplitude E_θ now grows larger until it reaches a maximum value in the arrangement shown in Fig. 37-6d. This arrangement corresponds to the first side maximum in the diffraction pattern.

If we increase θ a bit more, the resulting shrinkage of the coil decreases E_θ, which means that the intensity also decreases. When θ is increased enough, the head of the last phasor again meets the tail of the first phasor. We have then reached the second minimum.

We could continue this qualitative method of determining the maxima and minima of the diffraction pattern but, instead, we shall now turn to a quantitative method.

CHECKPOINT 2: The figures represent, in smoother form (with more phasors) than Fig. 37-6, the phasor diagrams for points on opposite sides of a certain diffraction maximum. (a) Which maximum is it? (b) What is the approximate value of m (in Eq. 37-3) that corresponds to this maximum?

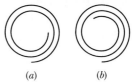

(a)　　　(b)

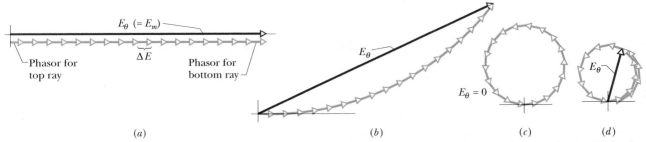

(a)

(b)

(c)

(d)

FIGURE 37-6 Phasor diagrams for $N = 18$ phasors, corresponding to 18 zones in a single slit. Resultant amplitudes E_θ are shown for (a) the central maximum at $\theta = 0$, (b) a point on the screen lying at a small angle θ to the central axis, (c) the first minimum, and (d) the first side maximum.

37-4 INTENSITY IN SINGLE-SLIT DIFFRACTION, QUANTITATIVELY

Equation 37-3 tells us how to locate the minima of the single-slit diffraction pattern on screen C of Fig. 37-4a as a function of the angle θ in that figure. Here we wish to derive an expression for the intensity I of the pattern as a function of θ. We state, and shall prove below, that the intensity is given by

$$I = I_m \left(\frac{\sin \alpha}{\alpha} \right)^2, \qquad (37\text{-}5)$$

where

$$\alpha = \tfrac{1}{2}\phi = \frac{\pi a}{\lambda} \sin \theta. \qquad (37\text{-}6)$$

The symbol α is just a convenient connection between the angle θ that locates a point on the viewing screen and the light intensity I at that point. I_m is the greatest value of the intensities I_θ in the pattern, and it occurs at the central maximum (where $\theta = 0$). And ϕ is the phase difference (in radians) between the top and bottom rays from the slit.

Study of Eq. 37-5 shows that intensity minima will occur when

$$\alpha = m\pi, \qquad \text{for } m = 1, 2, 3, \ldots . \qquad (37\text{-}7)$$

If we put this result into Eq. 37-6 we find

$$m\pi = \frac{\pi a}{\lambda} \sin \theta, \qquad \text{for } m = 1, 2, 3, \ldots$$

or $a \sin \theta = m\lambda, \qquad \text{for } m = 1, 2, 3, \ldots$

$$\text{(minima—dark fringes),} \qquad (37\text{-}8)$$

which is exactly Eq. 37-3, the expression that we derived earlier for the location of the minima.

Figure 37-7 shows plots of the intensity of a single-slit diffraction pattern, calculated with Eqs. 37-5 and 37-6 for three slit widths: $a = \lambda$, $a = 5\lambda$, and $a = 10\lambda$. Note that as the slit width increases (relative to the wavelength), the width of the *central diffraction maximum* (the central hill-like region of the graphs) decreases; that is, the light undergoes less flaring by the slit. The secondary maxima also decrease in width (and become weaker). In the limit of slit width a being much greater than wavelength λ, the secondary maxima due to the slit disappear; we then no longer have single-slit diffraction (but we still have diffraction due to the edges of the wide slit, like that produced by the edges of the razor blade in Fig. 37-2).

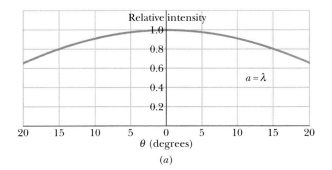

(a)

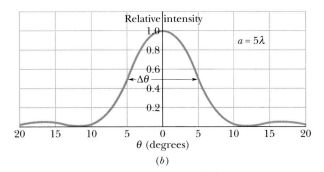

(b)

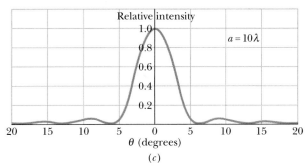

(c)

FIGURE 37-7   The relative intensity in single-slit diffraction for three values of the ratio a/λ. The wider the slit, the narrower is the central diffraction maximum.

Proof of Eqs. 37-5 and 37-6

The arc of phasors in Fig. 37-8 represents the wavelets that reach an arbitrary point P on the viewing screen of Fig. 37-4, corresponding to a particular small angle θ. The amplitude E_θ of the resultant wave at P is the vector sum of these phasors. If we divide the slit of Fig. 37-4 into infinitesimal zones of width Δx, the arc of phasors in Fig. 37-8 approaches the arc of a circle; we call its radius R as indicated in that figure. The length of the arc must be E_m, the amplitude at the center of the diffraction pattern, because if we straightened out the arc we would have the phasor arrangement of Fig. 37-6a (shown lightly in Fig. 37-8).

The angle ϕ in the lower part of Fig. 37-8 is the difference in phase between the infinitesimal vectors at the left

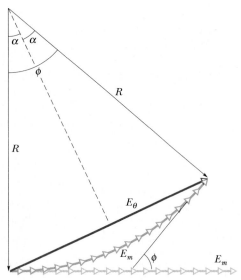

FIGURE 37-8 A construction used to calculate the intensity in single-slit diffraction. The situation shown corresponds to that of Fig. 37-6b.

and right ends of arc E_m. From the geometry, ϕ is also the angle between the two radii marked R in Fig. 37-8. The dashed line in that figure then forms two congruent triangles with angle $\frac{1}{2}\phi$. From either triangle we can write

$$\sin \tfrac{1}{2}\phi = \frac{E_\theta}{2R}. \tag{37-9}$$

In radian measure, ϕ is (with E_m considered to be a circular arc)

$$\phi = \frac{E_m}{R}.$$

Solving this equation for R and substituting in Eq. 37-9 yield, after some manipulation,

$$E_\theta = \frac{E_m}{\frac{1}{2}\phi} \sin \tfrac{1}{2}\phi. \tag{37-10}$$

In Section 34-4 we saw that the intensity of an electromagnetic wave is proportional to the square of the amplitude of its electric field. Here, this means that the maximum intensity I_m (at the center of the diffraction pattern) is proportional to E_m^2 and the intensity I at angle θ is proportional to E_θ^2. Thus, we may write

$$\frac{I}{I_m} = \frac{E_\theta^2}{E_m^2}. \tag{37-11}$$

Substituting for E_θ with Eq. 37-10 and then substituting $\alpha = \frac{1}{2}\phi$, we are led to the following expression for the

intensity as a function of θ:

$$I = I_m \left(\frac{\sin \alpha}{\alpha}\right)^2.$$

This is exactly Eq. 37-5, one of the two equations we set out to prove.

The second equation we wish to prove relates α to θ. The phase difference ϕ between the rays from the top and bottom of the entire slit may be related to a path length difference with Eq. 37-4; it tells us that

$$\phi = \left(\frac{2\pi}{\lambda}\right) (a \sin \theta),$$

where a is the sum of the widths Δx of the infinitesimal strips. But $\phi = 2\alpha$, so this equation reduces to Eq. 37-6.

SAMPLE PROBLEM 37-2

Find the intensities of the first three secondary maxima (side maxima) in the single-slit diffraction pattern of Fig. 37-1, measured relative to the intensity of the central maximum.

SOLUTION: The secondary maxima lie approximately halfway between the minima, which are given by Eq. 37-7 ($\alpha = m\pi$). The secondary maxima are then given (approximately) by

$$\alpha = (m + \tfrac{1}{2})\pi, \qquad \text{for } m = 1, 2, 3, \ldots,$$

with α in radian measure. If we substitute this result into Eq. 37-5 we obtain

$$\frac{I}{I_m} = \left(\frac{\sin \alpha}{\alpha}\right)^2 = \left(\frac{\sin(m + \tfrac{1}{2})\pi}{(m + \tfrac{1}{2})\pi}\right)^2,$$

$$\text{for } m = 1, 2, 3, \ldots.$$

The first of the secondary maxima occurs for $m = 1$, its relative intensity being

$$\frac{I_1}{I_m} = \left(\frac{\sin(1 + \tfrac{1}{2})\pi}{(1 + \tfrac{1}{2})\pi}\right)^2 = \left(\frac{\sin 1.5\pi}{1.5\pi}\right)^2$$

$$= 4.50 \times 10^{-2} \approx 4.5\%. \qquad \text{(Answer)}$$

For $m = 2$ and $m = 3$ we find that

$$\frac{I_2}{I_m} = 1.6\% \quad \text{and} \quad \frac{I_3}{I_m} = 0.83\%. \qquad \text{(Answer)}$$

Successive secondary maxima decrease rapidly in intensity. The pattern of Fig. 37-1 was deliberately overexposed to reveal them.

CHECKPOINT 3: Two wavelengths, 650 and 430 nm, are used separately in a single-slit diffraction experiment. The figure shows the results as graphs of intensity I versus angle θ for the two diffraction patterns. If both wavelengths are then used simultaneously, what color will be seen in the combined diffraction pattern at (a) angle *A* and (c) angle *B*?

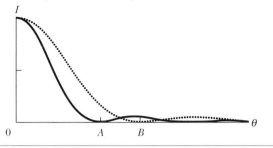

37-5 DIFFRACTION BY A CIRCULAR APERTURE

Here we consider diffraction by a circular aperture, that is, a circular opening such as a circular lens, through which light can pass. Figure 37-9 shows the image of a distant point source of light (a star, for instance) formed on photographic film placed in the focal plane of a converging lens. This image is not a point, as the geometrical optics treatment would suggest, but a circular disk surrounded by several progressively fainter secondary rings. Comparison

with Fig. 37-1 leaves little doubt that we are dealing with a diffraction phenomenon. Here, however, the aperture is a circle of diameter *d* rather than a rectangular slit.

The analysis of such patterns is complex. It shows, however, that the first minimum for the diffraction pattern of a circular aperture of diameter *d* is given by

$$\sin \theta = 1.22 \frac{\lambda}{d} \qquad \text{(first minimum; circular aperture).} \qquad (37\text{-}12)$$

Compare this with Eq. 37-1,

$$\sin \theta = \frac{\lambda}{a} \qquad \text{(first minimum; single slit),} \qquad (37\text{-}13)$$

which locates the first minimum for a long narrow slit of width *a*. The main difference is the factor 1.22, which enters because of the circular shape of the aperture.

Resolvability

The fact that lens images are diffraction patterns is important when we wish to *resolve* (distinguish) two distant point objects whose angular separation is small. Figure 37-10 shows the visual appearances and corresponding intensity patterns for two distant point objects (stars, say) with small angular separations. In Figure 37-10*a*, the objects are not resolved because of diffraction; that is, their diffraction patterns overlap so much that the two objects cannot be distinguished from a single point object. In Fig. 37-10*b* the objects are barely resolved, and in Fig. 37-10*c* they are fully resolved.

In Fig. 37-10*b* the angular separation of the two point sources is such that the central maximum of the diffraction

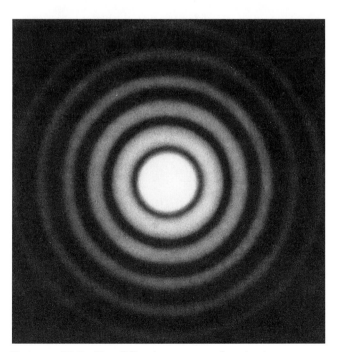

FIGURE 37-9 The diffraction pattern of a circular aperture. Note the central maximum and the circular secondary maxima. The figure has been overexposed to bring out these secondary maxima, which are much less intense than the central maximum.

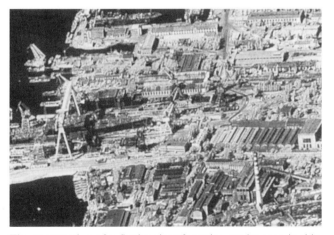

The construction of a Soviet aircraft carrier can be seen in this image made by a spy satellite and published in 1984. The image has been "cleaned" by a computer to remove diffraction effects and to improve resolution. Today, images from spy satellites can resolve much smaller details than shown here.

FIGURE 37-10 Above, the images of two point sources (stars), formed by a converging lens. Below, representations of the image intensities. In (a) the angular separation of the sources is too small for them to be distinguished; in (b) they can be marginally distinguished, and in (c) they are clearly distinguished. Rayleigh's criterion is just satisfied in (b), with the central maximum of one diffraction pattern coinciding with the first minimum of the other.

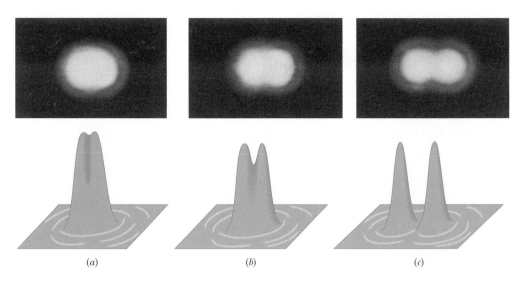

(a)   (b)   (c)

pattern of one source is centered on the first minimum of the diffraction pattern of the other, a condition called **Rayleigh's criterion** for resolvability. From Eq. 37-12, two objects that are barely resolvable by this criterion must have an angular separation θ_R of

$$\theta_R = \sin^{-1} \frac{1.22\lambda}{d}.$$

Since the angles involved are small, we can replace $\sin \theta_R$ with θ_R expressed in radians:

$$\theta_R = 1.22 \frac{\lambda}{d} \quad \text{(Rayleigh's criterion).} \quad (37\text{-}14)$$

Rayleigh's criterion for resolvability is only an approximation, because resolvability depends on many factors, such as the relative brightness of the sources and their surroundings, turbulence in the air between the sources and the observer, and the functioning of the observer's visual system. However, for the sake of calculations here, we shall take Eq. 37-14 as being a precise criterion: if the angular separation θ between the sources is greater than θ_R, we can resolve the sources; if it is less, we cannot.

When we wish to use a lens to resolve objects of small angular separation, it is desirable to make the diffraction pattern as small as possible. According to Eq. 37-14, this can be done either by increasing the lens diameter or by using light of a shorter wavelength.

For this reason ultraviolet light is often used with microscopes; because of its shorter wavelength, it permits finer detail to be examined than would be possible for the same microscope operated with visible light. In Chapter 40 of the extended version of this text, we show that beams of electrons behave like waves under some circumstances. In an *electron microscope* such beams may have an effective

wavelength that is 10^{-5} of the wavelength of visible light. They permit the detailed examination of tiny structures, like that in Fig. 37-11, that would be blurred by diffraction if viewed with an optical microscope.

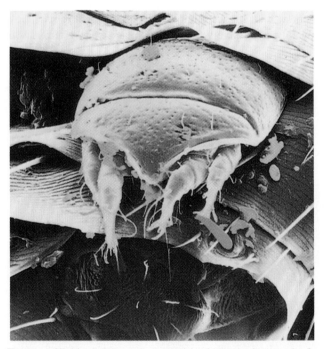

FIGURE 37-11 A false-color scanning electron micrograph of a mite that is on the back of a hedgehog flea.

SAMPLE PROBLEM 37-3

A circular converging lens, with diameter $d = 32$ mm and focal length $f = 24$ cm, forms images of distant point objects in the focal plane of the lens. Light of wavelength $\lambda = 550$ nm is used.

(a) Considering diffraction by the lens, what angular separation must two such objects have to satisfy Rayleigh's criterion for resolvability?

SOLUTION: Figure 37-12 shows two distant point objects P_1 and P_2, the lens, and a viewing screen in the focal plane of the lens. It also shows, at the right, plots of the light intensity I versus position on the screen for the central maxima of the images formed by the lens. From the perspective of the lens, the angular separation θ_o of the objects equals the angular separation θ_i of the images. So, if the images are to satisfy Rayleigh's criterion for resolvability, the angular separations on both sides of the lens must be given by Eq. 37-14 (assuming small angles). Substituting the given data, we obtain from Eq. 37-14

$$\theta_o = \theta_i = \theta_R = 1.22\frac{\lambda}{d}$$

$$= \frac{(1.22)(550 \times 10^{-9} \text{ m})}{32 \times 10^{-3} \text{ m}} = 2.1 \times 10^{-5} \text{ rad.} \quad \text{(Answer)}$$

At this angular separation, each central maximum in the two intensity curves of Fig. 37-12 is centered on the first minimum of the other curve.

(b) What is the separation Δx of the centers of the *images* in the focal plane? (That is, what is the separation of the *central* peaks in the two curves?)

SOLUTION: From either triangle between the lens and the screen in Fig. 37-12, we see that $\tan \theta_i/2 = \Delta x/2f$. Rearranging this and making the approximation $\tan \theta \approx \theta$, we find

$$\Delta x = f\theta_i, \quad (37\text{-}15)$$

where θ_i is in radian measure. Substituting known data then yields

$$\Delta x = (0.24 \text{ m})(2.1 \times 10^{-5} \text{ rad}) = 5.0 \ \mu\text{m.} \quad \text{(Answer)}$$

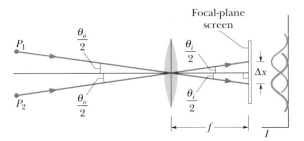

FIGURE 37-12 Sample Problem 37-3. Light from two distant point objects P_1 and P_2 passes through a converging lens and forms images on a viewing screen in the focal plane of the lens. Only one representative ray from each object is shown. The images are not points but diffraction patterns, with intensities approximately as plotted at the right. The angular separation of the objects is θ_o and that of the images is θ_i; the central maxima of the images have a separation Δx.

SAMPLE PROBLEM 37-4

Approximate the colored dots in Seurat's *Sunday Afternoon on the Island of La Grande Jatte* as closely spaced circles with center-to-center separations $D = 2.0$ mm (Fig. 37-13). If the diameter of the pupil of your eye is $d = 1.5$ mm, what is the minimum viewing distance from which you cannot distinguish any dots?

SOLUTION: Consider any two adjacent dots that you can distinguish when you are close to the painting. As you move away, you can distinguish the dots until their angular separation θ (in your view) decreases to that given by Rayleigh's criterion (Eq. 37-14):

$$\theta_R = 1.22\frac{\lambda}{d}. \quad (37\text{-}16)$$

Because the angular separation is then small, we can approximate $\sin \theta$ as θ and then write

$$\theta = \frac{D}{L}, \quad (37\text{-}17)$$

in which L is your distance from the dots.

Setting θ of Eq. 37-17 equal to θ_R of Eq. 37-16 and solving for L, we obtain

$$L = \frac{Dd}{1.22\lambda}. \quad (37\text{-}18)$$

Equation 37-18 tells us that L is larger for smaller λ. Thus, as you move away from the painting, adjacent red dots (corresponding to a long wavelength) become indistinguishable before adjacent blue dots do. So to find the least distance L at which *no* colored dots are distinguishable, we substitute $\lambda = 400$ nm (blue or violet light) and the given data into Eq. 37-18, finding

$$L = \frac{(2.0 \times 10^{-3} \text{ m})(1.5 \times 10^{-3} \text{ m})}{(1.22)(400 \times 10^{-9} \text{ m})} = 6.1 \text{ m.} \quad \text{(Answer)}$$

At this or a greater distance, the colors of all adjacent dots blend together. The color you then perceive at any given spot on the painting is a blended color that may not actually exist there. In other words, Seurat uses the viewer's eyes to create the colors of his art.

FIGURE 37-13 Sample Problem 37-4. Representation of dots on a Seurat painting.

CHECKPOINT 4: Suppose that you can barely resolve two red dots, owing to diffraction by the pupil of your eye. If we increase the general illumination around you so that the pupil decreases in diameter, does the resolvability of the dots improve or diminish? Consider only diffraction. (You might experiment to check your answer.)

37-6 DIFFRACTION BY A DOUBLE SLIT

In the double-slit experiments of Chapter 36, we implicitly assumed that the slits were narrow compared to the wavelength of the light illuminating them; that is, $a \ll \lambda$. For such narrow slits, the central maximum of the diffraction pattern of either slit covers the entire viewing screen. Moreover, the interference of light from the two slits produces bright fringes that all have approximately the same intensity (Fig. 36-9).

In practice with visible light, however, the condition $a \ll \lambda$ is often not met. For relatively wide slits, the interference of light from two slits produces bright fringes that do not all have the same intensity. In fact, their intensity is modified by the diffraction of the light through each slit.

As an example, the intensity plot of Fig. 37-14a suggests the double-slit fringe pattern that would occur if the slits were infinitely narrow (and thus $a \ll \lambda$); all the bright interference fringes would have the same intensity. The intensity plot of Fig. 37-14b is that of a single actual slit; the diffraction pattern has a broad central maximum and weaker secondary maxima at $\pm 17°$. The plot of Fig. 37-14c suggests the resulting interference pattern for two actual slits. The plot was constructed by using the curve of Fig. 37-14b as an *envelope* on the intensity plot in Fig. 37-14a. The positions of the fringes are not changed; only the intensity is affected.

Figure 37-15a shows an actual pattern in which both double-slit interference and diffraction are evident. If one slit is covered, the single-slit diffraction pattern of Fig.

FIGURE 37-14 (a) The intensity pattern to be expected in a double-slit interference experiment with vanishingly narrow slits. (b) The intensity pattern in diffraction by a typical slit of width a (not vanishingly narrow). (c) The intensity pattern to be expected for two slits of width a. The curve of (b) acts as an envelope, limiting the intensity of the double-slit fringes in (a). Note that the first minima of the diffraction pattern of (b) eliminate the double-slit fringes that would occur near $12°$ in (c).

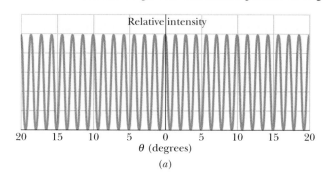

(a)

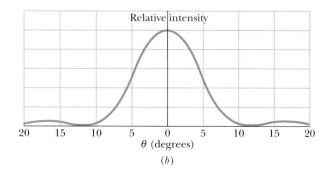

(b)

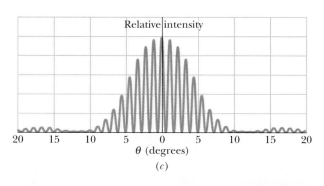

(c)

(a)

(b)

FIGURE 37-15 (a) Interference fringes for a double-slit system; compare with Fig. 37-14c. (b) The diffraction pattern of a single slit; compare with Fig. 37-14b.

37-15b results. Note the correspondence between Figs. 37-15a and 37-14c, and between Figs. 37-15b and 37-14b. In comparing these figures bear in mind that Fig. 37-15 has been deliberately overexposed to bring out the faint secondary maxima and that two secondary maxima (rather than one) are shown.

With diffraction effects taken into account, the intensity of a double-slit interference pattern is given by

$$I = I_m (\cos^2 \beta) \left(\frac{\sin \alpha}{\alpha} \right)^2 \quad \begin{matrix} \text{(double} \\ \text{slit),} \end{matrix} \quad (37\text{-}19)$$

in which

$$\beta = \left(\frac{\pi d}{\lambda} \right) \sin \theta \qquad (37\text{-}20)$$

and

$$\alpha = \left(\frac{\pi a}{\lambda} \right) \sin \theta. \qquad (37\text{-}21)$$

Here d is the distance between the centers of the slits, and a is the slit width. Note carefully that the right side of Eq. 37-19 is the product of I_m and two factors. (1) The *interference factor* $\cos^2 \beta$ is due to the interference between two slits with slit separation d (as given by Eqs. 36-21 and 36-22). (2) The *diffraction factor* $[(\sin \alpha)/\alpha]^2$ is due to diffraction by a single slit of width a (as given by Eqs. 37-5 and 37-6).

Let us check these factors. If we let $a \to 0$ in Eq. 37-21, for example, then $\alpha \to 0$ and $(\sin \alpha)/\alpha \to 1$. Equation 37-19 then reduces, as it must, to an equation describing the interference pattern for a pair of vanishingly narrow slits with slit separation d. Similarly, putting $d = 0$ in Eq. 37-20 is equivalent physically to causing the two slits to merge into a single slit of width a. Then Eq. 37-20 yields $\beta = 0$ and $\cos^2 \beta = 1$. In this case Eq. 37-19 reduces, as it must, to an equation describing the diffraction pattern for a single slit of width a.

The double-slit pattern described by Eq. 37-19 and displayed in Fig. 37-15a combines interference and diffraction in an intimate way. Both are superposition effects, in that they result from the combining of waves with different phases at a given point. If the combining waves originate from a finite (and usually small) number of elementary coherent sources—as in a double-slit experiment with $a \ll \lambda$—we call the process *interference*. If the combining waves originate in a single wavefront—as in a single-slit experiment—we call the process *diffraction*. This distinction between interference and diffraction (which is somewhat arbitrary and not always adhered to) is a convenient one, but we should not forget that both are superposition effects and usually both are present simultaneously (as in Fig. 37-15a).

SAMPLE PROBLEM 37-5

In a double-slit experiment, the wavelength λ of the light source is 405 nm, the slit separation d is 19.44 μm, and the slit width a is 4.050 μm.

(a) How many bright fringes are within the central peak of the diffraction envelope?

SOLUTION: The limits of the central diffraction peak are the first diffraction minima, each of which is located at the angle θ given by Eq. 37-3 with $m = 1$:

$$a \sin \theta = \lambda. \qquad (37\text{-}22)$$

The locations of the bright fringes of the double-slit interference pattern are given by Eq. 36-14:

$$d \sin \theta = m\lambda, \quad \text{for } m = 0, 1, 2, \ldots . \quad (37\text{-}23)$$

We can locate the first diffraction minimum within the double-slit fringe pattern by dividing Eq. 37-23 by Eq. 37-22 and solving for m. By doing so and then substituting the given data, we obtain

$$m = \frac{d}{a} = \frac{19.44 \ \mu\text{m}}{4.050 \ \mu\text{m}} = 4.8.$$

This tells us that the first diffraction minimum occurs just before the bright fringe for $m = 5$ in Eq. 37-23. So, within the central diffraction peak we have the central bright fringe ($m = 0$) and four bright fringes (up to $m = 4$) on each side of it. Thus a total of nine bright fringes of the double-slit interference pattern are within the central peak of the diffraction envelope. The bright fringes to one side of the central bright fringe are shown in Fig. 37-16.

(b) How many bright fringes are within either of the first side peaks of the diffraction envelope?

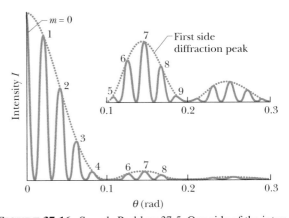

FIGURE 37-16 Sample Problem 37-5. One side of the intensity pattern for a two-slit interference experiment; the diffraction envelope is indicated by dots. The insert shows (vertically expanded) the intensity pattern for the first and second side diffraction peaks.

SOLUTION: The outer limits of the first side diffraction peaks are the second diffraction minima, each of which is at the angle θ given by Eq. 37-3 with $m = 2$:

$$a \sin \theta = 2\lambda. \qquad (37\text{-}24)$$

Dividing Eq. 37-23 by Eq. 37-24, we find

$$m = \frac{2d}{a} = \frac{(2)(19.44 \ \mu m)}{4.050 \ \mu m} = 9.6.$$

This tells us that the second diffraction minimum occurs just before the bright fringe for $m = 10$ in Eq. 37-23. So, within the first side diffraction peak we have the fringes from $m = 5$ to $m = 9$ and thus a total of five bright fringes of the double-slit interference pattern (shown in the insert of Fig. 37-16). However, if the $m = 5$ bright fringe, which is almost eliminated by the first diffraction minimum, is considered too dim to count, then only four bright fringes are in the first side diffraction peak.

CHECKPOINT 5: If we increase the wavelength of the light source in Sample Problem 37-5 to 550 nm, do (a) the width of the central diffraction peak and (b) the number of bright fringes within that peak increase, decrease, or remain the same?

37-7 DIFFRACTION GRATINGS

One of the most useful tools in the study of light and of objects that emit and absorb light is the **diffraction grating.** Somewhat like the double-slit arrangement of Fig. 36-8, this device has a much greater number N of slits, often called *rulings*, perhaps as many as several thousand per millimeter. An idealized grating consisting of only five slits is represented in Fig. 37-17. When monochromatic light is sent through the slits, it forms narrow interference fringes that can be analyzed to determine the wavelength of

the light. (Diffraction gratings can also be opaque surfaces with narrow parallel grooves arranged like the slits in Fig. 37-17. Light then scatters back from the grooves to form interference fringes rather than being transmitted through open slits.)

With monochromatic light incident on a diffraction grating, if we gradually increase the number of slits from two to a large number N, the intensity pattern changes from the typical double-slit pattern of Fig. 37-14c to a much more complicated pattern and then eventually to a simple pattern like that shown in Fig. 37-18a. The maxima are now very narrow (and so are called *lines*); they are separated by relatively wide dark regions. What you would see on a viewing screen using monochromatic red light from, say, a helium–neon laser, is shown in Fig. 37-18b.

We use a familiar procedure to find the locations of the bright lines on the viewing screen. We first assume that the screen is far enough from the grating that the rays reaching a particular point P on the screen are approximately parallel when they leave the grating (Fig. 37-19). Then we apply to each pair of adjacent rulings the same reasoning we used for double-slit interference. The separation d between rulings is called the *grating spacing*. (If N rulings occupy a total width w, then $d = w/N$.) The path length difference between adjacent rays is again $d \sin \theta$ (Fig. 37-19), where θ is the angle from the central axis of the grating (and of the pattern) to point P. A line is located at P if the path length difference between adjacent rays is an integer number of wavelengths, that is, if

$$d \sin \theta = m\lambda, \qquad \text{for } m = 0, 1, 2, \ldots$$
$$\text{(maxima—lines),} \qquad (37\text{-}25)$$

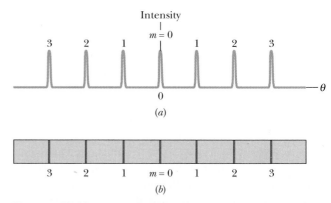

FIGURE 37-18 (a) The intensity pattern produced by a diffraction grating with a great many rulings consists of narrow peaks that are labeled with an order number m. (b) The corresponding bright fringes seen on the screen are called lines and are also labeled with m. Lines of the zeroth, first, second, and third orders are shown.

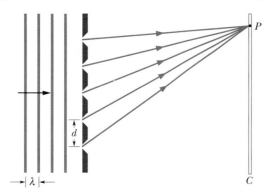

FIGURE 37-17 An idealized diffraction grating, consisting of only five rulings, that produces an interference pattern on a distant viewing screen C.

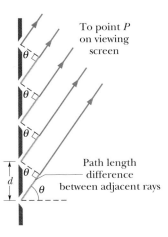

FIGURE 37-19 The rays from the rulings in a diffraction grating to a distant point P are approximately parallel. The path length difference between each two adjacent rays is $d \sin \theta$, where θ is measured as shown. (The rulings extend into and out of the page.)

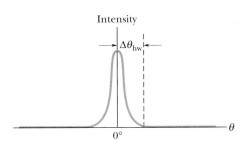

FIGURE 37-20 The half-width $\Delta\theta_{hw}$ of the central line is measured from the center of that line to the adjacent minimum on a plot of I versus θ like Fig. 37-18a.

where λ is the wavelength of the light. Each integer m represents a different line; hence these integers can be used to label the lines, as in Fig. 37-18. The integers are then called the *order numbers*, and the lines are called the zeroth-order line (the central line, with $m = 0$), the first-order line, the second-order line, and so on.

If we rewrite Eq. 37-25 as $\theta = \sin^{-1}(m\lambda/d)$ we see that, for a given diffraction grating, the angle from the central axis to any line (say, the third-order line) depends on the wavelength of the light being used. Thus, when light of an unknown wavelength is sent through a diffraction grating, measurements of the angles to the higher order lines can be used in Eq. 37-25 to determine the wavelength. Even light of several unknown wavelengths can be distinguished and identified in this way. We cannot do that with the double-slit arrangement of Section 36-4, even though the same equation and wavelength dependence apply there. In double-slit interference, the bright fringes due to different wavelengths overlap too much to be distinguished.

Width of the Lines

A grating's ability to resolve (separate) lines of different wavelengths depends on the width of the lines. We shall here derive an expression for the *half-width* of the central line (the line for which $m = 0$) and then state an expression for the half-widths of the higher order lines. We measure the half-width of the central line as the angle $\Delta\theta_{hw}$ from the center of the line at $\theta = 0$ outward to where the line effectively ends and darkness effectively begins with the first minimum (Fig. 37-20). At such a minimum, the N rays from the N slits of the grating cancel one another. (The actual width of the central line is, of course $2\Delta\theta_{hw}$, but line widths are usually compared via half-widths.)

In Section 37-2 we were also concerned with the cancellation of a great many rays, there due to diffraction through a single slit. We obtained Eq. 37-3 which, owing to the similarity of the two situations, we can use to find the first minimum here. It tells us that the first minimum

occurs where the path length difference between the top and bottom rays equals λ. For single-slit diffraction, this difference is $a \sin \theta$. For a grating of N rulings, each separated from the next by distance d, the distance between the top and bottom rulings is Nd (Fig. 37-21). So, the path length difference between the top and bottom rays here is $Nd \sin \Delta\theta_{hw}$. Thus, the first minimum occurs where

$$Nd \sin \Delta\theta_{hw} = \lambda. \qquad (37\text{-}26)$$

Because $\Delta\theta_{hw}$ is small, $\sin \Delta\theta_{hw} = \Delta\theta_{hw}$ (in radian measure). Substituting this in Eq. 37-26 gives the half-width of the central line as

$$\Delta\theta_{hw} = \frac{\lambda}{Nd} \qquad \text{(half-width of central line).} \qquad (37\text{-}27)$$

We state without proof that the half-width of any other line depends on its location relative to the central axis and is

$$\Delta\theta_{hw} = \frac{\lambda}{Nd \cos \theta} \qquad \text{(half-width of line at } \theta\text{).} \qquad (37\text{-}28)$$

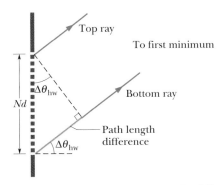

FIGURE 37-21 The top and bottom rulings of a diffraction grating of N rulings are separated by distance Nd. The top and bottom rays passing through these rulings have a path length difference of $Nd \sin \Delta\theta_{hw}$, if $\Delta\theta_{hw}$ is measured as shown. (The angle here is greatly exaggerated for clarity.)

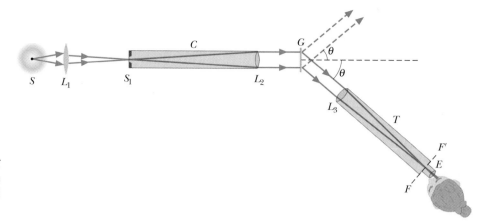

FIGURE 37-22 A simple type of grating spectroscope used to analyze the wavelengths of the light emitted by source S.

Note that for light of a given wavelength λ and a given ruling separation d, the widths of the lines decrease with an increase in the number N of rulings. Thus, of two diffraction gratings, the grating with the larger value of N is better able to distinguish between wavelengths because its diffraction lines are narrower and so produce less overlap.

An Application of Diffraction Gratings

Diffraction gratings are widely used to determine the wavelengths that are emitted by sources of light ranging from lamps to stars. Figure 37-22 shows a simple *grating spectroscope* in which a grating is used for this purpose. Light from source S is focused by lens L_1 on a slit S_1 placed in the focal plane of lens L_2. The light emerging from tube C (called a *collimator*) is a plane wave and is incident perpendicularly on grating G, where it is diffracted into a diffraction pattern, with the $m = 0$ order diffracted at angle $\theta = 0$ along the central axis of the grating.

We can view the diffraction pattern that would appear on a viewing screen at any angle θ simply by orienting telescope T in Fig. 37-22 to that angle. Lens L_3 of the telescope then focuses the light diffracted at angle θ (and at slightly smaller and larger angles) onto a focal plane FF' within the telescope. When we look through eyepiece E, we see a magnified view of this focused image.

By changing the angle θ of the telescope, we can examine the entire diffraction pattern. For any order number other than $m = 0$, the original light is spread out according to wavelength (or color) so that we can determine, with Eq. 37-25, just what wavelengths are being emitted by the source. If the source emits a broad band of wavelengths, what we see as we rotate the telescope through the angles corresponding to an order m is a broad band of color, with the shorter wavelength end at a smaller angle θ than the longer wavelength end. If the source emits discrete wavelengths, what we see are discrete vertical lines of color corresponding to those wavelengths.

For example, the light emitted by a hydrogen lamp, which contains hydrogen gas, has four discrete wavelengths in the visible range. If our eyes intercept this light directly, it appears to be white. If, instead, we view it through a grating spectroscope, we can distinguish, in several orders, the lines of the four colors corresponding to these visible wavelengths. (Such lines are called *emission lines*.) Four orders are represented in Fig. 37-23. In the central order ($m = 0$), the lines corresponding to all four wavelengths are superimposed, giving a single white line at $\theta = 0$. The colors are separated in the higher orders.

The third order is not shown in Fig. 37-23 for the sake of clarity; it actually overlaps the second and fourth orders. The fourth-order red line is missing because it is not formed by the grating used here (which is the grating of Sample Problem 37-6). That is, when we attempt to solve Eq. 37-25 for the angle θ for the red wavelength when $m = 4$, we find that sin θ is greater than unity, which is not possible. The fourth order is then said to be *incomplete* for this grating; it might not be incomplete for a grating with greater spacing d, which will spread the lines less than in Fig. 37-23. Figure 37-24 is a photograph of the visible emission lines produced by cadmium.

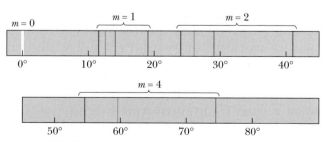

FIGURE 37-23 The zeroth, first, second, and fourth orders of the visible emission lines from hydrogen. Note that the lines are farther apart at greater angles. (They are also dimmer and wider, although that is not shown here.)

FIGURE 37-24 The visible emission lines of cadmium, as seen through a grating spectroscope.

SAMPLE PROBLEM 37-6

A diffraction grating has 1.26×10^4 rulings uniformly spaced over width $w = 25.4$ mm. It is illuminated at normal incidence by blue light of wavelength 450 nm.

(a) At what angles to the central axis do the second-order maxima occur?

SOLUTION: The grating spacing d is

$$d = \frac{w}{N} = \frac{25.4 \times 10^{-3} \text{ m}}{1.26 \times 10^4}$$

$$= 2.016 \times 10^{-6} \text{ m} = 2016 \text{ nm}.$$

The second-order maxima correspond to $m = 2$ in Eq. 37-25. For $\lambda = 450$ nm, we thus have

$$\theta = \sin^{-1} \frac{m\lambda}{d} = \sin^{-1} \frac{(2)(450 \text{ nm})}{2016 \text{ nm}}$$

$$= 26.51° \approx 26.5°. \qquad \text{(Answer)}$$

(b) What is the half-width of the second-order line?

SOLUTION: From Eq. 37-28,

$$\Delta\theta_{\text{hw}} = \frac{\lambda}{Nd \cos \theta} = \frac{450 \text{ nm}}{(1.26 \times 10^4)(2016 \text{ nm})(\cos 26.51°)}$$

$$= 1.98 \times 10^{-5} \text{ rad}. \qquad \text{(Answer)}$$

CHECKPOINT 6: The figure shows lines of different orders produced by a diffraction grating in monochromatic red light. (a) Is the center of the pattern to the left or right? (b) If we switch to monochromatic green light, will the half-widths of the lines then produced in the same orders be greater than, less than, or the same as the half-widths of the lines shown?

37-8 GRATINGS: DISPERSION AND RESOLVING POWER (OPTIONAL)

Dispersion

To be useful in distinguishing wavelengths that are close to each other (as in a grating spectroscope), a grating must spread apart the diffraction lines associated with the

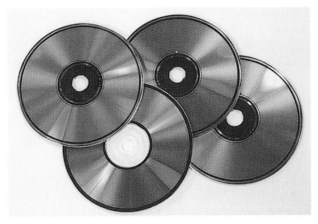

The fine rulings, each 0.5 μm wide, on a compact disc function as a diffraction grating. When a small source of white light illuminates a disc, the diffracted light forms colored "lanes" that are the composite of the diffraction patterns from the rulings.

various wavelengths. This spreading, called **dispersion,** is defined as

$$D = \frac{\Delta\theta}{\Delta\lambda} \qquad \text{(dispersion defined).} \qquad (37\text{-}29)$$

Here $\Delta\theta$ is the angular separation of two lines whose wavelengths differ by $\Delta\lambda$. The greater D is, the greater is the distance between two emission lines whose wavelengths differ by $\Delta\lambda$. We show below that the dispersion of a grating at angle θ is given by

$$D = \frac{m}{d \cos \theta} \qquad \begin{array}{l} \text{(dispersion} \\ \text{of a grating).} \end{array} \qquad (37\text{-}30)$$

Thus to achieve high dispersion, we must use a grating of small grating spacing (small d) and work in high orders (large m). Note that the dispersion does not depend on the number of rulings. The SI unit for D is the degree per meter or the radian per meter.

Resolving Power

To distinguish lines whose wavelengths are close together, the line widths should also be as narrow as possible. Expressed otherwise, the grating should have a high **resolving power** R, defined as

$$R = \frac{\lambda_{\text{av}}}{\Delta\lambda} \qquad \begin{array}{l} \text{(resolving power} \\ \text{defined).} \end{array} \qquad (37\text{-}31)$$

Here λ_{av} is the mean wavelength of two spectrum lines that can barely be recognized as separate, and $\Delta\lambda$ is the wavelength difference between them. The greater R is, the closer two emission lines can be and still be resolved. We shall show below that the resolving power of a grating is given by the simple expression

$$R = Nm \quad \text{(resolving power of a grating).} \quad (37\text{-}32)$$

To achieve high resolving power, we must use many rulings (large N in Eq. 37-32).

Proof of Eq. 37-30

Let us start with Eq. 37-25, the expression for the locations of the lines in the diffraction pattern of a grating:

$$d \sin \theta = m\lambda.$$

Let us regard θ and λ as variables and take differentials of this equation. We find

$$d \cos \theta \, d\theta = m \, d\lambda.$$

For small enough angles, we can write these differentials as small differences; thus

$$d \cos \theta \, \Delta\theta = m \, \Delta\lambda \quad (37\text{-}33)$$

or

$$\frac{\Delta\theta}{\Delta\lambda} = \frac{m}{d \cos \theta}.$$

The ratio on the left is simply D (see Eq. 37-29), so we have indeed derived Eq. 37-30.

Proof of Eq. 37-32

We start with Eq. 37-33, which was derived from Eq. 37-25, the expression for the locations of the lines in the diffraction pattern formed by a grating. Here $\Delta\lambda$ is the small wavelength difference between two waves that are diffracted by the grating, and $\Delta\theta$ is the angular separation between them in the diffraction pattern. If $\Delta\theta$ is to be the smallest angle that will permit the two lines to be resolved, it must (by Rayleigh's criterion) be equal to the half-width of each line, which is given by Eq. 37-28:

$$\Delta\theta_{\text{hw}} = \frac{\lambda}{Nd \cos \theta}.$$

If we substitute $\Delta\theta_{\text{hw}}$ as given here for $\Delta\theta$ in Eq. 37-33, we find that

$$\frac{\lambda}{N} = m \, \Delta\lambda,$$

from which it readily follows that

$$R = \frac{\lambda}{\Delta\lambda} = Nm.$$

This is Eq. 37-32, which we set out to derive.

Dispersion and Resolving Power Compared

The resolving power of a grating must not be confused with its dispersion. Table 37-1 shows the characteristics of three gratings, all illuminated with light of wavelength $\lambda = 589$ nm, whose diffracted light is viewed in the first order ($m = 1$ in Eq. 37-25). You should verify that the values of D and R as given in the table can be calculated with Eqs. 37-30 and 37-32, respectively. (In the calculations for D, you will need to convert radians per meter to degrees per micrometer.)

For the conditions noted in Table 37-1, gratings A and B have the same *dispersion* and A and C have the same *resolving power.*

Figure 37-25 shows the intensity patterns (also called *line shapes*) that would be produced by these gratings for two lines of wavelengths λ_1 and λ_2, in the vicinity of $\lambda = 589$ nm. Grating B, with the higher resolving power, produces narrower lines and thus is capable of distinguishing

TABLE 37-1 THREE GRATINGS[a]

GRATING	N	d (nm)	θ	D ($°/\mu$m)	R
A	10,000	2540	13.4°	23.2	10,000
B	20,000	2540	13.4°	23.2	20,000
C	10,000	1370	25.5°	46.3	10,000

[a]Data are for $\lambda = 589$ nm and $m = 1$.

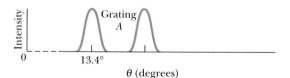

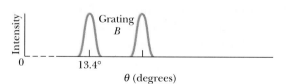

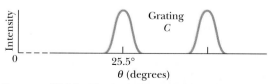

FIGURE 37-25 The intensity patterns for light of two wavelengths sent through the gratings of Table 37-1. Grating B has the highest resolving power, and grating C the highest dispersion.

lines that are much closer together in wavelength than those in the figure. Grating *C*, with the higher dispersion, produces the greater angular separation between the lines.

SAMPLE PROBLEM 37-7

The diffraction grating of Sample Problem 37-6 is illuminated at normal incidence by yellow light from a sodium vapor lamp. This light contains two closely spaced emission lines (known as the sodium doublet) of wavelengths 589.00 nm and 589.59 nm.

(a) At what angle does the first-order maximum occur for the first of these wavelengths?

SOLUTION: The first-order maximum corresponds to $m = 1$ in Eq. 37-25. From Sample Problem 37-6a, we know that the grating spacing *d* is 2016 nm. We thus have

$$\theta = \sin^{-1}\frac{m\lambda}{d} = \sin^{-1}\frac{(1)(589.00 \text{ nm})}{2016 \text{ nm}}$$

$$= 16.99° \approx 17.0°. \qquad \text{(Answer)}$$

(b) In the first order, what is the angular separation between the two lines?

SOLUTION: Here the *dispersion* of the grating comes into play. From Eq. 37-30, the dispersion is

$$D = \frac{m}{d \cos \theta} = \frac{1}{(2016 \text{ nm})(\cos 16.99°)}$$

$$= 5.187 \times 10^{-4} \text{ rad/nm}.$$

From Eq. 37-29, the defining equation for dispersion, we have

$$\Delta\theta = D \, \Delta\lambda$$

$$= (5.187 \times 10^{-4} \text{ rad/nm})$$

$$\times (589.59 \text{ nm} - 589.00 \text{ nm})$$

$$= 3.06 \times 10^{-4} \text{ rad} = 0.0175°. \quad \text{(Answer)}$$

This result depends on the grating spacing *d* but not on the number of rulings there are in the grating.

(c) How close in wavelength can two lines be and still be separated by this grating in the first order?

SOLUTION: Here the *resolving power* of the grating comes into play. From Eq. 37-32, the resolving power is

$$R = Nm = (1.26 \times 10^4)(1) = 1.26 \times 10^4.$$

From Eq. 37-31, the defining equation for resolving power, we have

$$\Delta\lambda = \frac{\lambda}{R} = \frac{589 \text{ nm}}{1.26 \times 10^4} = 0.0467 \text{ nm}. \quad \text{(Answer)}$$

Thus this grating can easily resolve the two sodium lines, which have a wavelength separation of 0.59 nm. Note that this result depends only on the number of grating rulings and is independent of *d*, the spacing between adjacent rulings.

(d) How many rulings must a grating have to just resolve the sodium doublet lines?

SOLUTION: From Eq. 37-31, the defining equation for *R*, the grating must have a resolving power of

$$R = \frac{\lambda}{\Delta\lambda} = \frac{589 \text{ nm}}{0.59 \text{ nm}} = 998.$$

From Eq. 37-32, the number of rulings needed to achieve this resolving power (in the first order) is

$$N = \frac{R}{m} = \frac{998}{1} = 998 \text{ rulings.} \qquad \text{(Answer)}$$

Since our grating has about 13 times as many rulings as this, it can easily resolve the sodium doublet lines, as we have already shown in (c).

37-9 X-RAY DIFFRACTION

X rays are electromagnetic radiation whose wavelengths are of the order of 1 Å ($= 10^{-10}$ m). Compare this with a wavelength of 550 nm ($= 5.5 \times 10^{-7}$ m) at the center of the visible spectrum. Figure 37-26 shows that x rays are produced when electrons escaping from a heated filament *F* are accelerated by a potential difference *V* and strike a metal target *T*.

A standard optical diffraction grating cannot be used to discriminate between different wavelengths in the x-ray wavelength range. For $\lambda = 1$ Å ($= 0.1$ nm) and $d = 3000$ nm, for example, Eq. 37-25 shows that the first-order maximum occurs at

$$\theta = \sin^{-1}\frac{m\lambda}{d} = \sin^{-1}\frac{(1)(0.1 \text{ nm})}{3000 \text{ nm}} = 0.0019°.$$

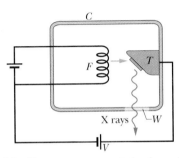

FIGURE 37-26 X rays are generated when electrons from heated filament *F*, accelerated through a potential difference *V*, strike a metal target *T*. The "window" *W* in the evacuated chamber *C* is transparent to x rays.

This is too close to the central maximum to be practical. A grating with $d \approx \lambda$ is desirable, but, since x-ray wavelengths are about equal to atomic diameters, such gratings cannot be constructed mechanically.

In 1912 it occurred to German physicist Max von Laue that a crystalline solid, which consists of a regular array of atoms, might form a natural three-dimensional "diffraction grating" for x rays. The idea is that in a crystal such as sodium chloride (NaCl) a basic unit of atoms (called the *unit cell*) repeats itself throughout the array. In NaCl four sodium ions and four chlorine ions are associated with each unit cell. Figure 37-27a represents a section through a crystal of NaCl and identifies this basic unit. The unit cell is a cube measuring a_0 on each side.

When an x-ray beam enters a crystal such as NaCl, x rays are *scattered*, that is, redirected, in all directions by the crystal structure. In some directions the scattered waves undergo destructive interference, resulting in intensity minima; in other directions the interference is constructive, resulting in intensity maxima. This process of scattering and interference is a form of diffraction, although it is unlike the diffraction of light traveling through a slit or past an edge as we discussed earlier.

Although the process of diffraction of x rays by a crystal is complicated, the maxima turn out to be in directions as *if* the x rays were reflected by a family of parallel *reflecting planes* (or *crystal planes*) that extend through the atoms within the crystal and that contain regular arrays of the atoms. (The x rays are not actually reflected; we use these fictional planes only to simplify the analysis of the actual diffraction process.)

Figure 37-27b shows three of the family of planes, with *interplanar spacing d*, from which the incident rays shown are said to reflect. Rays 1, 2, and 3 reflect from the first, second, and third planes, respectively. At each reflection the angle of incidence and the angle of reflection are represented with θ. Contrary to the custom in optics, these angles are defined relative to the *surface* of the reflecting plane rather than a normal to it. For the situation of Fig. 37-27b, the interplanar spacing happens to be equal to the unit cell dimension a_0.

Figure 37-27c shows an edge-on view of reflection from an adjacent pair of planes. The waves of rays 1 and 2 arrive at the crystal in phase. After they are reflected, they must again be in phase, because the reflections and the reflecting planes have been defined solely to explain the intensity maxima in the diffraction of x rays by a crystal. Unlike light rays, the x rays do not refract upon entering the crystal; moreover, we do not define an index of refraction for this situation. So the relative phase between the waves of rays 1 and 2 as they leave the crystal is set solely by their path length difference. For these rays to be in phase, the path length difference must be equal to an integer multiple of the wavelength λ of the x rays.

By drawing the dashed perpendiculars in Fig. 37-27c, we find that the path length difference is $2d \sin \theta$. In fact, this is true for any pair of adjacent planes in the family of planes represented in Fig. 37-27b. Thus we have, as the criterion for intensity maxima for x-ray diffraction,

$$2d \sin \theta = m\lambda, \quad \text{for } m = 1, 2, 3, \ldots$$
(Bragg's law), (37-34)

FIGURE 37-27 (*a*) The cubic structure of NaCl, showing the sodium and chlorine ions and a unit cell (shaded). (*b*) Incident x rays undergo diffraction by the structure of (*a*). The x rays are diffracted as if they were reflected by a family of parallel planes, with the angle of reflection equal to the angle of incidence, both angles measured relative to the planes (not relative to a normal as in optics). (*c*) The path length difference between waves effectively reflected by two adjacent planes is $2d \sin \theta$. (*d*) A different orientation of the x rays relative to the structure. A different family of parallel planes now effectively reflects the x rays.

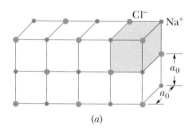
(a)

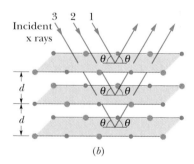
(b)

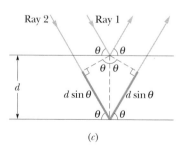
(c)

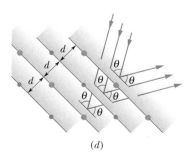
(d)

where m is the order number of an intensity maximum. Equation 37-34 is called **Bragg's law** after British physicist W. L. Bragg, who first derived it. (He and his father shared the 1915 Nobel prize for their use of x rays to study the structures of crystals.) The angle of incidence and reflection in Eq. 37-34 is called a *Bragg angle*.

Regardless of the angle at which x rays enter a crystal, there is always a family of planes from which they can be said to reflect so that we can apply Bragg's law. In Fig. 37-27d, the crystal structure has the same orientation as it does in Fig. 37-27a but the angle at which the beam enters the structure differs from that shown in Fig. 37-27b. This new angle requires a new family of planes, with a different interplanar spacing d and different Bragg angle θ, in order to explain the x-ray diffraction via Bragg's law.

Figure 37-28 shows how the interplanar spacing d can be related to the unit cell dimension a_0. For the particular family of planes shown there,

$$5d = \sqrt{5}a_0,$$

or
$$d = \frac{a_0}{\sqrt{5}}. \qquad (37\text{-}35)$$

Figure 37-28 suggests how the dimensions of the unit cell can be found once the interplanar spacing has been measured by means of x-ray diffraction.

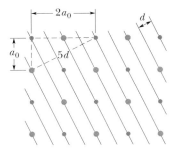

FIGURE 37-28 A family of planes through the structure of Fig. 37-27a, and a way to relate the edge length a_0 of a unit cell to the interplanar spacing d.

X-ray diffraction is a powerful tool for studying both x-ray spectra and the arrangement of atoms in crystals. To study spectra, a particular set of crystal planes, having a known spacing d, is chosen. These planes effectively reflect different wavelengths at different angles. A detector that can discriminate one angle from another can then be used to determine the wavelength of radiation reaching it. The crystal itself can be studied with a monochromatic x-ray beam, to determine not only the spacing of various crystal planes but also the structure of the unit cell.

SAMPLE PROBLEM 37-8

At what Bragg angles must x rays with $\lambda = 1.10$ Å be incident on the family of planes represented in Fig. 37-28 if effective reflections from the planes are to result in diffraction intensity maxima? Assume the material to be sodium chloride ($a_0 = 5.63$ Å).

SOLUTION: The interplanar spacing d for these planes is given by Eq. 37-35 as

$$d = \frac{a_0}{\sqrt{5}} = \frac{5.63 \text{ Å}}{\sqrt{5}} = 2.518 \text{ Å}.$$

Equation 37-34 then gives, for the Bragg angles,

$$\theta = \sin^{-1}\frac{m\lambda}{2d} = \sin^{-1}\left(\frac{(m)(1.10 \text{ Å})}{(2)(2.518 \text{ Å})}\right)$$
$$= \sin^{-1}(0.2184m).$$

Maxima are possible for $\theta = 12.6°$ ($m = 1$), $\theta = 25.9°$ ($m = 2$), $\theta = 40.9°$ ($m = 3$), and $\theta = 60.9°$ ($m = 4$). Higher order maxima cannot exist because they require that $\sin \theta$ be greater than 1.

Actually, the unit cell in cubic crystals such as NaCl has diffraction properties such that the intensity of diffracted x-ray beams corresponding to odd values of m is zero. Thus beams are expected only for $\theta = 25.9°$ and $\theta = 60.9°$.

REVIEW & SUMMARY

Diffraction

When waves encounter an edge or an obstacle or aperture with a size comparable to the wavelength of the waves, those waves spread in their direction of travel and undergo interference. This is called **diffraction.**

Single-Slit Diffraction

Waves passing through a long narrow slit of width a produce a **single-slit diffraction pattern** that includes a central maximum and other maxima, separated by minima located at angles θ to the

central axis that satisfy

$$a \sin \theta = m\lambda, \qquad \text{for } m = 1, 2, 3, \ldots$$
$$\text{(minima).} \quad (37\text{-}3)$$

The intensity of the diffraction pattern at any given angle θ is

$$I = I_m \left(\frac{\sin \alpha}{\alpha}\right)^2, \qquad \text{where} \quad \alpha = \frac{\pi a}{\lambda} \sin \theta \quad (37\text{-}5, 37\text{-}6)$$

and I_m is the intensity at the center of the pattern.

Circular Aperture Diffraction

Diffraction by a circular aperture or a lens with diameter d produces a central maximum and concentric maxima and minima, with the first minimum at an angle θ given by

$$\sin \theta = 1.22 \frac{\lambda}{d} \quad \begin{array}{l}\text{(first minimum;}\\ \text{circular aperture).}\end{array} \quad (37\text{-}12)$$

Rayleigh's Criterion

Rayleigh's criterion suggests that two objects are on the verge of resolvability if the central diffraction maximum of one is at the first minimum of the other. Their angular separation must then be at least

$$\theta_R = 1.22 \frac{\lambda}{d} \quad \text{(Rayleigh's criterion),} \quad (37\text{-}14)$$

in which d is the diameter of the aperture.

Double-Slit Diffraction

Waves passing through two slits, each of width a, whose centers are a distance d apart, display diffraction patterns whose intensity I at various diffraction angles θ is given by

$$I = I_m (\cos^2 \beta) \left(\frac{\sin \alpha}{\alpha}\right)^2 \quad \text{(double slit),} \quad (37\text{-}19)$$

with $\beta = (\pi d/\lambda) \sin \theta$ and α the same as for the case of single-slit diffraction.

Multiple-Slit Diffraction

Diffraction by N (multiple) slits results in maxima (lines) at angles θ such that

$$d \sin \theta = m\lambda, \quad \text{for } m = 0, 1, 2 \ldots$$
$$\text{(maxima),} \quad (37\text{-}25)$$

with the half-widths of the lines given by

$$\Delta\theta_{hw} = \frac{\lambda}{Nd \cos \theta} \quad \text{(half-widths).} \quad (37\text{-}28)$$

Diffraction Gratings

A *diffraction grating* is a series of "slits" used to separate an incident wave into its component wavelengths by separating and displaying their diffraction maxima. A grating is characterized by its dispersion D and resolving power R:

$$D = \frac{\Delta\theta}{\Delta\lambda} = \frac{m}{d \cos \theta}$$

$$R = \frac{\lambda_{av}}{\Delta\lambda} = Nm. \quad (37\text{-}29 \text{ to } 37\text{-}32)$$

X-Ray Diffraction

The regular array of atoms in a crystal is a three-dimensional diffraction grating for short-wavelength waves such as x rays. For analysis purposes, the atoms can be visualized as being arranged in planes with characteristic interplanar spacing d. Diffraction maxima (due to constructive interference) occur if the incident direction of the wave, measured from the surfaces of these planes, and the wavelength λ of the radiation satisfy **Bragg's law:**

$$2d \sin \theta = m\lambda, \quad \text{for } m = 1, 2, 3 \ldots$$
$$\text{(Bragg's law).} \quad (37\text{-}34)$$

QUESTIONS

1. Light of frequency f illuminating a long narrow slit produces a diffraction pattern. (a) If we switch to light of frequency $1.3f$, does the pattern expand away from the center or contract toward it? (b) Does the pattern expand or contract if, instead, we submerge the equipment in clear corn syrup?

2. You are conducting a single-slit diffraction experiment with light of wavelength λ. What appears, on a distant viewing screen, at a point at which the top and bottom rays through the slit have a path length difference equal to (a) 5λ and (b) 4.5λ?

3. If you speak with the same intensity with and without a megaphone in front of your mouth, in which situation do you sound louder to someone directly in front of you?

4. Figure 37-29 shows four choices for the rectangular opening of a source of either sound waves or light waves. The sides have lengths of either L or $2L$, with L being 3.0 times the wavelength of the waves. Rank the openings according to the extent of (a)

left–right spreading and (b) up–down spreading of the waves due to diffraction, greatest first.

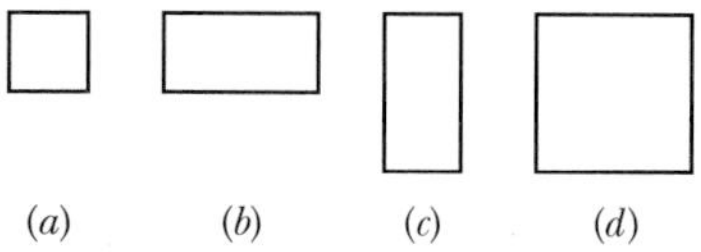

5. In a single-slit diffraction experiment, the top and bottom rays through the slit arrive at a certain point on the viewing screen with a path length difference of 4.0 wavelengths. In a phasor representation like those in Fig 37-6, how many overlapping circles does the chain of phasors make?

6. A vertical spider thread lies between you and the early morning Sun. As you move perpendicular to a line that extends through the thread and the Sun, toward that line, you begin to see the diffraction pattern of sunlight produced by the thread. As your eyes move through the first side maximum of the pattern, what color, red or blue, do you see first? (That is, in a diffraction pattern of white light, is red or blue diffracted at a greater angle?)

7. At night many people see rings (called *entoptic halos*) surrounding bright outdoor lamps in otherwise dark surroundings. The rings are the first of the side maxima in diffraction patterns produced by structures that are thought to be within the cornea (or possibly the lens) of the observer's eye. (The central maxima of such patterns overlap the lamp.) (a) Would a particular ring become smaller or larger if the lamp were switched from

FIGURE 37-29
Question 4.   (a)   (b)   (c)   (d)

blue to red light? (b) If a lamp emits white light, is blue or red on the outside edge of the ring?

8. Figure 37-30 shows the bright fringes that lie within the central diffraction envelope in two double-slit diffraction experiments using the same wavelength of light. Are (a) the slit width a (b) the slit separation d, and (c) the ratio d/a in experiment B greater than, less than, or the same as those in experiment A?

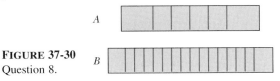

FIGURE 37-30
Question 8.

9. Figure 37-31 shows a red line and a green line of the same order in the pattern produced by a diffraction grating. If we increased the number of rulings in the grating, say, by removing tape that had covered half the rulings, would (a) the half-widths of the lines and (b) the separation of the lines increase, decrease, or remain the same? (c) Would the lines shift to the right, shift to the left, or remain in place?

FIGURE 37-31   Questions 9 and 10.

10. For the situation of Question 9 and Fig. 37-31, if instead we increased the grating spacing, would (a) the half-widths of the lines and (b) the separation of the lines increase, decrease, or remain the same? (c) Would the lines shift to the right, shift to the left, or remain in place?

11. (a) Figure 37-32a shows the lines produced by diffraction gratings A and B using light of the same wavelength; the lines are of the same order and at the same angles θ. Which grating has the greater number of rulings? (b) Figure 37-32b shows lines of two orders produced by a single diffraction grating using light of two wavelengths, both in the red region of the spectrum. Which lines, the left pair or right pair, are in the order with greater m? Is the center of the diffraction pattern to the left or right in (c) Fig. 37-32a and (d) Fig. 37-32b?

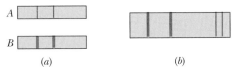

(a)   *(b)*

FIGURE 37-32   Question 11.

12. (a) For a given diffraction grating, does the least difference $\Delta\lambda$ in two wavelengths that can be resolved increase, decrease, or remain the same as the wavelength increases? (b) For a given wavelength region (say, around 500 nm), is $\Delta\lambda$ greater in the first order or in the third order?

EXERCISES & PROBLEMS

SECTION 37-2 Diffraction by a Single Slit: Locating the Minima

1E. When monochromatic light is incident on a slit 0.022 mm wide, the first diffraction minimum is observed at an angle of 1.8° from the direction of the incident light. What is the wavelength?

2E. Monochromatic light of wavelength 441 nm is incident on a narrow slit. On a screen 2.00 m away, the distance between the second diffraction minimum and the central maximum is 1.50 cm. (a) Calculate the angle of diffraction θ of the second minimum. (b) Find the width of the slit.

3E. Light of wavelength 633 nm is incident on a narrow slit. The angle between the first diffraction minimum on one side of the central maximum and the first minimum on the other side is 1.20°. What is the width of the slit?

4E. A single slit is illuminated by light of wavelengths λ_a and λ_b, so chosen that the first diffraction minimum of the λ_a component coincides with the second minimum of the λ_b component. (a) What relationship exists between the two wavelengths? (b) Do any other minima in the two diffraction patterns coincide?

5E. The distance between the first and fifth minima of a single-slit diffraction pattern is 0.35 mm with the screen 40 cm away from the slit, using light of wavelength 550 nm. (a) Find the slit width. (b) Calculate the angle θ of the first diffraction minimum.

6E. What must be the ratio of the slit width to the wavelength for a single slit to have the first diffraction minimum at $\theta = 45.0°$?

7E. A plane wave of wavelength 590 nm is incident on a slit with $a = 0.40$ mm. A thin converging lens of focal length $+70$ cm is placed between the slit and a viewing screen and focuses the light on the screen. (a) How far is the screen from the lens? (b) What is the distance on the screen from the center of the diffraction pattern to the first minimum?

8P. A slit 1.00 mm wide is illuminated by light of wavelength 589 nm. We see a diffraction pattern on a screen 3.00 m away. What is the distance between the first two diffraction minima on the same side of the central diffraction maximum?

9P. Sound waves with frequency 3000 Hz and speed 343 m/s diffract through the rectangular opening of a speaker cabinet and into a large auditorium. The opening, which has a horizontal width of 30.0 cm, faces a wall 100 m away (Fig. 37-33). Where

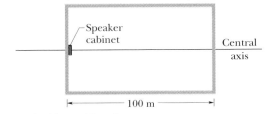

FIGURE 37-33   Problem 9.

along that wall will a listener be at the first diffraction minimum and thus have difficulty hearing the sound? (Neglect reflections from the walls.)

10P. Manufacturers of wire (and other objects of small dimensions) sometimes use a laser to continually monitor the thickness of the product. The wire intercepts the laser beam, producing a diffraction pattern like that of a single slit of the same width as the wire diameter (see Fig. 37-34). Suppose a helium–neon laser, of wavelength 632.8 nm, illuminates a wire, and the diffraction pattern appears on a screen 2.60 m away. If the desired wire diameter is 1.37 mm, what is the observed distance between the two tenth-order minima (one on each side of the central maximum)?

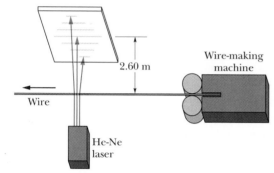

FIGURE 37-34 Problem 10.

SECTION 37-4 Intensity in Single-Slit Diffraction, Quantitatively

11E. A 0.10-mm-wide slit is illuminated by light of wavelength 589 nm. Consider rays that are diffracted at $\theta = 30°$ and calculate the phase difference at the screen of Huygens' wavelets from the top and midpoint of the slit. (*Hint:* See Eq. 37-4.)

12E. Monochromatic light with wavelength 538 nm is incident on a slit with width 0.025 mm. The distance from the slit to a screen is 3.5 m. Consider a point on the screen 1.1 cm from the central maximum. (a) Calculate θ for that point. (b) Calculate α. (c) Calculate the ratio of the intensity at this point to the intensity at the central maximum.

13P. If you double the width of a single slit, the intensity of the central maximum of the diffraction pattern increases by a factor of 4, even though the energy passing through the slit only doubles. Explain this quantitatively.

14P. *Babinet's Principle.* A monochromatic beam of parallel light is incident on a "collimating" hole of diameter $x \gg \lambda$. Point P lies in the geometrical shadow region on a *distant* screen (Fig. 37-35). Two obstacles, shown in Fig. 37-35*b*, are placed in turn over the collimating hole. A is an opaque circle with a hole in it and B is the "photographic negative" of A. Using superposition concepts, show that the intensity at P is identical for the two diffracting objects A and B.

15P. The full width at half-maximum (FWHM) of the central diffraction maximum is defined as the angle between the two points in the pattern where the intensity is one-half that at the center of the pattern. (See Fig. 37-7*b*.) (a) Show that the intensity

drops to one-half the maximum value when $\sin^2 \alpha = \alpha^2/2$. (b) Verify that $\alpha = 1.39$ radians (about 80°) is a solution to the transcendental equation of (a). (c) Show that the FWHM is $\Delta\theta = 2 \sin^{-1}(0.443\lambda/a)$. (d) Calculate the FWHM of the central maximum for slits whose widths are 1.0, 5.0, and 10 wavelengths.

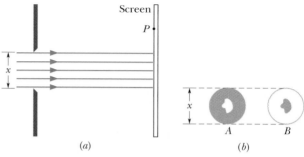

FIGURE 37-35 Problem 14.

16P. (a) Show that the values of α at which intensity maxima for single-slit diffraction occur can be found exactly by differentiating Eq. 37-5 with respect to α and equating the result to zero, obtaining the condition $\tan \alpha = \alpha$. (b) Find the values of α satisfying this relation by plotting the curve $y = \tan \alpha$ and the straight line $y = \alpha$ and finding their intersections or by using a pocket calculator to find an appropriate value of α by trial and error. (c) Find the (noninteger) values of m corresponding to successive maxima in the single-slit pattern. Note that the secondary maxima do not lie exactly halfway between minima.

17P*. Derive this expression for the intensity pattern for a three-slit "grating":

$$I = \tfrac{1}{9}I_m(1 + 4 \cos \phi + 4 \cos^2 \phi),$$

where $\phi = (2\pi d \sin \theta)/\lambda$. Assume that $a \ll \lambda$; be guided by the derivation of the corresponding double-slit formula (Eq. 36-21).

SECTION 37-5 Diffraction by a Circular Aperture

18E. Assume that the lamp in Question 7 emits light at wavelength 550 nm. If a ring has an angular diameter of 2.5°, approximately what is the (linear) diameter of the structure in the eye that causes the ring?

19E. The two headlights of an approaching automobile are 1.4 m apart. At what (a) angular separation and (b) maximum distance will the eye resolve them? Assume that the pupil diameter is 5.0 mm, and use a wavelength of 550 nm. Also assume that diffraction effects alone limit the resolution.

20E. An astronaut in a space shuttle claims she can just barely resolve two point sources on Earth's surface, 160 km below. Calculate their (a) angular and (b) linear separation, assuming ideal conditions. Take $\lambda = 540$ nm and the pupil diameter of the astronaut's eye to be 5.0 mm.

21E. Find the separation of two points on the Moon's surface that can just be resolved by the 200 in. (= 5.1 m) telescope at Mount Palomar, assuming that this separation is determined by diffraction effects. The distance from Earth to the Moon is 3.8×10^5 km. Assume a wavelength of 550 nm.

22E. The wall of a large room is covered with acoustic tile in which small holes are drilled 5.0 mm from center to center. How far can a person be from such a tile and still distinguish the individual holes, assuming ideal conditions, the pupil diameter of the observer's eye to be 4.0 mm, and the wavelength of the room light to be 550 nm?

23E. The pupil of a person's eye has a diameter of 5.00 mm. What distance apart must two small objects be if their images are just resolved when they are 250 mm from the eye and illuminated with light of wavelength 500 nm?

24E. Under ideal conditions, estimate the linear separation of two objects on the planet Mars that can just be resolved by an observer on Earth (a) using the naked eye and (b) using the 200 in. (= 5.1 m) Mount Palomar telescope. Use the following data: distance to Mars = 8.0×10^7 km; diameter of pupil = 5.0 mm; wavelength of light = 550 nm.

25E. If Superman really had x-ray vision at 0.10 nm wavelength and a 4.0 mm pupil diameter, at what maximum altitude could he distinguish villains from heroes, assuming that he needs to resolve points separated by 5.0 cm to do this?

26E. A navy cruiser employs radar with a wavelength of 1.6 cm. The circular antenna has a diameter of 2.3 m. At a range of 6.2 km, what is the smallest distance that two speedboats can be from each other and still be resolved as two separate objects by the radar system?

27P. Nuclear-pumped x-ray lasers are seen as a possible weapon to destroy ICBM booster rockets at ranges up to 2000 km. One limitation on such a device is the spreading of the beam due to diffraction, with resulting dilution of beam intensity. Consider such a laser operating at a wavelength of 1.40 nm. The element that emits light is the end of a wire with diameter 0.200 mm. (a) Calculate the diameter of the central beam at a target 2000 km away from the beam source. (b) By what factor is the beam intensity reduced in transit to the target? (The laser is fired from space, so that atmospheric absorption can be ignored.)

28P. (a) How far from grains of red sand must you be to position yourself just at the limit of resolving the grains if your pupil diameter is 1.5 mm, the grains are spherical with radius 50 μm, and the light from the grains has wavelength 650 nm? (b) If the grains were blue and the light from them had wavelength 400 nm, would the answer to (a) be larger or smaller?

29P. The wings of tiger beetles (Fig. 37-36) are colored by interference due to thin cuticle-like layers. In addition, these layers are arranged in patches that are 60 μm across and produce different colors. The color you see is a pointillistic mixture of thin-film interference colors that varies with perspective. Approximately what viewing distance from a wing puts you at the limit of resolving the different colored patches according to Rayleigh's criterion? Use 550 nm as the wavelength of light and 3.00 mm as the diameter of your pupil.

30P. (a) A circular diaphragm 60 cm in diameter oscillates at a frequency of 25 kHz as an underwater source of sound used for submarine detection. Far from the source the sound intensity is distributed as the diffraction pattern of a circular hole whose diameter equals that of the diaphragm. Take the speed of sound in

water to be 1450 m/s and find the angle between the normal to the diaphragm and the direction of the first minimum. (b) Repeat for a source having an (audible) frequency of 1.0 kHz.

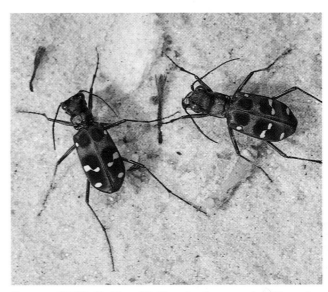

FIGURE 37-36 Problem 29. Tiger beetles are colored by pointillistic mixtures of thin-film interference colors.

31P. In June 1985 a laser beam was fired from the Air Force Optical Station on Maui, Hawaii, and reflected back from the shuttle *Discovery* as it sped by, 220 mi overhead. The diameter of the central maximum of the beam at the shuttle position was said to be 30 ft, and the beam wavelength was 500 nm. What is the effective diameter of the laser aperture at the Maui ground station? (*Hint:* A laser beam spreads only because of diffraction; assume a circular exit aperture.)

32P. A spy satellite orbiting at 160 km above Earth's surface has a lens with a focal length of 3.6 m and can resolve objects on the ground as small as 30 cm; it can easily measure the size of an aircraft's air intake. What is the effective lens diameter, determined by diffraction consideration alone? Assume $\lambda = 550$ nm.

33P. Millimeter-wave radar generates a narrower beam than conventional microwave radar, making it less vulnerable to antiradar missiles. (a) Calculate the angular width of the central maximum, from first minimum to first minimum, produced by a 220 GHz radar beam emitted by a 55.0-cm-diameter circular antenna. (The frequency is chosen to coincide with a low-absorption atmospheric "window.") (b) Calculate the same quantity for the ship's radar described in Exercise 26.

34P. (a) How small is the angular separation of two stars if their images are barely resolved by the Thaw refracting telescope at the Allegheny Observatory in Pittsburgh? The lens diameter is 76 cm and its focal length is 14 m. Assume $\lambda = 550$ nm. (b) Find the distance between these barely resolved stars if each of them is 10 light-years distant from Earth. (c) For the image of a single star in this telescope, find the diameter of the first dark ring in the diffraction pattern, as measured on a photographic plate placed at the focal plane of the telescope lens. Assume that the structure of the image is associated entirely with diffraction at the lens aperture and not with lens "errors."

35P. A circular obstacle produces the same diffraction pattern as a circular hole of the same diameter (except very near $\theta = 0$). Airborne water drops are examples of such obstacles. When you see the Moon through suspended water drops, such as in a fog, you intercept the diffraction pattern from many drops; the composite is a bright circular pattern surrounding the Moon (Fig. 37-37). Next to the Moon, the pattern is white. (a) What color, red or blue, outlines that white pattern? (b) Suppose the outlining ring has an angular diameter that is 1.5 times the angular diameter of the Moon, which is 0.50°. Suppose also that the drops all have about the same diameter; approximately what is that diameter?

FIGURE 37-37 Problem 35. The corona around the Moon is a composite of the diffraction patterns of airborne water drops.

36P. In a joint Soviet–French experiment to monitor the Moon's surface with a light beam, pulsed radiation from a ruby laser ($\lambda = 0.69 \ \mu m$) was directed to the Moon through a reflecting telescope with a mirror radius of 1.3 m. A reflector on the Moon behaved like a circular plane mirror with radius 10 cm, reflecting the light directly back toward the telescope on Earth. The reflected light was then detected after being brought to a focus by this telescope. What fraction of the original light energy was picked up by the detector? Assume that for each direction of travel all the energy is in the central diffraction peak.

SECTION 37-6 Diffraction by a Double Slit

37E. Suppose that the central diffraction envelope of a double-slit diffraction pattern contains 11 bright fringes and the first diffraction minima eliminate (are coincident with) bright fringes. How many bright fringes lie between the first and second minima of the diffraction envelope?

38E. For $d = 2a$ in Fig. 37-38, how many bright interference fringes lie in the central diffraction envelope?

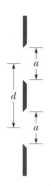

FIGURE 37-38 Exercise 38 and Problem 39.

39P. If we put $d = a$ in Fig. 37-38, the two slits coalesce into a single slit of width $2a$. Show that Eq. 37-19 reduces to the diffraction pattern for such a slit.

40P. (a) In a double-slit system, what ratio of d to a causes diffraction to eliminate the fourth bright side fringe? (b) What other bright fringes are also eliminated?

41P. Two slits of width a and separation d are illuminated by a coherent beam of light of wavelength λ. What is the linear separation of the bright interference fringes observed on a screen that is at a distance D away?

42P. (a) How many fringes appear between the first diffraction-envelope minima to either side of the central maximum for a double-slit pattern if $\lambda = 550$ nm, $d = 0.150$ mm, and $a = 30.0 \ \mu m$? (b) What is the ratio of the intensity of the third bright fringe to the intensity of the central fringe?

43P. Light of wavelength 440 nm passes through a double slit, yielding a diffraction pattern whose graph of intensity I versus deflection angle θ is shown in Fig. 37-39. Calculate (a) the slit width and (b) the slit separation. (c) Verify the displayed intensities of the $m = 1$ and $m = 2$ interference fringes.

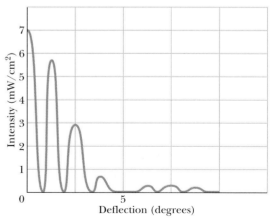

FIGURE 37-39 Problem 43.

44P. An acoustic double-slit system (of slit separation d and slit width a) is driven by two loudspeakers as shown in Fig. 37-40. By use of a variable delay line, the phase of one of the speakers may be varied. Describe in detail what changes occur in the double-slit diffraction pattern at large distances as the phase difference between the speakers is varied from zero to 2π. Take both interference and diffraction effects into account.

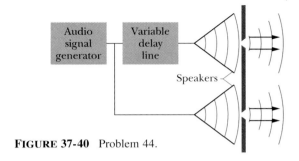

FIGURE 37-40 Problem 44.

SECTION 37-7 Diffraction Gratings

45E. A diffraction grating 20.0 mm wide has 6000 rulings. (a) Calculate the distance d between adjacent rulings. (b) At what angles will intensity maxima occur if the incident radiation has a wavelength of 589 nm?

46E. A diffraction grating has 200 rulings/mm, and it produces an intensity maximum at $\theta = 30.0°$. (a) What are the possible wavelengths of the incident visible light? (b) To what colors do they correspond?

47E. A grating has 315 rulings/mm. For what wavelengths in the visible spectrum can fifth-order diffraction be observed?

48E. Given a grating with 400 lines/mm, how many orders of the entire visible spectrum (400–700 nm) can it produce in addition to the $m = 0$ order?

49E. A diffraction grating 3.00 cm wide produces the second order at 33.0° with light of wavelength 600 nm. What is the total number of lines on the grating?

50E. Some tropical gyrinid beetles (whirligig beetles) are colored by optical interference that is due to scales whose alignment forms a diffraction grating (which uses scattered instead of transmitted light). If the incident light is perpendicular on the grating, the angle between the first-order maxima (on opposite sides of the zeroth-order maximum) is about 26°. What is the grating spacing of the beetle? Use 550 nm as the wavelength of light.

51E. A diffraction grating 1.0 cm wide has 10,000 parallel slits. Monochromatic light that is incident normally is deviated through 30° in the first order. What is the wavelength of the light?

52P. Light of wavelength 600 nm is incident normally on a diffraction grating. Two adjacent maxima occur at angles given by $\sin \theta = 0.2$ and $\sin \theta = 0.3$, respectively. The fourth-order maxima are missing. (a) What is the separation between adjacent slits? (b) What is the smallest possible individual slit width? (c) Which orders of intensity maxima are produced by the grating, assuming the values derived in (a) and (b)?

53P. A diffraction grating is made up of slits of width 300 nm with separation 900 nm. The grating is illuminated by monochromatic plane waves of wavelength $\lambda = 600$ nm at normal incidence. (a) How many diffraction maxima are there in the full pattern? (b) What is the width of a spectral line observed in the first order if the grating has 1000 slits?

54P. Assume that the limits of the visible spectrum are arbitrarily chosen as 430 and 680 nm. Calculate the number of rulings per millimeter of a grating that will spread the first-order spectrum through an angle of 20°.

55P. With light from a gaseous discharge tube incident normally on a grating with slit separation 1.73 μm, sharp maxima of green light are produced at angles $\theta = \pm17.6°$, 37.3°, $-37.1°$, 65.2°, and $-65.0°$. Compute the wavelength of the green light that best fits these data.

56P. Light is incident on a grating at an angle ψ as shown in Fig. 37-41. Show that bright fringes occur at angles θ that satisfy the equation

$$d(\sin \psi + \sin \theta) = m\lambda, \qquad \text{for } m = 0, 1, 2, \dots.$$

(Compare this equation with Eq. 37-25.) Only the special case $\psi = 0$ has been treated in this chapter.

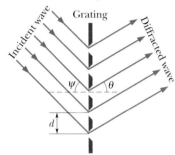

FIGURE 37-41 Problem 56.

57P. A grating with $d = 1.50$ μm is illuminated at various angles of incidence by light of wavelength 600 nm. Plot, as a function of the angle of incidence (0 to 90°), the angular deviation of the first-order maximum from the incident direction. (See Problem 56.)

58P. Two emission lines have wavelengths λ and $\lambda + \Delta\lambda$, respectively, where $\Delta\lambda \ll \lambda$. Show that their angular separation $\Delta\theta$ in a grating spectrometer is given approximately by

$$\Delta\theta = \frac{\Delta\lambda}{\sqrt{(d/m)^2 - \lambda^2}},$$

where d is the slit separation and m is the order at which the lines are observed. Note that the angular separation is greater in the higher orders than in lower orders.

59P. White light (consisting of wavelengths from 400 nm to 700 nm) is normally incident on a grating. Show that, no matter what the value of the grating spacing d, the second order and third order overlap.

60P. Show that a grating made up of alternately transparent and opaque strips of equal width eliminates all the even orders of maxima (except $m = 0$).

61P. A grating has 350 rulings per millimeter and is illuminated at normal incidence by white light. A spectrum is formed on a screen 30 cm from the grating. If a hole 10 mm square is cut in the screen, its inner edge being 50 mm from the central maximum and parallel to it, what range of wavelengths passes through the hole?

62P. Derive Eq. 37-28, the expression for the line widths.

SECTION 37-8 Gratings: Dispersion and Resolving Power

63E. The *D* line in the spectrum of sodium is a doublet with wavelengths 589.0 and 589.6 nm. Calculate the minimum number of lines needed in a grating that will resolve this doublet in the second-order spectrum. See Sample Problem 37-7.

64E. A grating has 600 rulings/mm and is 5.0 mm wide. (a) What is the smallest wavelength interval it can resolve in the third order at $\lambda = 500$ nm? (b) How many higher orders of maxima can be seen?

65E. A source containing a mixture of hydrogen and deuterium atoms emits red light at two wavelengths whose mean is 656.3 nm and whose separation is 0.180 nm. Find the minimum number of lines needed in a diffraction grating that can resolve these lines in the first order.

66E. (a) How many rulings must a 4.00-cm-wide diffraction grating have to resolve the wavelengths 415.496 and 415.487 nm in the second order? (b) At what angle are the maxima found?

67E. With a particular grating the sodium doublet (see Sample Problem 37-7) is viewed in the third order at 10° to the normal and is barely resolved. Find (a) the grating spacing and (b) the total width of the rulings.

68E. Show that the dispersion of a grating is $D = (\tan \theta)/\lambda$.

69E. A grating has 40,000 rulings spread over 76 mm. (a) What is its expected dispersion *D* for sodium light ($\lambda = 589$ nm) in the first three orders? (b) What is the grating's resolving power in these orders?

70P. Light containing a mixture of two wavelengths, 500 and 600 nm, is incident normally on a diffraction grating. It is desired (1) that the first and second maxima for each wavelength appear at $\theta \leq 30°$, (2) that the dispersion be as high as possible, and (3) that the third order for 600 nm be a missing order. (a) What should be the slit separation? (b) What is the smallest possible individual slit width? (c) For the 600 nm wavelength, which orders of intensity maxima are produced by the grating, assuming the values derived in (a) and (b)?

71P. (a) In terms of the angle θ locating a line produced by a grating, find the product of that line's half-width and the resolving power of the grating. (b) Evaluate that product for the grating of Problem 53, for first order.

72P. A diffraction grating has resolving power $R = \lambda_{av}/\Delta\lambda = Nm$. (a) Show that the corresponding frequency range Δf that can just be resolved is given by $\Delta f = c/Nm\lambda$. (b) From Fig. 37-19, show that the times required for light to travel along the two extreme rays differ by an amount $\Delta t = (Nd/c) \sin \theta$. (c) Show that $(\Delta f)(\Delta t) = 1$, this relation being independent of the various grating parameters. Assume $N \gg 1$.

SECTION 37-9 X-Ray Diffraction

73E. X rays of wavelength 0.12 nm are found to undergo second-order reflection at a Bragg angle of 28° from a lithium fluoride crystal. What is the interplanar spacing of the reflecting planes in the crystal?

74E. What is the smallest Bragg angle for x rays of wavelength 30 pm to undergo reflection from reflecting planes of spacing 0.30 nm in a calcite crystal?

75E. If first-order reflection occurs in a crystal at Bragg angle 3.4°, at what Bragg angle does second-order reflection occur from the same family of reflecting planes?

76E. Figure 37-42 is a graph of intensity versus diffraction angle for the diffraction of an x-ray beam by a crystal. The beam consists of two wavelengths, and the spacing between the reflecting planes is 0.94 nm. What are the two wavelengths?

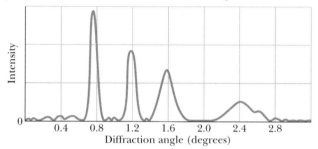

FIGURE 37-42 Exercise 76.

77E. An x-ray beam of wavelength *A* undergoes a first-order reflection from a crystal when its angle of incidence to a crystal face is 23°, and an x-ray beam of wavelength 97 pm undergoes third-order reflection when its angle of incidence to that face is 60°. Assuming that the two beams reflect from the same family of reflecting planes, find (a) the interplanar spacing and (b) the wavelength *A*.

78E. An x-ray beam of a certain wavelength is incident on a NaCl crystal, at 30.0° to a certain family of reflecting planes of spacing 39.8 pm. If the reflection from those planes is of the first order, what is the wavelength of the x rays?

79P. Prove that it is not possible to determine both wavelength of radiation and spacing of reflecting planes in a crystal by measuring the Bragg angles in several orders.

80P. In Fig. 37-43, an x-ray beam of wavelengths from 95.0 pm to 140 pm is incident on a family of reflecting planes with spacing $d = 275$ pm. At which wavelengths will these planes produce intensity maxima in their reflections?

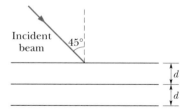

FIGURE 37-43 Problems 80 and 83.

81P. In Fig. 37-44, first-order reflection from the reflection planes shown occurs when an x-ray beam of wavelength 0.260 nm makes an angle of 63.8° with the top face of the crystal. What is the unit cell size a_0?

82P. Consider a two-dimensional square crystal structure, such as one side of the structure shown in Fig. 37-27a. One interplanar spacing of reflecting planes is the unit cell size a_0. Calculate and sketch the next five smaller interplanar spacings. (b) Show that your results in (a) obey the general formula

$$d = \frac{a_0}{\sqrt{h^2 + k^2}},$$

where h and k are relatively prime integers (they have no common factor other than unity).

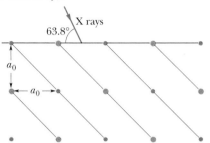

FIGURE 37-44   Problem 81.

83P.   In Fig. 37-43, let a beam of x rays of wavelength 0.125 nm be incident on an NaCl crystal at an angle of 45.0° to the top face of the crystal. Let the reflecting planes have separation $d = 0.252$ nm. Through what angles must the crystal be turned about an axis that is perpendicular to the plane of the page for these reflecting planes to give intensity maxima in their reflections?

Electronic Computation

84.   A computer can be used to sum the phasors corresponding to Huygens' wavelets and so find a diffraction pattern. Suppose light with a wavelength of 500 nm is incident normally on a single slit with a width of 5.00×10^{-6} m. To approximate the diffraction pattern, sum the phasors corresponding to $N = 200$ wavelets spreading from uniformly distributed sources within the slit. The horizontal and vertical components of the resultant are proportional to

$$E_h = \sum_{i=1}^{N} \cos \phi_i \quad \text{and} \quad E_v = \sum_{i=1}^{N} \sin \phi_i,$$

respectively, where ϕ_i is the phase of wavelet i. The intensity ratio is $I/I_m = (E_h^2 + E_v^2)/N^2$. The factor $1/N^2$ assures that $I/I_m = 1$ when all the wavelets have the same phase. If you consider light that is diffracted at the angle θ to the straight-ahead direction, then you may take the phase of the first wavelet to be zero and the phase of each successive wavelet to be $(2\pi/\lambda)\Delta x \sin \theta$ greater than that of the preceding wavelet. Here Δx is the distance between wavelet sources; that is, $\Delta x = a/(N - 1)$, where a is the slit width. Use this technique to search for the diffraction angles corresponding to the first three secondary maxima and find the intensity ratios for those maxima.

38
Relativity

In modern long-range navigation, the precise location and speed of moving craft are continuously monitored and updated. A system of navigation satellites called NAVSTAR permits locations and speeds anywhere on Earth to be determined to within about 16 m and 2 cm/s. However, if relativity effects were not taken into account, speeds could not be determined any closer than about 20 cm/s, which is unacceptable for modern navigation systems. How can something as abstract as Einstein's special theory of relativity be involved in something as practical as navigation?

Tracks of tiny vapor bubbles in this bubble-chamber image reveal where electrons (tracks color-coded green) and positrons (red) moved. A gamma ray (which left no track when it entered at the top) kicked an electron out of one of the hydrogen atoms filling the chamber and then converted to an electron–positron pair. Another gamma ray underwent another pair production farther down. These tracks (curved because of a magnetic field) clearly show that electrons and positrons are particles that move along narrow paths. Yet, those particles can also be interpreted in terms of waves. Can a particle be a wave?

39-1 A NEW DIRECTION

Our discussion of Einstein's theory of relativity took us into a world far beyond that of ordinary experience—the world of objects moving at speeds close to the speed of light. Among other surprises, Einstein's theory predicts that the rate at which a clock runs depends on how fast the clock is moving relative to the observer: the faster the motion, the slower the clock rate. This and other predictions of the theory have passed every experimental test devised thus far, and relativity theory has led us to a deeper and more satisfying view of the nature of space and time.

Now you are about to explore a second world that is outside ordinary experience—the subatomic world. You will encounter a new set of surprises that, though they may sometimes seem bizarre, have led physicists step by step to a deeper view of the nature of reality.

Quantum mechanics, as our new subject is called, answers such questions as: Why do the stars shine? Why do the elements exhibit the order that is so apparent in the periodic table? How do transistors and other microelectronic devices work? Why does copper conduct electricity but glass does not? Because quantum mechanics accounts for all of chemistry, including biochemistry, we need to understand it if we are to understand life itself.

Some of the predictions of quantum mechanics seem strange even to the physicists and philosophers who study its foundations. Nevertheless, this theory too has passed every experimental test—and there have been many—with flying colors. Its predictions have never failed.

39-2 LIGHT WAVES AND PHOTONS

We have described light as a wave, having a wavelength λ, a frequency f, and a speed c, such that

$$c = \lambda f. \qquad (39\text{-}1)$$

In Chapter 34 we used Maxwell's equations to show that a light wave is an interdependent combination of electric and magnetic fields, each alternating at frequency f. We showed further that visible light is part of an electromagnetic spectrum that extends, in a continuous range of wavelengths, from gamma rays to long radio waves.

In 1905 Einstein proposed a property of visible light and other electromagnetic radiation that is *not* predicted by Maxwell's equations and gives us the first of our quantum surprises: when an atom emits or absorbs light, energy is transferred not in a smooth continuous fashion but in small, discrete "lumps" of energy. We now call such lumps of energy **photons** (the word was not introduced until 1926).

According to Einstein's proposal, the energy E transferred by a single photon associated with a light wave of frequency f is

$$E = hf \qquad \text{(photon energy)}. \qquad (39\text{-}2)$$

Here h is the **Planck constant,** which has the value

$$h = 6.63 \times 10^{-34} \text{ J} \cdot \text{s} = 4.14 \times 10^{-15} \text{ eV} \cdot \text{s}. \qquad (39\text{-}3)$$

The Planck constant is the basic constant of quantum mechanics, much as the speed of light c is the basic constant of relativity. If c were infinite (it is "large" but it isn't infinite), there would be no special relativity; if h were zero (it is "small" but it isn't zero), there would be no quantum mechanics.

CHECKPOINT 1: Rank the following radiations according to their associated photon energies, greatest first: (a) yellow light from a sodium vapor lamp, (b) a gamma ray emitted by a radioactive nucleus, (c) a radio wave emitted by the antenna of a commercial radio station, (d) a microwave beam emitted by an airport traffic control radar.

SAMPLE PROBLEM 39-1

A 100 W sodium vapor lamp is placed at the center of a large sphere, which absorbs all the sodium light that falls on it. At what rate are photons delivered to the sphere? The wavelength of sodium light is 590 nm.

SOLUTION: From Eq. 39-2 the energy per photon for sodium light is

$$\begin{aligned} E = hf &= \frac{hc}{\lambda} \\ &= \frac{(6.63 \times 10^{-34} \text{ J} \cdot \text{s})(3.00 \times 10^8 \text{ m/s})}{590 \times 10^{-9} \text{ m}} \\ &= 3.37 \times 10^{-19} \text{ J}. \end{aligned}$$

Thus, every time a sodium atom emits a photon, the atom loses 3.37×10^{-19} J, or 2.1 eV, of energy. When sodium light is absorbed by the sphere, energy is transferred to the sphere in "lumps" of this same size.

To find the rate R at which photons are absorbed by the sphere, we divide E into the rate (the power P) at which the lamp emits energy:

$$\begin{aligned} R = \frac{P}{E} &= \frac{100 \text{ W}}{3.37 \times 10^{-19} \text{ J/photon}} \\ &= 3.0 \times 10^{20} \text{ photons/s}. \qquad \text{(Answer)} \end{aligned}$$

That's a lot of photons! If you could read words ("photons" of information?) at this rate, you could read every book in the Library of Congress in about one nanosecond.

39-3 THE PHOTOELECTRIC EFFECT

If you shine a beam of light of short enough wavelength onto a clean metal surface, the light will knock electrons out of that surface. This **photoelectric effect** is used in many devices, including TV cameras, camcorders, and night vision viewers. Einstein supported his photon concept by using it to explain this effect, which simply cannot be understood in terms of classical physics.

Let us analyze two photoelectric experiments, each using the apparatus of Fig. 39-1 in which light of frequency f falls on target T and knocks electrons out of it. A potential difference V is maintained between target T and collector cup C to sweep up these electrons, said to be **photoelectrons**. This collection produces a **photoelectric current** i in meter A.

First Photoelectric Experiment

We adjust the potential difference V by moving the sliding contact in Fig. 39-1 so that collector C is negative with respect to target T. This potential difference acts to slow down the ejected electrons. We then vary V until it reaches a certain value, called the **stopping potential** V_{stop}, at which the reading of meter A has just dropped to zero. When $V = V_{stop}$, the most energetic ejected electrons are turned back just before reaching the collector. Then K_{max}, the kinetic energy of these most energetic electrons, is

$$K_{max} = eV_{stop}, \qquad (39\text{-}4)$$

where e is the elementary charge.

Measurements show that for light of a given frequency, K_{max} *does not depend on the intensity of the light source.* Whether the source is dazzling bright or so feeble that you can scarcely detect it (or has some intermediate brightness), the maximum kinetic energy of the ejected electrons always has the same value.

This is a puzzle for classical physics. If you view the incident light as a classical electromagnetic wave, you have in mind the image of an electron in the target oscillating back and forth under the influence of the alternating electric field of the incident light wave. Under certain conditions, the oscillating electron will pick up enough energy to break through the surface of the target. If you increase the intensity of the incident light beam, you increase the amplitude of the alternating electric field, and it seems reasonable to suppose that this stronger alternating field will give a more energetic ''kick'' to the ejected electron. *That is not what happens.* For a given frequency, intense light beams and feeble light beams give exactly the same maximum kick to breakaway electrons.

The actual result follows naturally if we think in terms of photons. Now the maximum energy that an electron of

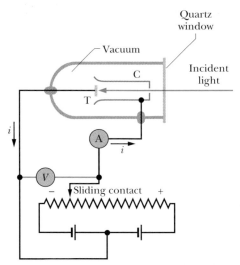

FIGURE 39-1 An apparatus used to study the photoelectric effect. The incident light falls on target T, ejecting electrons, which are collected by collector cup C. The electrons move in the circuit in a direction opposite the conventional current arrows. The batteries and the variable resistor are used to produce and adjust the electric potential difference between T and C.

target T in Fig. 39-1 can pick up from the incident light is only that of a single photon. Increasing the light intensity increases the *number* of photons at the target surface, but the *energy per photon*, given by Eq. 39-2, remains unchanged. Hence the maximum kinetic energy imparted to an electron does not change.

Second Photoelectric Experiment

Now we vary the frequency f of the incident light and measure the associated stopping potential V_{stop}. Figure 39-2 is a plot of V_{stop} against f. Note that the photoelectric effect does not occur if the frequency is less than a certain **cutoff frequency** f_0; it turns out that this is so *no matter how intense the incident light is.*

This is another puzzle for classical physics. If you view light as an electromagnetic wave, you must expect that no matter how low the frequency, electrons can always be ejected if you supply them with enough energy — that is, if you use a bright enough light source. *That is not what happens.* For light below a certain frequency, the photoelectric effect does not occur, no matter how bright the light source.

The existence of a cutoff frequency, however, is just what we should expect if the energy is transferred via photons. The electrons within the target are held there by electric forces. (If they weren't, they would drip out of the target under the influence of gravity!) To just escape from the target, an electron must pick up a certain minimum

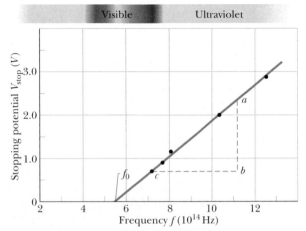

FIGURE 39-2 The stopping potential V_{stop} as a function of the frequency f of the incident light for a sodium target T in the apparatus of Fig. 39-1. (Data reported by R. A. Millikan in 1916.)

energy Φ, where Φ is a property of the target material called its **work function**. If the energy hf transferred to an electron by a photon exceeds the work function of the material (that is, if $hf > \Phi$), the electron can escape through the target surface. If the energy transferred does not exceed the work function (that is, if $hf < \Phi$), the electron cannot escape. This is just what Fig. 39-2 shows.

The Photoelectric Equation

Einstein summed up the results of our two photoelectric experiments in the equation

$$hf = K_{max} + \Phi \qquad \text{(photoelectric equation)}, \qquad (39\text{-}5)$$

which is a statement of the conservation of energy for a single interaction between a photon of frequency f and an electron in a target made of a material with work function Φ. If the electron is to escape from the target, it must pick up energy at least equal to Φ. Any remaining energy $(hf - \Phi)$ that the electron acquires from the interaction appears as kinetic energy of the electron. In the most favorable circumstance, the electron can escape through the surface without losing any of this kinetic energy in the process; it then appears outside the target with the maximum possible kinetic energy K_{max}.

Let us rewrite Eq. 39-5 by substituting for K_{max} from Eq. 39-4. After a little rearranging we get

$$V_{stop} = \left(\frac{h}{e}\right) f - \frac{\Phi}{e}. \qquad (39\text{-}6)$$

The ratios h/e and Φ/e are constants, so we expect a plot of the measured stopping potential V_{stop} against the frequency f to be a straight line, as in Fig. 39-2. Further, the slope of

that straight line should be h/e. As a check, we measure ab and bc in Fig. 39-2 and write

$$\frac{h}{e} = \frac{ab}{bc} = \frac{2.35\ \text{V} - 0.72\ \text{V}}{(11.2 \times 10^{14} - 7.2 \times 10^{14})\ \text{Hz}}$$

$$= 4.1 \times 10^{-15}\ \text{V} \cdot \text{s}.$$

Multiplying this result by the elementary charge e, we find

$$h = (4.1 \times 10^{-15}\ \text{V} \cdot \text{s})(1.6 \times 10^{-19}\ \text{C})$$

$$= 6.6 \times 10^{-34}\ \text{J} \cdot \text{s}.$$

This value of the Planck constant agrees with values measured by many other methods.

CHECKPOINT 2: The figure shows data like those of Fig. 39-2 for targets of cesium, potassium, sodium, and lithium. The plots are parallel. (a) Rank the targets according to their work functions, greatest first. (b) Rank the plots according to the value of h they yield, greatest first.

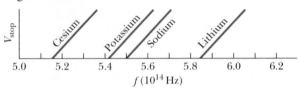

SAMPLE PROBLEM 39-2

A potassium foil is a distance $r = 3.5$ m from an isotropic light source that emits energy at the rate $P = 1.5$ W. The work function Φ of potassium is 2.2 eV. Suppose that the energy transported by the incident light were transferred to the target foil continuously and smoothly (that is, if classical physics prevailed and there were no photons). How long would it take for the foil to soak up enough energy to eject an electron? Assume that the foil absorbs all the energy that falls on it and that the to-be-ejected electron collects energy from a circular patch of the foil whose radius is 5.0×10^{-11} m, about that of a typical atom.

SOLUTION: Let us calculate the rate R at which light energy falls on the target patch. Knowing this, we can easily find how long it takes for the target patch to absorb 2.2 eV.

We assume that the energy emitted by the light source is spread uniformly over expanding spherical wavefronts centered on the source. From Eq. 34-27, the light intensity at the patch is

$$I = \frac{P}{4\pi r^2}$$

$$= \frac{1.5\ \text{W}}{4\pi(3.5\ \text{m})^2} = 9.74 \times 10^{-3}\ \text{W/m}^2.$$

The patch has area $A = \pi(5.0 \times 10^{-11} \text{ m})^2$, which is $7.85 \times 10^{-21} \text{ m}^2$. The rate at which it absorbs energy is then

$$R = IA = (9.74 \times 10^{-3} \text{ W/m}^2)(7.85 \times 10^{-21} \text{ m}^2)$$
$$= 7.65 \times 10^{-23} \text{ W}.$$

If all this energy were delivered to a single electron, the time required for the electron to soak up 2.2 eV would be

$$t = \frac{2.2 \text{ eV}}{R} = \left(\frac{2.2 \text{ eV}}{7.65 \times 10^{-23} \text{ J/s}}\right)\left(\frac{1.60 \times 10^{-19} \text{ J}}{1 \text{ eV}}\right)$$
$$= 4600 \text{ s} \approx 1.3 \text{ h}. \qquad \text{(Answer)}$$

Thus, you would have to wait more than an hour after turning on the light source for a photoelectron to be ejected. The actual waiting time is less than 10^{-9} s. Apparently, then, the electron does *not* have to "soak up" energy from an incoming wave; it absorbs that energy *all at once* in a single photon–electron interaction.

SAMPLE PROBLEM 39-3

Find the work function Φ of sodium from the data plotted in Fig. 39-2.

SOLUTION: The cutoff frequency f_0 at which the graph in Fig. 39-2 intercepts the frequency axis appears to be about 5.5×10^{14} Hz. Photons at the cutoff frequency have energy just equal to the work function, so we may write Eq. 39-2 as

$$E = hf_0 = \Phi,$$

which gives us

$$\Phi = hf_0 = (6.63 \times 10^{-34} \text{ J·s})(5.5 \times 10^{14} \text{ Hz})$$
$$= 3.6 \times 10^{-19} \text{ J} = 2.3 \text{ eV}. \qquad \text{(Answer)}$$

39-4 PHOTONS HAVE MOMENTUM

In 1916 Einstein extended his photon concept by asserting that when light interacts with matter, not only energy but also linear momentum is transferred via photons. Like energy, momentum is transferred in discrete amounts and at pointlike locations instead of broad regions.

The magnitude p of the momentum of a photon associated with a wave of frequency f is

$$p = \frac{hf}{c} = \frac{h}{\lambda} \qquad \text{(photon momentum).} \qquad (39\text{-}7)$$

Equation 39-2 ($E = hf = hc/\lambda$) and Eq. 39-7 tell us, for example, that photons associated with a beam of x rays ($\lambda \approx 50$ pm) have much greater values of both energy and momentum than do photons associated with a beam of visible light ($\lambda \approx 500$ nm $= 5 \times 10^5$ pm.)

Some years later, in 1923, Arthur Compton at Washington University in St. Louis carried out an experiment that gave solid support to the view that both momentum and energy are transferred via photons. He arranged for a beam of x rays of wavelength λ to fall on a target made of carbon, as shown in Fig. 39-3. Compton measured the wavelengths and intensities of the x rays scattered in various directions from this target.

Figure 39-4 shows his results. Although there is only a single wavelength ($\lambda = 71.1$ pm) in the incident x-ray beam, we see that the scattered x rays contain a range of wavelengths with two prominent intensity peaks. One peak is centered about the incident wavelength λ, the other about a wavelength λ' that is larger than λ by an amount $\Delta\lambda$, which is called the **Compton shift**. The value of the Compton shift varies with the angle at which the scattered x rays are detected.

Figure 39-4 is still another puzzle for classical physics. If you think of the incident x-ray beam as an electromagnetic wave, you must imagine an electron in the carbon target oscillating back and forth under the influence of the alternating electric field of the incident wave. The electron will oscillate at the frequency of the alternating electric field and—like a tiny radio transmitting antenna—it will radiate *at this same frequency*. The scattered x rays should have the same frequency, and thus the same wavelength, as the incident beam. But they don't.

Compton interpreted the scattering of x rays from carbon in terms of energy and momentum transfers, via photons, between the incident x-ray beam and loosely bound electrons in the carbon target. Let us see, first conceptually and then quantitatively, how this quantum mechanical picture leads to an understanding of Compton's results.

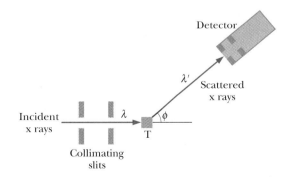

FIGURE 39-3 Compton's apparatus. A beam of x rays of wavelength $\lambda = 71.1$ pm falls on a carbon target T. The x rays scattered from the target are observed at various angles ϕ to the direction of the incident beam. The detector measures both the intensity of the scattered x rays and their wavelength.

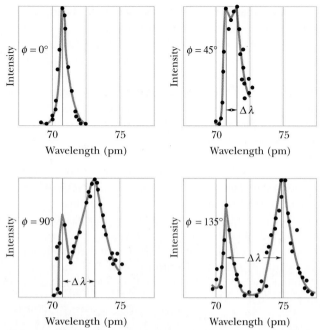

FIGURE 39-4 Compton's results for four values of the scattering angle ϕ. Note that the Compton shift $\Delta\lambda$ increases as the scattering angle increases.

Suppose a single photon (of energy $E = hf$) is associated with the interaction between the incident x-ray beam and a stationary electron. In general, the x-ray direction will change (an x-ray photon is said to be scattered) and the electron will recoil. Thus the electron will pick up some kinetic energy. Because energy is conserved in the interaction, the energy of the scattered photon ($E' = hf'$) must be less than that of the incident photon. The scattered x rays must then have a lower frequency f' and thus a longer wavelength λ' than the incident x rays, just as Compton's experimental results in Fig. 39-4 show.

For the quantitative part, we first apply the law of conservation of energy. Figure 39-5 suggests a "collision" between an x ray and an initially stationary free electron in the target. As a result of the collision, an x ray of wave-

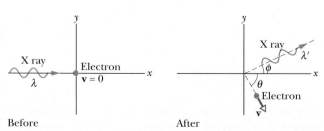

Before · After

FIGURE 39-5 An x ray of wavelength λ interacts with a stationary electron. The x ray is scattered at angle ϕ, with an increased wavelength λ'. The electron moves off with speed v at angle θ.

length λ' moves off at an angle ϕ and the electron moves off at an angle θ, as shown. The conservation of energy then gives us

$$hf = hf' + K,$$

in which hf is the energy of the incident x-ray photon, hf' is the energy of the scattered x-ray photon, and K is the kinetic energy of the recoiling electron. Because the electron may recoil with a speed comparable to that of light, we must use the relativistic expression of Eq. 38-33,

$$K = mc^2(\gamma - 1),$$

for its kinetic energy. Here m is the electron's mass and γ is the Lorentz factor

$$\gamma = 1/\sqrt{1 - (v/c)^2}.$$

Substituting for K in the conservation of energy equation yields

$$hf = hf' + mc^2(\gamma - 1).$$

Substituting c/λ for f and c/λ' for f' then leads to the energy conservation equation

$$\frac{h}{\lambda} = \frac{h}{\lambda'} + mc(\gamma - 1). \qquad (39\text{-}8)$$

Now we need to apply the (vector) law of conservation of momentum to the x-ray–electron collision of Fig. 39-5. The momentum of the incident and scattered photons is given by Eq. 39-7 ($p = h/\lambda$) and that of the scattered electron by Eq. 38-31 ($p = \gamma mv$). By writing separate equations for the conservation of momentum for the x and y directions, we get

$$\frac{h}{\lambda} = \frac{h}{\lambda'}\cos\phi + \gamma mv\cos\theta \qquad (x\text{ direction}) \quad (39\text{-}9)$$

and

$$0 = \frac{h}{\lambda'}\sin\phi - \gamma mv\sin\theta \qquad (y\text{ direction}). \quad (39\text{-}10)$$

We want to find $\Delta\lambda$ ($= \lambda' - \lambda$), the Compton shift of the scattered x rays. Of the five collision variables (λ, λ', v, ϕ, and θ) that appear in Eqs. 39-8, 39-9, and 39-10, we choose to eliminate v and θ, which deal only with the recoiling electron. Carrying out the algebra (it is somewhat complicated) leads to an equation for the Compton shift as a function of the scattering angle ϕ:

$$\Delta\lambda = \frac{h}{mc}(1 - \cos\phi) \qquad \text{(Compton shift)}. \quad (39\text{-}11)$$

Here the quantity h/mc, called the **Compton wavelength** of the electron, is a constant. Equation 39-11 agrees exactly with Compton's experimental results.

A Loose End

It remains to explain the peak at the incident wavelength λ (= 71.1 pm) in Fig. 39-4. This peak arises not from encounters between x rays and the very loosely bound electrons in the target but from encounters between x rays and the electrons that are *tightly* bound to the carbon atoms making up the target. Effectively, each of these latter collisions is between an incident x ray and an entire carbon atom. If we substitute for m in Eq. 39-11 the mass of a carbon atom (which is about 22,000 times that of an electron), we see that $\Delta\lambda$ is about 22,000 times smaller than the Compton shift for an electron—too small to detect. Thus the x rays scattered in these collisions have a detected wavelength equal to that of the incident x rays.

SAMPLE PROBLEM 39-4

X rays of wavelength $\lambda = 22$ pm (photon energy = 56 keV) are scattered from a carbon target, and the scattered rays are detected at 85° to the incident beam.

(a) What is the Compton shift of the scattered rays?

SOLUTION: From Eq. 39-11 we have

$$\Delta\lambda = \frac{h}{mc}(1 - \cos\phi)$$

$$= \frac{(6.63 \times 10^{-34}\text{ J}\cdot\text{s})(1 - \cos 85°)}{(9.11 \times 10^{-31}\text{ kg})(3.00 \times 10^8\text{ m/s})}$$

$$= 2.21 \times 10^{-12}\text{ m} \approx 2.2\text{ pm.} \qquad \text{(Answer)}$$

(b) What percentage of the initial x-ray photon energy is transferred to an electron in such scattering?

SOLUTION: The fractional energy loss *frac* is

$$frac = \frac{E - E'}{E} = \frac{hf - hf'}{hf} = \frac{c/\lambda - c/\lambda'}{c/\lambda} = \frac{\lambda' - \lambda}{\lambda'}$$

$$= \frac{\Delta\lambda}{\lambda + \Delta\lambda}. \qquad (39\text{-}12)$$

Substitution yields

$$frac = \frac{2.21\text{ pm}}{22\text{ pm} + 2.21\text{ pm}} = 0.091 \quad \text{or} \quad 9.1\%. \quad \text{(Answer)}$$

Although the Compton shift $\Delta\lambda$ is independent of the wavelength λ of the incident x rays (see Eq. 39-11), the *fractional* photon energy loss of the x rays does depend on λ, increasing as the wavelength of the incident radiation decreases, as indicated by Eq. 39-12.

CHECKPOINT 3: Compare Compton scattering for x rays ($\lambda \approx 20$ pm) and visible light ($\lambda \approx 500$ nm) at a particular angle of scattering. Which has the greater (a) Compton shift, (b) fractional wavelength shift, (c) fractional photon energy change, and (d) energy imparted to the electron?

39-5 LIGHT AS A PROBABILITY WAVE

You may wonder how light can be a wave and still be generated and absorbed as fixed amounts of energy—photons—in interactions. A new look at the double-slit experiment of Section 36-4 provides some insights. We consider three versions of this important experiment.

The Standard Version

Figure 39-6 reminds us of the original experiment carried out by Thomas Young in 1801, which we first saw in Fig. 36-6. Light falls on screen B, which contains two narrow parallel slits. The light waves emerging from each slit spread out by diffraction and overlap on screen C where, by interference, they form a pattern of alternating intensity maxima and minima. In Section 36-4 we took the existence of these interference fringes as evidence for the wave nature of light.

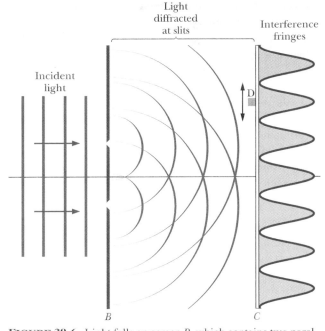

FIGURE 39-6 Light falls on screen B, which contains two parallel slits. Light emerging from these slits spreads out by diffraction. The two diffracted waves overlap at screen C and form a pattern of interference fringes. A small photon detector D in the plane of screen C generates a sharp click for each photon that it absorbs.

Let us place a tiny photon detector D—perhaps a photoelectric device that clicks when it absorbs a photon —at one point in the plane of screen C. We find that it produces a series of clicks, randomly spaced in time, each click signaling the transfer of energy from the light wave to the screen in a single photon-sized lump.

If we move the detector very slowly up or down as indicated in Fig. 39-6, we find that the click rate increases and decreases, passing through alternate maxima and minima that correspond exactly to the maxima and the minima of the interference fringes.

The point of this thought experiment is as follows. We cannot predict when a photon will be detected at any particular point on screen C; photons are detected at individual points at random intervals. We can, however, predict that the relative *probability* that a single photon will be detected at a particular point in a specified time interval is proportional to the intensity of the incident light at that point on screen C.

We saw in Section 34-4 that the intensity I of a light wave at any point is proportional to the square of E_m, the amplitude of the alternating electric field vector, at that point. Thus,

---

The probability (per unit time interval) that a photon will be detected in any small volume centered on a given point in a light wave is proportional to the square of the amplitude of the wave's electric field vector at that point.

We now have a probabilistic description of a light wave, hence another way to view light. It is not only an electromagnetic wave but it is also a **probability wave**. That is, to every point in a light wave we can attach a numerical probability (per unit time interval) that a photon can be detected in any small volume centered on that point.

The Single-Photon Version

A single-photon version of the double-slit experiment was first carried out by G. I. Taylor in 1909 and has been repeated many times since. It differs from the standard version in that the light source is so extremely feeble that it emits only one photon at a time, at random intervals. Astonishingly, interference fringes still build up on screen C if the experiment runs long enough (several months for Taylor's early experiment).

What explanation can we offer for this single-photon, double-slit experiment? Before we can even consider the results, we are compelled to ask questions like these: If the photons move through the apparatus one at a time, through

which of the two slits in screen B does a given photon pass? And how does a given photon even "know" that there is another slit present so that interference is a possibility? And can a single photon somehow pass through both slits and interfere with itself?

Bear in mind that photons manifest themselves only when light interacts with matter. Thus we know that photons *originate* in the source that generates the incident light of Fig. 39-6. And photons *vanish* in screen C, where light interacts with the solid matter that makes up the screen. Between source and detector, however, we *postulate* that light travels *not* as a stream of photons but as a probability wave. Such a wave, no matter how feeble the light source, can be diffracted at each slit. The two diffracted probability subwaves (one from each slit) can then interfere with each other when they meet at any point on screen C, producing a pattern of maximum and minimum "probability fringes" on that screen. Photons will tend to occur in regions of maximum probability and to not occur in regions of minimum probability.

That seems to be a satisfactory explanation of the single-photon experiment, since classical physics offers no explanation at all. According to physicist Richard Feynman,

> [the single-photon, double-slit experiment is] a phenomenon which is impossible, *absolutely* impossible, to explain in any classical way, and which has in it the heart of quantum mechanics.

The Single-Photon, Wide-Angle Version

Figure 39-7 shows the arrangement used in another version of the two-slit experiment, reported in 1992 by Ming Lai and Jean-Claude Diels of the University of New Mexico. Source S contains molecules that emit photons that are well

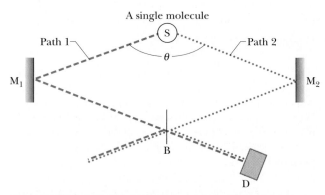

FIGURE 39-7 The light from a single photon emission in source S travels over two widely separated paths and interferes with itself at detector D after being recombined by the beam splitter B. (After Ming Lai and Jean-Claude Diels, *Journal of the Optical Society of America B*, **9**, 2290–2294, December 1992.)

separated in time. Mirrors M_1 and M_2 are positioned to reflect light that the source emits along two distinct paths, 1 and 2, that are separated by an angle θ, which is close to 180°. This arrangement differs from the standard two-slit experiment, in which the angle between the paths of the light waves falling on two slits is very small.

After reflection from mirrors M_1 and M_2, the light waves traveling along paths 1 and 2 meet at beam splitter B. (A beam splitter is an optical device that transmits half the light incident upon it and reflects the other half.) On the right side of the beam splitter in Fig. 39-7 the light wave traveling along path 2 and reflected by B combines with the light wave traveling along path 1 and transmitted by B. These two waves then interfere with each other as they arrive at detector D (a *photomultiplier tube* that can detect individual photons).

The output of the detector is a randomly spaced series of electronic pulses, one for each detected photon. In the experiment, the beam splitter is moved slowly in a horizontal direction (in the reported experiment, only about 50 μm maximum), and the detector output is recorded on a chart recorder. Moving the beam splitter changes the lengths of paths 1 and 2, producing a phase shift between the light waves arriving at detector D. Interference maxima and minima appear in the detector's output signal.

This experiment is difficult to understand in traditional terms. For example, when a molecule in the source emits a single photon, does that photon travel along path 1 or path 2 in Fig. 39-7 (or along any other path)? How can it move in both directions at once? To answer, we assume that when the emitting molecule makes a quantum transition to a lower energy level, a probability wave radiates in all directions from it. The experiment samples this wave in two of those directions, chosen to be nearly opposite each other.

We see that we can interpret all three versions of the double-slit experiment if we assume that (1) light is generated in the source as photons, (2) light is absorbed in the detector as photons, and (3) light travels between source and detector as a probability wave.

39-6 ELECTRONS AND MATTER WAVES

Physicists have rarely gone wrong by assuming the symmetry of nature. Thus, when you learn that a changing magnetic field produces an electric field, you might guess —as both Faraday and Maxwell did—that a changing electric field produces a magnetic field. And it does.

In 1924 French physicist Louis de Broglie made the following appeal to symmetry. A beam of light is a wave, but it transfers energy and momentum to matter in photon-sized lumps. Why can't a beam of particles have the same properties? That is, why can't we think of a moving electron—or any other particle, for that matter—as a **matter wave**?

In particular, de Broglie suggested that Eq. 39-7 ($p = h/\lambda$) might apply not only to photons but also to particles of matter, the electron being a convenient prototype. We used that equation in Section 39-4 to assign a momentum p to a photon, knowing the wavelength λ of its associated wave. We now use it, in the form

$$\lambda = \frac{h}{p} \quad \text{(de Broglie wavelength)} \quad (39\text{-}13)$$

to assign a wavelength λ to a particle whose momentum is p. The wavelength calculated from Eq. 39-13 is called the **de Broglie wavelength** of the moving particle.

De Broglie's prediction of the existence of matter waves was first verified experimentally in 1927, by C. J. Davisson and L. H. Germer of the Bell Telephone Laboratories and by George P. Thomson of the University of Aberdeen in Scotland. More recently, the wave nature of a beam of electrons was demonstrated in a 1989 double-slit experiment like that used to demonstrate the wave nature of light. Figure 39-8 suggests how the fringe pattern builds up with time in this experiment as individual electrons strike the detecting screen. And in 1994 interference fringes were generated with beams of iodine molecules, which are about 500,000 times more massive than electrons.

Figure 39-9a suggests another experiment in which a beam, of either x rays or electrons, is allowed to fall on a target consisting of a powder of tiny aluminum crystals. Scattered by the crystals, the beam emerges from the target with circular symmetry about its initial direction and, because of Bragg reflections on the atomic planes of the aluminum crystals (see Section 37-9), forms concentric rings on a sheet of photographic film placed as indicated. Figure 39-9b shows the result for an x-ray beam; Fig. 39-9c shows the result for an electron beam. The geometries of the rings are identical, showing that both x rays and electrons behave like waves in this experiment. (The energy of the x-ray photons and the momentum of the electrons were chosen so that both beams had the same wavelength.)

We now take the wave nature of matter for granted. Diffraction studies involving beams of electrons or neutrons are used routinely to study the atomic structures of solids and liquids. Matter waves are a valuable supplement to x rays in such studies. Electrons, for example, are less penetrating than x rays and so are particularly useful in studying surface features. Also, x rays interact largely with electrons in a target and for that reason are not effective in locating low-mass atoms—particularly hydrogen—that have few electrons. Neutrons, on the other hand, interact primarily with the nuclei of the target atoms and so are useful where x rays are not.

FIGURE 39-8 The buildup of an interference pattern by a beam of electrons in a two-slit interference experiment like that of Fig. 39-6. Matter waves, like light waves, are *probability waves*. From top to bottom the approximate numbers of electrons involved are 7, 100, 3000, 20,000, and 70,000.

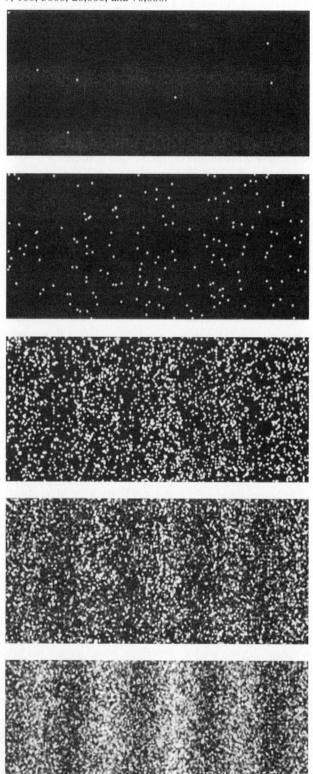

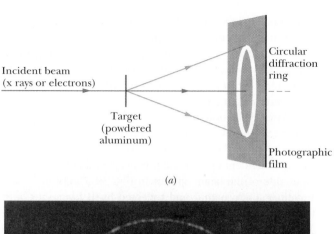

(a)

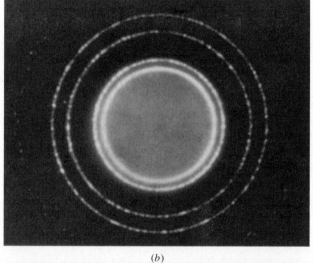

(b)

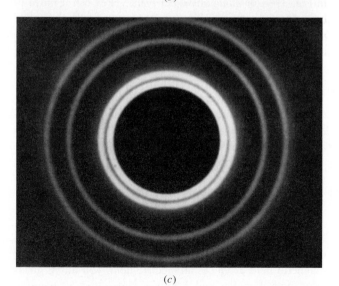

(c)

FIGURE 39-9 (a) An experimental arrangement used to demonstrate, by diffraction techniques, the wavelike character of the incident beam. (b) The diffraction pattern when the incident beam is an x-ray beam (light wave). (c) The diffraction pattern when the incident beam is an electron beam (matter wave). Note the basic geometrical identity of the patterns.

Figure 39-10 shows the structure of solid benzene as deduced from neutron diffraction studies. Each set of concentric blue circles shows the location of one of the six carbon atoms that form the familiar benzene ring. Each set of red circles shows the location of a hydrogen atom that is coupled to a carbon atom.

Waves and Particles

Figures 39-9 and 39-10 are convincing evidence of the *wave* nature of matter. But we have at least as many experiments that suggest the *particle* nature of matter. Consider the tracks generated by electrons and displayed in the opening photo of this chapter. Surely these tracks—which are strings of bubbles left in the liquid hydrogen that fills the bubble chamber—strongly suggest the passage of a particle. Where is the wave?

To simplify the situation, let us turn off the magnetic field so that the strings of bubbles will then be straight. We can view each bubble as a detection point for the electron. Matter waves traveling between detection points such as *I* and *F* in Fig. 39-11 explore all possible paths, a few of which are shown.

In general, for every path connecting *I* and *F* there will be a neighboring path such that matter waves following the two paths cancel each other by interference. This is not true, however, for the straight-line path joining *I* and *F*; in this case, matter waves traversing all neighboring paths reinforce the wave following the direct path. You can think of the bubbles that form the track as a series of detection points at which the matter wave undergoes constructive interference.

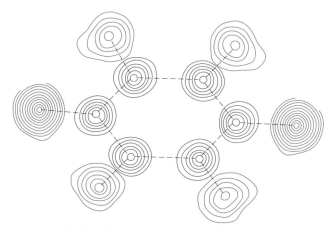

FIGURE 39-10 The atomic structure of solid benzene as revealed using neutron diffraction. The closed curves suggest the patterns of electron density in the solid target. You can easily see the familiar benzene ring of six carbon atoms (blue) and the hydrogen atoms (red) that are coupled to them.

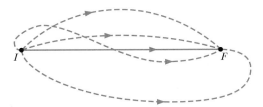

FIGURE 39-11 A few of the many paths that connect two particle detection points *I* and *F*. Only matter waves that follow paths close to the straight line between these points interfere constructively. For all other paths, the waves following neighboring paths interfere destructively. Thus a matter wave leaves a straight track.

SAMPLE PROBLEM 39-5

What is the de Broglie wavelength of an electron whose kinetic energy is 120 eV?

SOLUTION: We can find the de Broglie wavelength from Eq. 39-13 if we know the momentum of the electron. From the (nonrelativistic) relation $K = \frac{1}{2}mv^2$ you can show that, for $K = 120$ eV, $v = 6.5 \times 10^6$ m/s, which is well below the speed of light. This low value for v justifies our use of the nonrelativistic expressions for both kinetic energy and momentum ($p = mv$). Eliminating the particle speed v between these two equations yields

$$p = \sqrt{2mK}$$
$$= \sqrt{(2)(9.11 \times 10^{-31} \text{ kg})(120 \text{ eV})(1.60 \times 10^{-19} \text{ J/eV})}$$
$$= 5.91 \times 10^{-24} \text{ kg} \cdot \text{m/s}.$$

From Eq. 39-13 then

$$\lambda = \frac{h}{p} = \frac{6.63 \times 10^{-34} \text{ J} \cdot \text{s}}{5.91 \times 10^{-24} \text{ kg} \cdot \text{m/s}}$$
$$= 1.12 \times 10^{-10} \text{ m} = 112 \text{ pm}. \quad \text{(Answer)}$$

This is about the size of a typical atom.

CHECKPOINT **4:** An electron and a proton have the same (a) kinetic energy, (b) momentum, (c) speed. In each case, which particle has the shorter de Broglie wavelength?

39-7 SCHRÖDINGER'S EQUATION

A simple traveling wave of any kind, be it a wave on a string, a sound wave, or a light wave, is described in terms of some quantity that varies in a wavelike fashion. For light waves, for example, this quantity is **E** (*x, y, z, t*), the electric field component of the wave. Its observed value at any point depends on the location of that point and on the time at which the observation is made.

What varying quantity should we use to describe a matter wave? We should expect this quantity, which we call the **wave function** Ψ (x, y, z, t), to be more complicated than the corresponding quantity for a light wave because a matter wave, in addition to energy and momentum, transports mass and (often) electric charge. It turns out that Ψ, the uppercase Greek letter psi, usually represents a function that is complex in the mathematical sense; that is, we can always write its values in the form $a + ib$, in which a and b are real numbers and $i^2 = -1$.

In all the situations you will meet here, the space and time variables can be grouped separately and Ψ can be written in the form

$$\Psi (x, y, z, t) = \psi (x, y, z)\, e^{-i\omega t}, \quad (39\text{-}14)$$

where ω $(= 2\pi f)$ is the angular frequency of the matter wave. Note that ψ, the lowercase Greek letter psi, represents only the space-dependent part of the complete, time-dependent wave function Ψ. We shall deal almost exclusively with ψ. Two questions arise: What is meant by the wave function, and how do we find it?

What does the wave function mean? A matter wave, like a light wave, is a probability wave. Suppose, for example, that a matter wave falls on a particle detector that is small; then the probability that a particle will be detected in a specified time interval is proportional to $|\psi|^2$, where $|\psi|$ is the absolute value of the wave function at the location of the detector. Although ψ is usually a complex quantity, $|\psi|^2$ is always both real and positive. It is, then, $|\psi|^2$, which we call the **probability density**, and not ψ, that has *physical* meaning. Speaking loosely, the meaning is this:

The probability (per unit time) of detecting a particle in a small volume centered on a given point in a matter wave is proportional to the value of $|\psi|^2$ at that point.

Because ψ is usually a complex quantity, we find the square of its absolute value by multiplying ψ by ψ^*, the *complex conjugate* of ψ. (To find ψ^* we replace the imaginary number i in ψ with $-i$, wherever it occurs.)

How do we find the wave function? Sound waves and waves in strings are described by the equations of Newtonian mechanics. Light waves are described by Maxwell's equations. Matter waves are described by **Schrödinger's equation**, advanced in 1926 by Austrian physicist Erwin Schrödinger.

Many of the situations that we shall discuss involve a particle traveling in the x direction through a region in which forces acting on the particle cause it to have a potential energy $E_{pot}(x)$. In this special case, Schrödinger's equation reduces to

$$\frac{d^2\psi}{dx^2} + \frac{8\pi^2 m}{h^2}[E - E_{pot}(x)]\psi = 0$$

(Schrödinger's equation, one-dimensional motion), (39-15)

in which E is the total mechanical energy (potential energy plus kinetic energy) of the moving particle. We cannot derive Schrödinger's equation from more basic principles; it *is* the basic principle.

If $E_{pot}(x)$ in Eq. 39-15 is zero, that equation describes a **free particle**, that is, a moving particle on which no net force acts. The particle's total energy in this case is all kinetic, and thus E in Eq. 39-15 is $\frac{1}{2}mv^2$. That equation then becomes

$$\frac{d^2\psi}{dx^2} + \frac{8\pi^2 m}{h^2}\left(\frac{mv^2}{2}\right)\psi = 0,$$

which we can recast as

$$\frac{d^2\psi}{dx^2} + \left(2\pi \frac{p}{h}\right)^2\psi = 0.$$

To obtain this equation, we replaced mv with the momentum p and regrouped terms.

From Eq. 39-13 we recognize p/h in the equation above as $1/\lambda$, where λ is the de Broglie wavelength of the moving particle. We further recognize $2\pi/\lambda$ as the *angular wave number* k, which we defined in Eq. 17-5. With this substitution, the equation above becomes

$$\frac{d^2\psi}{dx^2} + k^2\psi = 0 \quad \text{(Schrödinger's equation, free particle).} \quad (39\text{-}16)$$

The most general solution of Eq. 39-16 is

$$\psi(x) = Ae^{ikx} + Be^{-ikx}, \quad (39\text{-}17)$$

in which A and B are arbitrary constants. You can show that this equation is indeed a solution of Eq. 39-16 by substituting $\psi(x)$ and its second derivative into that equation and noting that an identity results.

If we combine Eqs. 39-14 and 39-17 we find, for the time-dependent wave function Ψ of a free particle traveling in the x direction,

$$\Psi(x, t) = \psi(x)e^{-i\omega t}$$
$$= (Ae^{ikx} + Be^{-ikx})e^{-i\omega t}$$
$$= Ae^{i(kx - \omega t)} + Be^{-i(kx + \omega t)}. \quad (39\text{-}18)$$

Finding the Probability Density $|\psi|^2$

In Section 17-5 we saw that *any function F of the form $F(kx \pm \omega t)$ represents a traveling wave.* This applies to exponential functions like those in Eq. 39-18 as well as to the sinusoidal functions we have used to describe waves on strings. In fact, these two representations of functions are related by

$$e^{i\theta} = \cos\theta + i\sin\theta \quad \text{and} \quad e^{-i\theta} = \cos\theta - i\sin\theta,$$

where θ is any angle.

The first term on the right in Eq. 39-18 thus represents a wave traveling in the direction of increasing x and the second a wave traveling in the direction of decreasing x. However, we have assumed that the free particle we are considering travels only in the direction of *increasing x*. To reduce the general solution (Eq. 39-18) to our case of interest, we choose the arbitrary constant B in Eqs. 39-18 and 39-17 to be zero. At the same time, we relabel the constant A as ψ_0. Equation 39-17 then becomes

$$\psi(x) = \psi_0 e^{ikx}. \tag{39-19}$$

To calculate the probability density, we take the square of the absolute value of $\psi(x)$. We get

$$|\psi|^2 = |\psi_0 e^{ikx}|^2 = (\psi_0^2) |e^{ikx}|^2.$$

Now, because

$$|e^{ikx}|^2 = (e^{ikx})(e^{ikx})^* = e^{ikx} e^{-ikx} = e^{ikx-ikx} = e^0 = 1,$$

we get

$$|\psi|^2 = (\psi_0^2)(1)^2 = \psi_0^2 \quad \text{(a constant)}.$$

Figure 39-12 is a plot of the probability density $|\psi|^2$ versus x for a free particle—a straight line parallel to the x axis from $-\infty$ to $+\infty$. We see that the probability density $|\psi|^2$ is the same for all values of x, which means that the particle has equal probabilities of being *everywhere* along the x axis. There is no distinguishing feature by which we can predict a most likely position for the particle.

We'll see what this means in the next section.

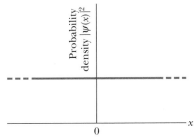

FIGURE 39-12 A plot of the probability density $|\psi|^2$ for a free particle moving in the positive x direction. Since $|\psi|^2$ has the same constant value for all values of x, the particle has the same probability of detection at all points.

39-8 HEISENBERG'S UNCERTAINTY PRINCIPLE

Our inability to predict the position of the free particle in Fig. 39-12 is our first example of **Heisenberg's uncertainty principle**, proposed in 1927 by German physicist Werner Heisenberg. It states that measured values cannot be assigned to the position **r** and the momentum **p** of a particle simultaneously with unlimited precision.

For the components of **r** and **p**, Heisenberg's principle gives the following limits in terms of $\hbar = h/2\pi$ (called "h-bar"):

$$
\begin{aligned}
\Delta x \cdot \Delta p_x &\geq \hbar \\
\Delta y \cdot \Delta p_y &\geq \hbar \\
\Delta z \cdot \Delta p_z &\geq \hbar
\end{aligned}
\qquad
\begin{array}{l}
\text{(Heisenberg's} \\
\text{uncertainty} \\
\text{principle).}
\end{array}
\qquad (39\text{-}20)
$$

Here Δx and Δp_x, as examples, represent the intrinsic uncertainties in the measurements of the x components of **r** and **p**. Even with the best measuring instruments that modern technology can provide, each product of a position uncertainty and a momentum uncertainty in Eq. 39-20 will be greater than $\hbar$; it can *never* be less.

The particle whose probability density is plotted in Fig. 39-12 is a free particle. That is, no force acts on it, so its momentum **p** must be constant. We implied—without making a point of it—that we can determine **p** with absolute precision. That is, we assumed that $\Delta p_x = \Delta p_y = \Delta p_z = 0$ in Eq. 39-20. That assumption then requires $\Delta x \to \infty$, $\Delta y \to \infty$, and $\Delta z \to \infty$. With such infinitely great uncertainties, the position of the particle is completely unspecified, just as Fig. 39-12 shows.

Do not think that the particle *really has* a sharply defined position that is, for some reason, hidden from us. If its momentum can be specified with absolute precision, the words "position of the particle" simply lose all meaning. The particle in Fig. 39-12 can be found *with equal probability* anywhere along the x axis.

SAMPLE PROBLEM 39-6

An electron of kinetic energy 12.0 eV can be shown to have a speed of 2.05×10^6 m/s. Assume that the electron is moving in the x direction and that you can measure its speed with a precision of 0.50%. What is the minimum uncertainty (that is, the uncertainty due to Heisenberg's uncertainty principle) with which you can simultaneously measure the position of the electron along the x axis?

SOLUTION: The electron's speed is well below the speed of light, so we can find its momentum from the nonrelativistic formula:

$$
\begin{aligned}
p = p_x = mv &= (9.11 \times 10^{-31} \text{ kg})(2.05 \times 10^6 \text{ m/s}) \\
&= 1.87 \times 10^{-24} \text{ kg} \cdot \text{m/s}.
\end{aligned}
$$

The uncertainty Δp_x in the momentum measurement is 0.50% of this, or 9.35×10^{-27} kg·m/s. From Heisenberg's principle (Eq. 39-20), the minimum uncertainty in the position measurement is then

$$\Delta x \approx \frac{\hbar}{\Delta p_x} = \frac{(6.63 \times 10^{-34} \text{ J·s})/2\pi}{9.35 \times 10^{-27} \text{ kg·m/s}}$$

$$= 1.13 \times 10^{-8} \text{ m} \approx 11 \text{ nm}, \quad \text{(Answer)}$$

which is about 100 atomic diameters. Given your measurement of the electron's momentum, it makes no sense to try to pin down the electron's position to any greater precision.

39-9 BARRIER TUNNELING

Suppose you repeatedly flip a jelly bean along a tabletop on which a book is positioned somewhere along the jelly bean's path. You would be very surprised to see the jelly bean appear on the other side of the book instead of bouncing from it. Don't expect this to happen for jelly beans. However, something very much like it, called **barrier tunneling**, *does* happen for electrons and other particles with small masses.

Figure 39-13a shows an electron of total energy E moving parallel to the x axis. Forces act on it such that its potential energy is zero except when it is in the region

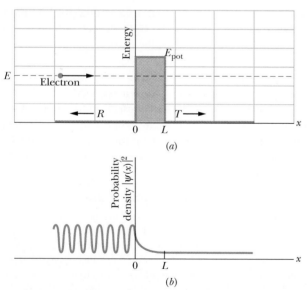

FIGURE 39-13 (a) An energy diagram showing a potential energy barrier of height E_{pot} and thickness L. An electron with total energy E approaches the barrier from the left. (b) The probability density $|\psi|^2$ of the matter wave representing the electron, showing the tunneling of the electron through the barrier. The pattern to the left of the barrier is a standing matter wave due to the superposition of the incident and reflected matter waves.

$0 < x < L$, where its potential energy has the constant value E_{pot}. We define this region as a **potential energy barrier** (often loosely called a **potential barrier**) of height E_{pot} and thickness L.

Classically, because $E < E_{pot}$, an electron approaching the barrier from the left would be reflected from the barrier and would move back in the direction from which it came. In quantum mechanics, however, there is a finite chance that the matter wave associated with the electron will "leak through" the barrier and appear on the other side. This means that there is a finite probability that the electron will be found on the far side of the barrier, moving to the right.

The wave function $\psi(x)$ describing the electron can be found by solving Schrödinger's equation (Eq. 39-15) separately for the three regions shown in Fig. 39-13a: (1) to the left of the barrier, (2) within the barrier, and (3) to the right of the barrier. The arbitrary constants that appear in the solutions are then chosen so that the values of $\psi(x)$ join smoothly (no jumps, no kinks) at $x = 0$ and at $x = L$. Squaring the absolute value of $\psi(x)$ then yields the probability density.

Figure 39-13b shows a plot of the result. The oscillating curve to the left of the barrier (for $x < 0$) in Fig. 39-13a is a combination of the incident matter wave and the reflected matter wave (which has a smaller amplitude than the incident wave). The oscillations occur because these two waves, traveling in opposite directions, interfere with each other, setting up a standing wave pattern.

Within the barrier (for $0 < x < L$) the probability density decreases exponentially with x. However, provided L is small, the probability density is not quite zero at $x = L$.

To the right of the barrier of Fig. 39-13 (for $x > L$), the probability density plot describes a transmitted wave with low but constant amplitude. Thus the electron can be found in this region with an equal but relatively small probability anywhere along the x axis if it happens to tunnel through the barrier. (Compare this part of the figure with Fig. 39-12 for a free particle.)

We can assign a *transmission coefficient T* to the incident matter wave and the barrier in Fig. 39-13a. This coefficient gives the probability with which an approaching electron will be transmitted through the barrier, that is, that tunneling will occur. As an example, if $T = 0.02$, then of every 1000 electrons fired at the barrier, 20 (on average) will tunnel through it and 980 will be reflected.

The **transmission coefficient T** is approximately

$$T \approx e^{-2kL}, \quad (39\text{-}21)$$

in which

$$k = \sqrt{\frac{8\pi^2 m(E_{pot} - E)}{h^2}}. \quad (39\text{-}22)$$

Because of the exponential form of Eq. 39-21, the value of T is very sensitive to the three variables on which it depends: particle mass m, barrier thickness L, and energy difference $E_{pot} - E$.

Barrier tunneling finds many applications in technology, among them the tunnel diode, in which the flow of electrons (by tunneling through a device) can be rapidly turned on or off by controlling the barrier height. This can be done very quickly (within 5 ps), so the device is suitable for applications demanding a high-speed response. The 1973 Nobel prize was shared by three "tunnelers," Leo Esaki (for tunneling in semiconductors), Ivar Giaever (for tunneling in superconductors), and Brian Josephson (for the Josephson junction, a rapid quantum switching device based on tunneling). The 1986 Nobel prize was awarded to Gerd Binnig and Heinrich Rohrer to recognize their development of another useful device based on tunneling, the scanning tunneling microscope.

CHECKPOINT 5: Is the wavelength of the transmitted wave in Fig. 39-13*b* larger than, smaller than, or the same as that of the incident wave?

The Scanning Tunneling Microscope (STM)

A device based on tunneling, the STM allows one to make detailed maps of surfaces, revealing features on the atomic scale with a resolution much greater than can be obtained with an optical or electron microscope. Figure 39-14 shows an example, the individual atoms of the surface being readily apparent.

Figure 39-15 shows the heart of the scanning tunneling microscope. A fine metallic tip, mounted at the intersection of three mutually perpendicular quartz rods, is

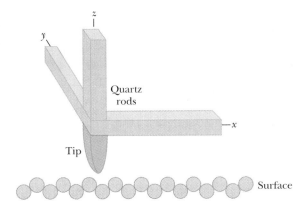

FIGURE 39-15 The essence of a scanning tunneling microscope (STM). Three quartz rods are used to scan a sharply pointed conducting tip across the surface of interest and to maintain a constant separation between tip and surface. The tip thus moves up and down to match the contours of the surface, and a record of its movement is a map like that of Fig. 39-14.

placed close to the surface to be examined. A small potential difference, perhaps only 10 mV, is applied between tip and surface.

Crystalline quartz has an interesting property called *piezoelectricity*: when an electric potential difference is applied across a sample of crystalline quartz, the dimensions of the sample will change slightly. This property is used to change the length of each of the three rods in Fig. 39-15, smoothly and by tiny amounts, so that the tip can be scanned across the surface (in the x and y directions) and also lowered or raised with respect to the surface (in the z direction).

The space between the surface and the tip forms a potential energy barrier, much like that of Fig. 39-13*a*. If the tip is close enough to the surface, electrons from the sample can tunnel through this barrier from the surface to the tip, forming a tunneling current.

In operation, an electronic feedback arrangement adjusts the vertical position of the tip to keep the tunneling current constant as the tip is scanned back and forth over the surface. This means that the tip–surface separation also remains constant during the scan. The output of the device—for example, Fig. 39-14—is a video display of the varying vertical position of the tip, hence of the surface contour, as a function of the tip position in the xy plane.

Scanning tunneling microscopes are available commercially and are used in laboratories all over the world.

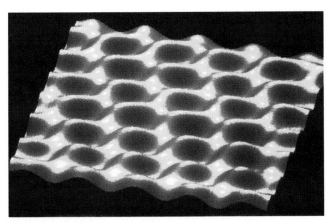

FIGURE 39-14 The contour of a graphite surface as revealed by a scanning tunneling microscope. The carbon atoms and the hexagonal patterns they form are visible.

SAMPLE PROBLEM 39-7

Suppose that the electron in Fig. 39-13*a*, having a total energy E of 5.1 eV, approaches a barrier of height $E_{pot} = 6.8$ eV and thickness $L = 750$ pm.

(a) What is the approximate transmission coefficient T for this electron–barrier combination?

SOLUTION: To compute T with Eq. 39-21, we first evaluate Eq. 39-22:

$$k = \sqrt{\frac{8\pi^2 m(E_{pot} - E)}{h^2}}.$$

The numerator of the fraction under the square-root sign is

$(8\pi^2)(9.11 \times 10^{-31}$ kg$)(6.8$ eV $- 5.1$ eV$)$

$\times (1.60 \times 10^{-19}$ J/eV$) = 1.956 \times 10^{-47}$ J·kg.

Thus

$$k = \sqrt{\frac{1.956 \times 10^{-47} \text{ J·kg}}{(6.63 \times 10^{-34} \text{ J·s})^2}} = 6.67 \times 10^9 \text{ m}^{-1}.$$

The (dimensionless) quantity $2kL$ is then

$2kL = (2)(6.67 \times 10^9 \text{ m}^{-1})(750 \times 10^{-12} \text{ m}) = 10.0$

and, from Eq. 39-21, the transmission coefficient is

$$T \approx e^{-2kL} = e^{-10.0} = 45 \times 10^{-6}. \quad \text{(Answer)}$$

Thus, of every million electrons that strike the barrier, about 45 will tunnel through it.

(b) What would be the transmission coefficient if the incident particle were a proton?

SOLUTION: Carrying out the calculation once more but with the proton mass (1.67×10^{-27} kg) substituted for the electron mass yields $T \approx 10^{-186}$. The transmission coefficient is enormously reduced for this more massive particle. *Imagine how small it would be for a jelly bean!*

REVIEW & SUMMARY

Photons

When light and matter interact, energy and momentum are transferred at pointlike locations in discrete amounts via "bundles" of energy called **photons**. The energy and momentum of a photon are

$$E = hf \quad \text{(photon energy)} \quad (39\text{-}2)$$

$$p = \frac{hf}{c} = \frac{h}{\lambda} \quad \text{(photon momentum),} \quad (39\text{-}7)$$

in which f and λ are, respectively, the frequency and wavelength of the associated light wave.

Photoelectric Effect

When light of high enough frequency falls on a clean metal surface, electrons are emitted from the surface by photon–electron interactions within the metal. The governing relation is

$$hf = K_{max} + \Phi, \quad (39\text{-}5)$$

in which hf is the photon energy, K_{max} is the kinetic energy of the most energetic emitted electrons, and Φ is the **work function** of the target material, that is, the minimum energy an electron must have if it is to emerge from the surface of the target. If hf is less than Φ, the photoelectric effect does not occur.

Compton Shift

When x rays are scattered by loosely bound electrons in a target, some of the scattered x rays have a longer wavelength than do the incident x rays. This **Compton shift** (in wavelength) is given by

$$\Delta\lambda = \frac{h}{mc}(1 - \cos\phi), \quad (39\text{-}11)$$

in which ϕ is the angle at which the x rays are scattered.

Light Waves and Photons

When light interacts with matter, energy and momentum are transferred via photons. When light is in transit, however, we interpret the light wave as a **probability wave**, in which the probability (per unit time) that a photon can be detected is proportional to E_m^2, where E_m is the amplitude of the oscillating electric field associated with the light wave at the detector.

Matter Waves

A moving particle such as an electron or a proton can be described as a **matter wave**; its wavelength (called the **de Broglie wavelength**) is given by $\lambda = h/p$, where p is the momentum of the particle.

The Wave Function

The displacement of a matter wave is given by its **wave function** $\Psi(x, y, z, t)$, which can be separated into a space-dependent part $\psi(x, y, z)$ and a time-dependent part $e^{-i\omega t}$. For a particle of mass m moving in the x direction with constant total energy E through a region in which its potential energy is $E_{pot}(x)$, $\psi(x)$ can be found by solving the simplified **Schrödinger equation**:

$$\frac{d^2\psi}{dx^2} + \frac{8\pi^2 m}{h^2}[E - E_{pot}(x)]\psi = 0. \quad (39\text{-}15)$$

A matter wave, like a light wave, is a probability wave in the sense that if a particle detector is inserted into the wave, the probability that the detector will register a particle during any specified time interval is proportional to $|\psi|^2$, a quantity called the **probability density**.

For a free particle—that is, a particle for which $E_{pot}(x) = 0$ —moving in the x direction, $|\psi|^2$ has a constant value for all positions along the x axis.

Heisenberg's Uncertainty Principle

The probabilistic nature of quantum mechanics places an important limitation on detecting a particle's position and momentum. That is, it is not possible to measure the position **r** and the momentum **p** of a particle simultaneously with unlimited precision.

The uncertainties in the components of these quantities are given by

$$\Delta x \cdot \Delta p_x \geq \hbar$$
$$\Delta y \cdot \Delta p_y \geq \hbar \qquad (39\text{-}20)$$
$$\Delta z \cdot \Delta p_z \geq \hbar.$$

Barrier Tunneling

According to classical physics, an incident particle will be reflected from a potential energy barrier whose height is greater than the particle's kinetic energy. According to quantum mechanics, however, the probability wave associated with a particle has a finite probability of tunneling through such a barrier.

The probability that a given particle of mass m and energy E will tunnel through a barrier of height E_{pot} and thickness L is given by the transmission coefficient T:

$$T \approx e^{-2kL}, \qquad (39\text{-}21)$$

in which

$$k = \sqrt{\frac{8\pi^2 m(E_{pot} - E)}{h^2}}. \qquad (39\text{-}22)$$

QUESTIONS

1. Of the electromagnetic waves generated in a microwave oven and those generated in your dentist's x-ray machine, which has (a) the greater wavelength, (b) the greater frequency, and (c) the greater photon energy?

2. Of the following statements about the photoelectric effect, which are true and which are false? (a) The greater the frequency of the incident light, the greater the stopping potential. (b) The greater the intensity of the incident light, the greater the cutoff frequency. (c) The greater the work function of the target material, the greater the stopping potential. (d) The greater the work function of the target material, the greater the cutoff frequency. (e) The greater the frequency of the incident light, the greater the maximum kinetic energy of the ejected electrons. (f) The greater the energy of the photons, the smaller the stopping potential.

3. According to the figure for Checkpoint 2, is the maximum kinetic energy of the ejected electrons greater for a target made of sodium or of potassium for a given frequency of incident light?

4. In the photoelectric effect (for a given target and a given frequency of the incident light), which of these quantities, if any, depend on the intensity of the incident light beam: (a) the maximum kinetic energy of the electrons, (b) the maximum photoelectric current, (c) the stopping potential, (d) the cutoff frequency?

5. If you shine ultraviolet light on an isolated metal plate, the plate emits electrons for a while. Why does it eventually stop?

6. A metal plate is illuminated with light of a certain frequency. Which of the following determine whether or not electrons are emitted: (a) the intensity of the light; (b) the length of time of exposure to the light; (c) the thermal conductivity of the plate; (d) the area of the plate; (e) the material of the plate?

7. In a Compton-shift experiment, an x-ray photon is scattered in the forward direction, at $\phi = 0$ in Fig. 39-3. How much energy does the electron acquire during this encounter?

8. According to Eq. 39-11 the Compton shift is the same for x rays and for visible light. Why is it that the Compton shift for x rays can be measured readily but that for visible light cannot?

9. Photon A has twice the energy of photon B. (a) Is the momentum of A less than, equal to, or greater than that of B? (b) Is the wavelength of A less than, equal to, or greater than that of B?

10. Compare a photon from a dental x-ray unit (photon A) and one from a microwave oven (photon B). Which has the greater (a) wavelength, (b) energy, (c) frequency, and (d) momentum?

11. The data shown in Fig. 39-4 were taken by allowing x rays to strike a carbon target. In what essential way, if any, would these data differ if the target were sulfur instead of carbon?

12. An electron and a proton have the same kinetic energy. Which has the greater de Broglie wavelength?

13. (a) If you double the kinetic energy of a nonrelativistic particle, how does its de Broglie wavelength change? (b) What if you double the speed of the particle?

14. The following nonrelativistic particles all have the same kinetic energy. Rank them in order of their de Broglie wavelengths, greatest first: electron, alpha particle, neutron.

15. Is the de Broglie wavelength of a speeding bullet extremely large or extremely small?

16. Compare the Compton wavelength of an electron to its de Broglie wavelength. Which of these statements (if any) is true? (a) The Compton wavelength is always larger. (b) The Compton wavelength is always smaller. (c) The two wavelengths are always the same. (d) They are independent of each other.

17. Figure 39-16 shows four situations in which an electron is moving through a field. It is moving (a) opposite an electric field, (b) in the same direction as an electric field, (c) in the same direction as a magnetic field, (d) perpendicular to a magnetic field. For each situation, is the de Broglie wavelength of the electron increasing, decreasing, or remaining the same?

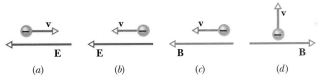

FIGURE 39-16 Question 17.

18. A proton and a deuteron, each having a kinetic energy of 3 MeV, approach a potential energy barrier whose height E_{pot} is 10 MeV. Which particle has the greater chance of tunneling through the barrier? (A deuteron is twice as massive as a proton.)

19. Which has the greater effect on the transmission coefficient T of a potential energy barrier: (a) raising the barrier height E_{pot} by 1% or (b) lowering the kinetic energy E of the incident electron by 1%?

20. At the left in Fig. 39-13b, why are the minima in the values of $|\psi|^2$ greater than zero?

21. Suppose that the height of the potential energy barrier in Fig. 39-13a is infinite. (a) What value would you expect for the transmission coefficient of electrons approaching the barrier? (b) Does Eq. 39-21 predict your expected result?

22. The table gives relative values for three situations for the barrier tunneling experiment of Fig. 39-13. Rank the situations according to the probability of the electron tunneling through the barrier, greatest first.

	ELECTRON ENERGY	BARRIER HEIGHT	BARRIER THICKNESS
(a)	E	$5E$	L
(b)	E	$17E$	$L/2$
(c)	E	$2E$	$2L$

EXERCISES & PROBLEMS

SECTION 39-2 Light Waves and Photons

1E. Show that the energy E of a photon, in electron-volts, is related to its wavelength λ, in nanometers, by $E = 1240/\lambda$.

2E. The orange-colored light from a highway sodium lamp has a wavelength of 589 nm. What is the energy of the photons associated with this light?

3E. Express the Planck constant h in terms of the unit electron-volt–femtoseconds.

4E. Monochromatic light falls on a sheet of photographic film. Individual photons will be recorded if they have enough energy to dissociate an AgBr molecule in the film, and the minimum energy required to do this is about 0.6 eV. What is the greatest wavelength of light that will be recorded? In what region of the spectrum does this light fall?

5E. A spectral emission line that is important in astronomy has a wavelength of 21 cm. What is its corresponding photon energy?

6E. How fast must an electron move to have a kinetic energy equal to the energy of a photon of sodium light ($\lambda = 590$ nm)?

7E. At what rate does the Sun emit photons? Assume for simplicity that the Sun's light is monochromatic, with $\lambda = 550$ nm. The Sun emits energy at the rate of 3.9×10^{26} W.

8E. A helium–neon laser emits a beam of red light ($\lambda = 633$ nm) that is about 3.5 mm in diameter. If the emitted power is 5.0 mW, at what rate per unit area are photons transferred to a detector placed across the beam path? Assume that the detector absorbs the beam completely.

9E. At one time the meter was defined as 1,650,763.73 wavelengths of the orange light emitted by a light source containing krypton-86 atoms. What is the corresponding photon energy of this radiation?

10P. Under ideal conditions, the human eye will record a visual sensation for light whose wavelength is 550 nm if energy is transferred to the eye at a rate as low as 100 photons per second. To what power does this correspond?

11P. An ultraviolet lightbulb emitting light of wavelength 400 nm and an infrared lightbulb emitting light of wavelength 700 nm are both rated at 400 W. (a) Which bulb generates photons at the greater rate and (b) what is that rate?

12P. A satellite in Earth orbit maintains a panel of solar cells of 2.60 m² area perpendicular to the direction of the Sun's rays. Solar energy arrives at the rate of 1.39 kW/m². (a) At what rate does solar energy strike the panel? (b) At what rate are solar photons absorbed by the panel? Assume that the solar radiation is monochromatic, with a wavelength of 550 nm, and that all the solar radiation striking the panel is absorbed. (c) How long would it take for a "mole of photons" to be absorbed by the panel?

13P. A special kind of lightbulb emits monochromatic light of wavelength 630 nm. It is rated at 60 W and is 93% efficient in converting electric energy to light. How many photons will the bulb generate over its 730 h lifetime?

14P. The emerging beam from a 1.5 W argon laser ($\lambda = 515$ nm) has a diameter d of 3.0 mm. The beam is focused by a lens system whose effective focal length f_L is 2.5 mm. The focused beam falls on a totally absorbing screen, where it forms a circular diffraction pattern whose central disk has a radius R given by $1.22 f_L \lambda/d$. It can be shown that 84% of the incident energy falls within this central disk, the rest falling in the fainter, concentric diffraction rings that surround the central disk. At what rate are photons absorbed by the screen in the central disk of the diffraction pattern?

15P. A 100 W sodium lamp ($\lambda = 589$ nm) radiates energy uniformly in all directions. (a) At what rate are photons generated in the lamp? (b) At what distance from the lamp will a totally absorbing screen absorb photons at the rate of 1.00 photon/cm²·s? (c) What is the photon flux (photons per unit area per unit time) on a small screen 2.00 m from the lamp?

SECTION 39-3 The Photoelectric Effect

16E. The work functions for potassium and cesium are 2.25 and 2.14 eV, respectively. (a) Will the photoelectric effect occur for either of these elements with incident light of wavelength 565 nm? (b) With light of wavelength 518 nm?

17E. You wish to pick a substance for a photocell that will operate via the photoelectric effect with visible light. Which of the following will do (work functions are in parentheses): tantalum (4.2 eV), tungsten (4.5 eV), aluminum (4.2 eV), barium (2.5 eV), lithium (2.3 eV)?

18E. (a) The energy needed to remove an electron from metallic sodium is 2.28 eV. Does sodium show a photoelectric effect for red light, with $\lambda = 680$ nm? (b) What is the cutoff wavelength for photoelectric emission from sodium? To what color does that correspond?

19E. Find the maximum kinetic energy of electrons emitted from a certain material if the material's work function is 2.3 eV and the frequency of the incident radiation is 3.0×10^{15} Hz.

20E. Light strikes a sodium surface, causing photoelectric emission. The stopping potential for the emitted electrons is 5.0 V, and the work function of sodium is 2.2 eV. What is the wavelength of the incident light?

21E. The work function of tungsten is 4.50 eV. Calculate the speed of the fastest electrons emitted when light whose photon energy is 5.80 eV falls on a tungsten surface.

22P. Light of wavelength 200 nm falls on an aluminum surface. In aluminum, 4.20 eV is required to remove an electron. What is the kinetic energy of (a) the fastest and (b) the slowest emitted electrons? (c) What is the stopping potential for this situation? (d) What is the cutoff wavelength for aluminum?

23P. (a) If the work function for a certain metal is 1.8 eV, what is its stopping potential for light of wavelength 400 nm? (b) What is the maximum speed of electrons emitted via the photoelectric effect as they leave the metal surface?

24P. The wavelength associated with the cutoff frequency for silver is 325 nm. Find the maximum kinetic energy of electrons ejected from a silver surface by ultraviolet light of wavelength 254 nm.

25P. An orbiting satellite can become charged by the photoelectric effect when sunlight ejects electrons from the vehicle's outer surface. Satellites must be designed to minimize such charging. Suppose a satellite is coated with platinum, a metal with a very large work function ($\Phi = 5.32$ eV). Find the longest wavelength of incident sunlight that can eject an electron from the platinum.

26P. The stopping potential for electrons emitted from a surface illuminated by light of wavelength 491 nm is 0.710 V. When the incident wavelength is changed to a new value, the stopping potential is found to be 1.43 V. (a) What is this new wavelength? (b) What is the work function for the surface?

27P. In a photoelectric experiment using a sodium surface, you find a stopping potential of 1.85 V for a wavelength of 300 nm and a stopping potential of 0.820 V for a wavelength of 400 nm. From these data find (a) a value for the Planck constant, (b) the

work function Φ for sodium, and (c) the cutoff wavelength λ_0 (the wavelength corresponding to the cutoff frequency) for sodium.

28P. In about 1916, R. A. Millikan found the following stopping-potential data for lithium in his photoelectric experiments:

Wavelength (nm)	433.9	404.7	365.0	312.5	253.5
Stopping potential (V)	0.55	0.73	1.09	1.67	2.57

Use these data to make a plot like Fig. 39-2 (which is for sodium) and then use the plot to find (a) the Planck constant and (b) the work function for lithium.

29P. Suppose the *fractional efficiency* of a cesium surface (with work function 1.80 eV) is 1.0×10^{-16}; that is, on average one electron is emitted for every 10^{16} photons that fall on the surface. What would be the current of electrons emitted from such a surface if it were illuminated with 600 nm light from a 2.00 mW laser and all the emitted electrons took part in the charge flow?

30P. X rays with a wavelength of 71 pm eject from a gold foil electrons originating deep within the gold atoms. The ejected electrons move in circular paths of radius r in a region of uniform magnetic field **B**, with $Br = 1.88 \times 10^{-4}$ T·m. Find (a) the maximum kinetic energy of the emitted electrons and (b) the work done in removing them from the gold atoms.

SECTION 39-4 Photons Have Momentum

31E. A certain x-ray beam has a wavelength of 35.0 pm. (a) What is the corresponding frequency? Calculate the corresponding (b) photon energy and (c) photon momentum.

32E. (a) What is the momentum of a photon whose energy equals the rest energy of an electron? What are (b) the wavelength and (c) the frequency of the corresponding radiation?

33E. Light of wavelength 2.4 pm falls on a target containing free electrons. (a) Find the wavelength of light scattered at 30° from the incident direction. (b) Do the same for a scattering angle of 120°.

34P. Gamma rays of photon energy 0.511 MeV fall on free electrons in an aluminum target and are scattered in various directions. (a) What is the wavelength of the incident gamma rays? (b) What is the wavelength of gamma rays scattered at 90.0° to the incident beam? (c) What is the photon energy of the rays scattered in this direction?

35P. Show, by analyzing a collision between a photon and a free electron (using relativistic mechanics), that it is impossible for a photon to give all its energy to a free electron.

36P. An x-ray beam of wavelength 0.01 nm strikes a target containing free electrons. Consider x rays scattered from the target at an angle of 180°. Determine (a) the change in wavelength of the scattered x rays, (b) the change in photon energy between the incident and scattered beams, (c) the kinetic energy transferred to an electron, and (d) the electron's direction of motion.

37P. Calculate the Compton wavelength for (a) an electron and (b) a proton. What is the energy of a photon whose associated wavelength is equal to the Compton wavelength of (c) the electron and (d) the proton?

38P. Calculate the percentage change in photon energy during a collision like that in Fig. 39-5 for $\phi = 90°$ and for radiation in (a) the microwave range, with $\lambda = 3.0$ cm, (b) the visible range, with $\lambda = 500$ nm, (c) the x-ray range, with $\lambda = 25$ pm, and (d) the gamma-ray range, the gamma photon energy being 1.0 MeV. (e) What are your conclusions about the feasibility of detecting the Compton shift in these various regions of the electromagnetic spectrum, judging solely by the criterion of energy loss in a single photon–electron encounter?

39P. What percentage increase in wavelength leads to a 75% loss of photon energy in a photon–free electron collision?

40P. What is the maximum wavelength shift for a Compton collision between a photon and a free *proton*?

41P. An electron of mass m and speed v undergoes a head-on collision with a gamma-ray photon of energy hf_0, scattering the gamma-ray photon back in the direction of incidence. Verify that the energy of the scattered gamma-ray photon, as measured in the laboratory system, is

$$E = hf_0 \left(1 + \frac{2hf_0}{mc^2} \sqrt{\frac{1 + v/c}{1 - v/c}} \right)^{-1}.$$

42P. What would be (a) the Compton shift, (b) the fractional Compton shift, and (c) the change in photon energy for light of wavelength 590 nm scattering from a free, initially stationary electron if the scattering is at 90° to the direction of the incident beam? (d) Calculate the same quantities for x rays whose photon energy is 50.0 keV.

43P. Consider a collision between an x-ray photon of initial energy 50.0 keV and an electron at rest, in which the photon is scattered backward and the electron is knocked forward. (a) What is the energy of the back-scattered photon? (b) What is the kinetic energy of the electron?

44P. Show that $\Delta E/E$, the fractional loss of energy of a photon during a collision with a particle of mass m, is given by

$$\frac{\Delta E}{E} = \frac{hf'}{mc^2} (1 - \cos \phi),$$

where E is the energy of the incident photon, f' is the frequency of the scattered photon, and ϕ is defined as in Fig. 39-5.

45P. Through what angle must a 200 keV photon be scattered by a free electron so that the photon loses 10% of its energy?

46P. Show that when a photon of energy E is scattered from a free electron, the maximum kinetic energy transferred to the electron is given by

$$K_{\max} = \frac{E^2}{E + mc^2/2}.$$

47P. What is the maximum kinetic energy of electrons knocked out of a thin copper foil by an incident beam of 17.5 keV x rays?

48P. Derive Eq. 39-11, the equation for the Compton shift, from Eqs. 39-8, 39-9, and 39-10 by eliminating v and θ.

SECTION 39-6   Electrons and Matter Waves

49E. A bullet of mass 40 g travels at 1000 m/s. (a) What wavelength can we associate with it? (b) Why is the wave nature of the bullet not revealed through diffraction effects?

50E. Using the classical relation between momentum and kinetic energy, shows that an electron's de Broglie wavelength in nanometers can be written as $\lambda = 1.226/\sqrt{K}$, in which K is the electron's kinetic energy in electron-volts.

51E. In an ordinary television set, electrons are accelerated through a potential difference of 25.0 kV. What is the de Broglie wavelength of such electrons? (Ignore relativistic effects.)

52E. Calculate the de Broglie wavelength of (a) a 1.00 keV electron, (b) a 1.00 keV photon, and (c) a 1.00 keV neutron.

53P. The wavelength of the yellow spectral emission line of sodium is 590 nm. At what kinetic energy would an electron have the same de Broglie wavelength?

54P. An electron and a photon each have a wavelength of 0.20 nm. Calculate (a) their momenta and (b) their energies.

55P. Neutrons in thermal equilibrium with matter have an average kinetic energy of $(3/2)kT$, where k is the Boltzmann constant and T, which may be taken to be 300 K, is the temperature of the environment of the neutrons. (a) What is the average kinetic energy of such a neutron? (b) What is the corresponding de Broglie wavelength?

56P. If the de Broglie wavelength of a proton is 100 fm, (a) what is the speed of the proton and (b) through what electric potential would the proton have to be accelerated to acquire this speed?

57P. Consider a balloon filled with helium gas at room temperature and pressure. (a) Calculate the average de Broglie wavelength of the helium atoms and the average distance between atoms under these conditions. The average kinetic energy of an atom is equal to $(3/2)kT$, where k is the Boltzmann constant. (b) Can the atoms be treated as particles under these conditions?

58P. (a) A photon has an energy of 1.00 eV, and an electron has a kinetic energy of that same amount. What are their wavelengths? (b) Repeat for an energy of 1.00 GeV.

59P. (a) A photon and an electron both have a wavelength of 1.00 nm. Give the energy of the photon and the kinetic energy of the electron. (b) Repeat for a wavelength of 1.00 fm.

60P. Singly charged sodium ions are accelerated through a potential difference of 300 V. (a) What is the momentum acquired by such an ion? (b) What is its de Broglie wavelength?

61P. The large electron accelerator at Stanford University provides a beam of electrons with kinetic energies of 50 GeV. Electrons with this energy have small wavelengths, suitable for probing the fine details of nuclear structure via scattering. What is the de Broglie wavelength of a 50 GeV electron? How does this wavelength compare with the radius of an average nucleus, taken to be about 5.0 fm? (At this energy it is sufficient to use the extreme relativistic relationship between momentum and energy, namely, $p = E/c$. This is the same relationship used for light and is justified when the kinetic energy of the particle is much greater than its rest energy, as in this case.)

62P. The existence of the atomic nucleus was discovered in 1911 by Ernest Rutherford, who properly interpreted some experiments in which a beam of alpha particles was scattered from a metal foil of atoms such as gold. (a) If the alpha particles had a kinetic energy of 7.5 MeV, what was their de Broglie wavelength? (b) Should the wave nature of the incident alpha particles have been taken into account in interpreting these experiments? The mass of an alpha particle is 4.00 u (atomic mass units), and its distance of closest approach to the nuclear center in these experiments was about 30 fm. (The wave nature of matter was not postulated until more than a decade after these crucial experiments were first performed.)

63P. A nonrelativistic particle is moving three times as fast as an electron. The ratio of the de Broglie wavelength of the particle to that of the electron is 1.813×10^{-4}. By calculating its mass, identify the particle.

64P. The highest achievable resolving power of a microscope is limited only by the wavelength used; that is, the smallest detail that can be separated has dimensions about equal to the wavelength. Suppose one wishes to "see" inside an atom. Assuming the atom to have a diameter of 100 pm, this means that one must resolve detail of separation of, say, 10 pm. (a) If an electron microscope is used, what minimum electron energy is required? (b) If a light microscope is used, what minimum photon energy is required? (c) Which microscope seems more practical? Why?

65P. What accelerating voltage for the electrons would be required if an electron microscope is to obtain the same ultimate resolving power as could be obtained using 100 keV gamma rays? (See Problem 64.)

SECTION 39-7 Schrödinger's Equation

66E. (a) Let $n = a + ib$ be a complex number, where a and b are real (positive or negative) numbers. Show that the product nn^* is always a positive real number. (b) Let $m = c + id$ be another complex number. Show that $|nm| = |n| \, |m|$.

67P. Show that Eq. 39-17 is indeed a solution of Eq. 39-16 by substituting $\psi(x)$ and its second derivative into Eq. 39-16 and noting that an identity results.

68P. (a) Write the wave function $\psi(x)$ displayed in Eq. 39-19 in the form $\psi(x) = a + ib$, where a and b are real quantities. (Assume that ψ_0 is real.) (b) Write the time-dependent wave function $\Psi(x, t)$ that corresponds to $\psi(x)$.

69P. Show that the angular wave number k for a free particle of mass m can be written as

$$k = \frac{2\pi \sqrt{2 \, mK}}{h},$$

in which K is the particle's kinetic energy.

70P. The function $\psi(x)$ displayed in Eq. 39-19 describes a free particle, for which we assumed that $E_{pot}(x) = 0$ in Schrödinger's equation (Eq. 39-15). Assume now that $E_{pot}(x) = E_0 = $ a constant in that equation. Show that Eq. 39-19 is still a solution of Schrödinger's equation, with the wave number k of the particle now given by

$$k = \frac{2\pi}{h} \sqrt{2m(E - E_0)}.$$

71P. Show that $|\psi|^2 = |\Psi|^2$, with ψ and Ψ defined as in Eq. 39-14. That is, show that the probability density does not depend on the time variable.

72P. Suppose that we had put $A = 0$ in Eq. 39-17 and relabeled B as ψ_0. What would the resulting wave function then describe? How, if at all, would Fig. 39-12 be altered?

73P. In Eq. 39-18 keep both terms, putting $A = B = \psi_0$. The equation then describes the superposition of two matter waves of equal amplitude, traveling in opposite directions. (Recall that this is the condition for a standing wave.) (a) Show that $|\Psi(x, t)|^2$ is then given by

$$|\Psi(x, t)|^2 = 2\psi_0^2[1 + \cos 2kx].$$

(b) Plot this function, and demonstrate that it describes the square of the amplitude of a standing matter wave. (c) Show that the nodes of this standing wave are located at

$$x = (2n + 1)(\tfrac{1}{4}\lambda), \qquad \text{where } n = 0, 1, 2, 3 \ldots$$

and λ is the de Broglie wavelength of the particle. (d) Write an expression for the locations of the most probable positions for finding the particle.

SECTION 39-8 Heisenberg's Uncertainty Principle

74E. Figure 39-12 shows that because of Heisenberg's uncertainty principle, it is not possible to assign an x coordinate to the position of the electron. (a) Can you assign a y or a z coordinate? (*Hint:* The momentum of the electron has no y or z component.) (b) Describe the extent of the matter wave in three dimensions.

75E. The uncertainty in the position of an electron is given as 50 pm, which is about equal to the radius of a hydrogen atom. What is the least uncertainty in any simultaneous measurement of the momentum of this electron?

76E. Imagine playing baseball in a universe (not ours!) where the Planck constant is $0.60 \; \text{J} \cdot \text{s}$. What would be the uncertainty in the position of a 0.50 kg baseball that is moving at 20 m/s along an axis if the uncertainty in the speed is 1.0 m/s?

77P. Figure 39-12 shows a case in which the momentum p_x of a particle is fixed so that $\Delta p_x = 0$; then, from Heisenberg's uncertainty principle (Eq. 39-20), the position x of the particle is completely unknown. From the same principle it follows that the opposite is also true. That is, if the position of a particle is exactly known ($\Delta x = 0$), the uncertainty in its momentum is infinite.

Consider an intermediate case, in which the position of a particle is measured, not to infinite precision, but to within a distance of $\lambda/2\pi$, where λ is the particle's de Broglie wavelength. Show that the uncertainty in the (simultaneously measured) momentum is then equal to the momentum itself; that is, $\Delta p_x = p$. Under these circumstances, would a measured momentum of zero surprise you? What about a measured momentum of $0.5p$? Of $2p$? Of $12p$?

78P. You will find in Chapter 40 that we no longer imagine electrons to move in definite orbits within atoms, like the planets in our solar system. To see why, let us try to "observe" such an orbiting electron by using a light microscope to measure the electron's presumed orbital position with a precision of, say 10 pm (a typical atom has a radius of about 100 pm). The wavelength of the light used in the microscope must then be about 10 pm. (a) What would be the photon energy of this light? (b) How much energy would such a photon impart to an electron in a head-on collision? (c) What do these results tell you about the possibility of "viewing" an atomic electron at two or more points along its presumed orbital path? (*Hint:* The outer electrons of atoms are bound to the atom by energies of only a few electron-volts.)

SECTION 39-9 Barrier Tunneling

79P. A proton and a deuteron (the latter has the same charge as a proton but twice the mass) strike a potential energy barrier that is 10 fm thick and 10 MeV high. Each particle has a kinetic energy of 3.0 MeV before it strikes the barrier. (a) What is the transmission probability for each? (b) What are their respective kinetic energies after they pass through the barrier (assuming that they do so)? (c) What are their respective kinetic energies if they are reflected from the barrier?

80P. Consider a potential energy barrier like that of Fig. 39-13*a* but whose height E_{pot} is 6.0 eV and whose thickness *L* is 0.70 nm. What is the energy of an incident electron whose transmission probability is 0.0010?

81P. (a) Suppose a beam of 5.0 eV protons strikes a potential energy barrier of height 6.0 eV and thickness 0.70 nm, at a rate equivalent to a current of 1000 A. How long would you have to wait—on average—for one proton to be transmitted? (b) How long would you have to wait if the particle was an electron rather than a proton?

82P. Consider the barrier-tunneling situation in Sample Problem 39-7. What percentage change in the transmission coefficient *T* occurs for a 1.0% change in (a) the barrier height, (b) the barrier thickness, and (c) the kinetic energy of the incident electron?

83P. A 1500 kg car moving at 20 m/s approaches a hill that is 24 m high and 30 m long. What is the probability that the car will tunnel quantum mechanically through the hill, appearing on the other side? That is, what is the car's transmission coefficient for this hill? (*Hint:* The potential energy is gravitational in this case.)

84P. A particle of momentum *p* approaches the barrier of Fig. 39-13*a* from the left. In the region to the left of the barrier, $E_{pot} = 0$ and Schrödinger's equation takes the form of Eq. 39-16. (a) Show that, in this region,

$$\psi(x) = Ae^{ikx} + Be^{-ikx}$$

is a solution of Schrödinger's equation. Here *A* and *B* are real but arbitrary constants and $k = 2\pi p/h$. (b) Show further that

$$|\psi|^2 = A^2 + B^2 + 2AB \cos 2kx.$$

(c) Show that $|\psi|^2$ oscillates between the limits of $(A + B)^2$ and $(A - B)^2$. Note that if $A \neq B$, $|\psi|^2$ is always positive and never zero. Check these results against the plot of $|\psi|^2$ in Fig. 39-13*b*.

85P. A particle of momentum *p* and kinetic energy *E* approaches the barrier of Fig. 39-13*a* from the left. In the region within the barrier, $E < E_{pot}$ and Schrödinger's equation, in the form of Eq. 39-16, still holds. (a) Show that in this region

$$\psi(x) = Ce^{-kx},$$

in which

$$k = \sqrt{\frac{8\pi^2 m(E_{pot} - E)}{h^2}}$$

and *C* is an arbitrary constant. (b) Show further that

$$|\psi|^2 = C^2 e^{-2kx}.$$

This function describes the exponential decay of the probability density within the barrier, as displayed in Fig. 39-13*b*.

This spectacular computer image was produced in 1993 at IBM's Almaden Research Center in California. The 48 peaks forming the circle mark the positions of individual atoms of iron on a specially prepared copper surface. The circle, which is about 14 nm in diameter, is called a quantum corral. How do these atoms come to be arranged in a circle? And what is the significance of the ripples that are visible within the corral''?

40-1 ATOM BUILDING

Early in the twentieth century nobody knew how the electrons in an atom are arranged, what their motions are, how atoms emit or absorb light, or even why atoms are stable. Without this knowledge it is not possible to understand how atoms combine to form molecules or stack up to form solids. As a consequence, the foundations of chemistry — including biochemistry, which underlies the nature of life itself — were more or less a mystery.

In 1926 all these questions and many others were answered with the development of **quantum mechanics.** Its basic premise is that moving electrons, protons, and particles of any kind are best viewed as matter waves, whose motions are governed by Schrödinger's equation. Although quantum mechanics also applies to massive particles, there is no point in treating baseballs, automobiles, planets, and so on with quantum mechanics. For such massive, slow-moving objects, Newtonian mechanics and quantum mechanics yield the same answers.

Before we can apply quantum mechanics to the problem of atomic structure, we need to develop some insights by applying quantum ideas in a few simpler situations. These "practice problems" may seem artificial but, as you will see, they provide a firm foundation for understanding a very real problem that we shall analyze in Section 40-6 — the structure of the hydrogen atom.

40-2 WAVES ON STRINGS AND MATTER WAVES

In Chapter 17 we saw that waves of two kinds can be set up on a stretched string. If the string is so long that we can take it to be infinitely long, we can set up a *traveling wave* of essentially any frequency. However, if the stretched string has only a finite length, perhaps because it is rigidly clamped at both ends, we can set up only *standing waves* on it; further, these standing waves can have only discrete frequencies. In other words, confining the wave to a finite region of space leads to *quantization* of the motion — to the existence of discrete *states* for the wave, each state with a sharply defined frequency.

This observation applies to waves of all kinds, including matter waves. For matter waves, however, it is more convenient to deal with the energy E of the associated particle than with the frequency f of the wave. In all that follows we shall focus on the matter wave associated with a moving electron, which we choose as a prototype particle for study.

Consider the matter wave associated with an electron moving in the x direction and subject to no net force — a so-called *free particle.* The energy of such an electron can have any reasonable value, just as a wave traveling along a stretched string of infinite length can have any reasonable frequency.

Consider next the matter wave associated with an atomic electron, perhaps the *valence* (least tightly bound) electron in a sodium atom. Such an electron — held within the atom by the attractive Coulomb force due to the positively charged nucleus — is *not* a free particle. It can exist only in a set of discrete states, each having a discrete energy E. This sounds much like the discrete states and quantized frequencies that are available to a stretched string of finite length. For matter waves, then, as for waves of all kinds, we may state a **confinement principle:**

> Confinement of a wave leads to quantization, that is, to the existence of discrete states with discrete energies.

40-3 TRAPPING AN ELECTRON

Here we examine the matter wave associated with an electron confined to a limited region of space. We do so by analogy with standing waves on a string of finite length, stretched along an x axis and confined between rigid supports. Because the supports are rigid, the two ends of the string are nodes, or points at which the string is always at rest. There may be other nodes along the string, but these two must always be present, as Fig. 17-17 shows.

The states, or discrete standing wave patterns in which the string can oscillate, are those for which the length L of the string is equal to an integer number of half-wavelengths. That is, the string can occupy only states for which

$$L = \frac{n\lambda}{2}, \qquad \text{for } n = 1, 2, 3, \cdots. \quad (40\text{-}1)$$

Each value of n identifies a state of the oscillating string; using the language of quantum mechanics, we can call the integer n a **quantum number.**

For each state of the string permitted by Eq. 40-1, the transverse displacement of the string at various positions along the string is given by

$$y_n(x) = A \sin\left(\frac{n\pi}{L}\right)x, \quad \text{for } n = 1, 2, 3, \cdots, \quad (40\text{-}2)$$

in which the quantum number n identifies the oscillation pattern and the amplitude A depends on the time at which you inspect the string. (Equation 40-2 is a short version of Eq. 17-51.) We see that for all values of n and for all times, there is a point of zero displacement (a node) at $x = 0$ and at $x = L$, as there must be. Figure 17-17 shows a time exposure of such a stretched string for $n = 2$, 3, and 4.

Now let us turn our attention to matter waves. Our first problem is to physically confine an electron that is moving along the x axis so that it remains within a finite segment of that axis. Figure 40-1 shows a conceivable "electron trap." It consists of two semi-infinitely long cylinders, each of which has an electric potential approaching $-\infty$; between them is a hollow cylinder of length L, which has an electric potential of zero. We introduce a single electron into this central cylinder, setting the electron in motion parallel to the x axis.

The trap of Fig. 40-1 is easy to analyze but is not very practical. Single electrons *can*, however, be trapped in the laboratory with traps that are more complex in design but similar in concept. At the University of Washington, for example, a single electron has been held in a trap for months on end, permitting scientists to make extremely precise measurements of its properties.

Finding the Quantized Energies

Figure 40-2 shows the potential energy of the electron as a function of its position along the x axis of the idealized trap of Fig. 40-1. When the electron is in the central cylinder, its potential energy E_{pot} $(= -eV)$ is zero because there the potential V is zero. If the electron could get outside this region, its potential energy would be positive and of infinite magnitude, because there $V \rightarrow -\infty$. We call the potential energy pattern of Fig. 40-2 an **infinitely deep potential energy well** or, for short, an *infinite potential well*. It is a "well" because an electron placed in the central cylinder of Fig. 40-1 cannot escape from it. As the electron approaches either end of the cylinder, a force of essentially infinite magnitude reverses the electron's motion.

Just like the standing wave in a length of stretched string, the matter wave describing the confined electron must have nodes at $x = 0$ and $x = L$. Moreover, Eq. 40-1 applies to such a matter wave if we interpret λ in that equation as the de Broglie wavelength associated with the moving electron.

The de Broglie wavelength λ is defined in Eq. 39-13 as $\lambda = h/p$, where p is the magnitude of the electron's momentum. This magnitude p is related to the kinetic energy K by $p = \sqrt{2mK}$, where m is the mass of the electron.

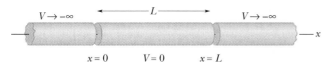

FIGURE 40-1 The elements of an idealized "trap" designed to confine an electron to the central cylinder. We take the semi-infinitely long end cylinders to be at an infinitely great negative potential and the central cylinder to be at zero potential.

FIGURE 40-2 The electric potential energy $E_{pot}(x)$ of an electron confined to the central cylinder of the idealized trap of Fig. 40-1. We see that $E_{pot} = 0$ for $0 < x < L$, and $E_{pot} \rightarrow \infty$ for $x < 0$ and $x > L$.

For an electron moving within the central cylinder of Fig. 40-1, where $E_{pot} = 0$, the total energy E is equal to the kinetic energy. Hence we can write the de Broglie wavelength of this electron as

$$\lambda = \frac{h}{p} = \frac{h}{\sqrt{2mE}}. \tag{40-3}$$

If we substitute Eq. 40-3 into Eq. 40-1 and solve for the energy E, we find that

$$E_n = \left(\frac{h^2}{8mL^2}\right) n^2, \quad \text{for } n = 1, 2, 3, \cdots . \tag{40-4}$$

Because the electron is confined, its energy can have only the values given by Eq. 40-4. The number n, which identifies the quantum state of the electron, is a quantum number. Figure 40-3 shows some of the discrete energy values (or *energy levels*) for an electron in an infinite well with $L = 100$ pm, according to Eq. 40-4. (This value for L was

FIGURE 40-3 Several of the allowed energies, given by Eq. 40-4, for an electron confined to the infinite well of Fig. 40-2, with width $L = 100$ pm. Such a plot is called an *energy level diagram*.

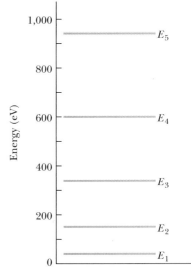

chosen because it corresponds roughly to the dimensions of a typical atom.)

The quantum state of a confined electron having the lowest possible energy is called the *ground state*; in Fig. 40-3, this state has energy E_1. The quantum states having greater energies are called *excited states*. In Fig. 40-3, the state with energy E_2 is the first excited state, the state with energy E_3 is the second excited state, and so on.

Energy Changes

To have the lowest allowed energy, the electron tends to occupy the ground state; it can move to an excited state (in which it has greater energy), only if an external source provides energy equal to the energy difference between the ground state and the excited state. An electron that receives such energy is said to make a *quantum jump* (or transition) to the excited state.

One way an electron can gain energy to make a quantum jump up to a greater energy level is to absorb a photon. However, this absorption and quantum jump can occur only if the following condition is met:

If a confined electron is to absorb a photon, the energy hf of the photon must equal the energy difference between the initial energy level of the electron and a higher level.

When an electron reaches an excited state, it does not stay there but quickly *de-excites* by decreasing its energy. One way it can decrease its energy is by emitting a photon under the following condition:

If a confined electron emits a photon, the energy hf of that photon equals the energy difference between the initial energy level of the electron and a lower level.

SAMPLE PROBLEM 40-1

An electron is confined to an infinitely deep potential energy well of width $L = 100$ pm.

(a) What is the energy difference between two adjacent energy levels, with quantum numbers n and $n + 1$? What is the energy difference if $n = 1$?

SOLUTION: From Eq. 40-4 we have

$$\Delta E = E_{n+1} - E_n$$

$$= \frac{h^2}{8mL^2} [(n + 1)^2 - n^2]$$

$$= \frac{h^2}{8mL^2} (2n + 1) \tag{40-5}$$

$$= \frac{(6.63 \times 10^{-34} \text{ J} \cdot \text{s})^2}{(8)(9.11 \times 10^{-31} \text{ kg})(100 \times 10^{-12} \text{ m})^2} (2n + 1)$$

$$= (6.03 \times 10^{-18} \text{ J})(1 \text{ eV}/1.6 \times 10^{-19} \text{ J})(2n + 1)$$

$$= (37.7 \text{ eV})(2n + 1). \tag{Answer}$$

Thus, the energy difference between adjacent levels becomes larger as the quantum number n increases.

The energy difference between the state with $n = 1$ and that with $n = 2$ is found by putting $n = 1$ in the preceding equation, obtaining

$$\Delta E = (37.7 \text{ eV})(3) = 113 \text{ eV}, \tag{Answer}$$

which is consistent with Fig. 40-3.

(b) What is the energy difference between adjacent energy levels for an electron confined to an evacuated tube 3.0 m long?

SOLUTION: We proceed exactly as in (a) except that we put $L = 3.0$ m in place of $L = 100$ pm. The result is

$$\Delta E = (4.19 \times 10^{-20} \text{ eV})(2n + 1). \tag{Answer}$$

For $n = 1$ this yields $\Delta E = 1.3 \times 10^{-19}$ eV, an energy too small to offer any hope of measurement. It is about equal to the energy required to lift a single electron two nanometers vertically against Earth's gravitational force on the electron. When an electron is "confined" to such a large region of space, the energies of its allowed states are so close together that they cannot be identified experimentally as discrete states. For all practical purposes, the quantization of energy and the existence of discrete states are then not detectable.

SAMPLE PROBLEM 40-2

An electron is in the initial state $n_i = 3$ of a infinite potential well of width 100 pm. If it is to make a quantum jump to the state $n_f = 6$ by absorbing a photon, what must be the energy hf of the photon and the wavelength λ associated with it?

SOLUTION: The electron is to jump from an energy level E_3 with $n_i = 3$ to an energy level E_6 with $n_f = 6$; this jump requires an increase in the electron's energy, which is to be provided by the photon absorption. From Eq. 40-4, the change ΔE in the energy of the electron is

$$\Delta E = E_6 - E_3 = \frac{h^2}{8mL^2} n_f^2 - \frac{h^2}{8mL^2} n_i^2$$

$$= \frac{h^2}{8mL^2} (n_f^2 - n_i^2).$$

Equating the photon energy hf to ΔE and then substituting known data, we find

$$hf = \frac{h^2}{8mL^2}(n_f^2 - n_i^2)$$

$$= \frac{(6.63 \times 10^{-34}\ \text{J}\cdot\text{s})^2}{(8)(9.11 \times 10^{-31}\ \text{kg})(100 \times 10^{-12}\ \text{m})^2}(6^2 - 3^2)$$

$$= 1.628 \times 10^{-16}\ \text{J} \approx 1.63 \times 10^{-16}\ \text{J}. \qquad \text{(Answer)}$$

To find the wavelength λ associated with the photon, we substitute c/λ for the frequency f associated with the photon. We then have

$$h\frac{c}{\lambda} = 1.628 \times 10^{-16}\ \text{J},$$

which yields

$$\lambda = \frac{(6.63 \times 10^{-34}\ \text{J}\cdot\text{s})(3.00 \times 10^8\ \text{m/s})}{1.628 \times 10^{-16}\ \text{J}}$$

$$= 1.22 \times 10^{-9}\ \text{m}. \qquad \text{(Answer)}$$

This wavelength is in the x-ray region of the electromagnetic spectrum.

$\mathbb{C}$HECKPOINT 1: Rank the following pairs of quantum states for an electron confined to an infinite well according to the energy differences between the states, greatest first: (a) $n = 3$ to $n = 1$, (b) $n = 5$ to $n = 4$, (c) $n = 4$ to $n = 3$.

Finding the Wave Functions

It turns out that the wave functions for the allowed states of the electron in an infinite potential well are given by

$$\psi_n(x) = A \sin\left(\frac{n\pi}{L}\right)x, \ \text{for}\ n = 1, 2, 3, \cdots, \quad (40\text{-}6)$$

for the range $0 \leq x \leq L$ (the wave function is zero outside that range). In Eq. 40-6, A is an arbitrary amplitude constant; you will see shortly how to evaluate A.

We could have derived Eq. 40-6 by solving Schrödinger's equation, given the potential energy function plotted in Fig. 40-2. It is far simpler, however, to assume— correctly, as it turns out—that the wave function $\psi_n(x)$ has the same form as the displacement function $y_n(x)$ for a standing wave on a string stretched between rigid supports (see Eq. 40-2).

We are more interested in the *probability density* $\psi_n^2(x)$ than in $\psi_n(x)$ because it is the probability density that has physical meaning. (Although wave functions are usually complex quantities, in Eq. 40-6 the wave function is a real quantity, so we do not have to be concerned about taking its absolute value before squaring.) Recall from Section 39-7 that the value of $\psi_n^2(x)$ at any point measures the probability that the electron will be found near that point. Specifically, the probability that an electron in an infinite well will be found to lie between the points x and $x + dx$ is $\psi_n^2(x)\ dx$. Thus $\psi_n^2(x)$ is a probability per unit length. From Eq. 40-6 we see that the probability density for an electron in an infinite well is

$$\psi_n^2(x) = A^2 \sin^2\left(\frac{n\pi}{L}\right)x,$$

$$\text{for}\ n = 1, 2, 3, \cdots, \quad (40\text{-}7)$$

for the range $0 \leq x \leq L$ (the probability density is zero outside that range). Figure 40-4 shows $\psi_n^2(x)$ for $n = 1, 2, 3,$ and 15 for an electron in an infinite well whose width L is 100 pm.

If classical physics prevailed, we would expect the trapped electron to appear with equal probability in all parts of the well. From Fig. 40-4 we see that it does not. For example, inspection of that figure and of Eq. 40-7 shows that for the state with $n = 2$, the electron is most likely to be found near $x = 25$ pm and $x = 75$ pm. It will be found with near-zero probability near $x = 0$, $x = 50$ pm, and $x = 100$ pm.

The case of $n = 15$ in Fig. 40-4 suggests that as n increases, it becomes more and more likely that the electron *will* be found with equal probability in all parts of the well. This result is an instance of a general principle called the **correspondence principle:**

> At large enough quantum numbers, the predictions of quantum mechanics merge smoothly with those of classical physics.

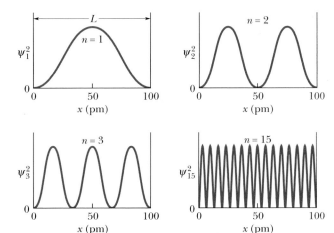

FIGURE 40-4 The probability density $\psi_n^2(x)$ for four states of an electron trapped in an infinite well; their quantum numbers are $n = 1, 2, 3,$ and 15. The electron is most likely to be found where $\psi_n^2(x)$ is high, and least likely to be found where it is low.

This principle, first advanced by Danish physicist Niels Bohr, holds for all quantum predictions. It should remind you of a similar principle concerning the theory of relativity, namely, that at low-enough particle speeds, the predictions of special relativity merge smoothly with those of classical physics.

CHECKPOINT 2: The figure shows three infinite potential wells of widths L, $2L$, and $3L$; each contains an electron in the state for $n = 10$. Rank the wells according to (a) the number of maxima for the probability density of the electron and (b) the energy of the electron, greatest first.

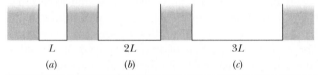

L	$2L$	$3L$
(a)	(b)	(c)

Normalization

The product $\psi_n^2(x)\,dx$ gives the probability that an electron in an infinite well will be found in the interval of the x axis that lies between x and $x + dx$. We know that the electron must be *somewhere* in the infinite well, so it must be that

$$\int_{-\infty}^{+\infty} \psi_n^2(x)\,dx = 1 \quad \text{(normalization equation),} \quad (40\text{-}8)$$

since the probability 1 corresponds to certainty. Although the integral is taken over the entire x axis, only the region from $x = 0$ to $x = L$ makes any contribution to the probability. Graphically, the integral in Eq. 40-8 represents the area under each of the plots of Fig. 40-4.

In Sample Problem 40-3 we shall show that if you substitute $\psi_n^2(x)$ from Eq. 40-7 into Eq. 40-8, it is possible to assign a specific value to the arbitrary amplitude constant A that appears in Eq. 40-7, namely, $A = \sqrt{2/L}$. This process of using Eq. 40-8 to evaluate the amplitude of a wave function is called **normalizing** the wave function. The process applies to *all* one-dimensional wave functions.

Zero-Point Energy

Substituting $n = 1$ in Eq. 40-4 defines the state of lowest energy for an electron in the infinite well, the ground state. It is the state that the confined electron will occupy unless energy is supplied to it to raise it to an excited state.

The question arises: Why can't we include $n = 0$ among the possibilities listed for n in Eq. 40-4? Putting $n = 0$ in this equation would indeed yield a ground-state

energy of zero. However, putting $n = 0$ in Eq. 40-7 would also yield $\psi_n^2(x) = 0$ for all x, which we can interpret only to mean that there is no electron in the well. But there is, so $n = 0$ is not a possible quantum number.

It is an important conclusion of quantum mechanics that confined systems cannot exist in states with zero energy. They must always have a certain minimum energy called the **zero-point energy.**

We can make the zero-point energy as small as we like by making the infinite well wider, that is, by increasing L in Eq. 40-4 for $n = 1$. In the limit as $L \to \infty$, the zero-point energy E_1 approaches zero. In this limit, however, with an infinitely wide well, the electron is a free particle, no longer confined in the x direction. And because the energy of a free particle is not quantized, that energy can have any value, including zero. Only a confined particle must have a finite zero-point energy and can never be at rest.

CHECKPOINT 3: Each of the following particles is confined to an infinite well of the same width: (a) an electron, (b) a proton, (c) a deuteron, and (d) an alpha particle. Rank their zero-point energies, greatest first. The particles are listed in order of increasing mass.

SAMPLE PROBLEM 40-3

Use Eq. 40-8, the normalization equation, to evaluate the arbitrary amplitude constant A in Eq. 40-6 for an infinite potential well extending from $x = 0$ to $x = L$.

SOLUTION: Substituting Eq. 40-7 into Eq. 40-8 and taking the constant outside the integral yield

$$A^2 \int_0^L \sin^2\left[\left(\frac{n\pi}{L}\right)x\right]dx = 1. \quad (40\text{-}9)$$

We have changed the limits of the integral from $-\infty$ and $+\infty$ to 0 and L because the wave function is zero outside these new limits (so there's no need to integrate out there).

We can further simplify this equation by changing the variable from x to the dimensionless variable y, where

$$y = \left(\frac{n\pi}{L}\right)x, \quad (40\text{-}10)$$

hence

$$dx = \left(\frac{L}{n\pi}\right)dy.$$

When we change the variable, we must also change the integration limits (again). Equation 40-10 tells us that $y = 0$ when $x = 0$ and that $y = n\pi$ when $x = L$. So 0 and $n\pi$ are our new limits. With all these substitutions, Eq. 40-9 becomes

$$A^2 \frac{L}{n\pi}\int_0^{n\pi}\sin^2 y\,dy = 1.$$

We can use integral 11 in Appendix E to evaluate the integral, obtaining the equation

$$\frac{A^2L}{n\pi}\left[\frac{y}{2}-\frac{\sin 2y}{4}\right]_0^{n\pi}=1.$$

Evaluating the limits yields

$$\frac{A^2L}{n\pi}\frac{n\pi}{2}=1,$$

so
$$A=\sqrt{\frac{2}{L}}. \qquad \text{(Answer)} \quad \text{(4-11)}$$

This result tells us that the dimension for A^2, and thus for $\psi_n^2(x)$, is an inverse length. This is appropriate because a probability density is a probability *per unit length*.

40-4 AN ELECTRON IN A FINITE WELL

A potential energy well of infinite depth is an idealization. Figure 40-5 shows a realizable potential energy well—one in which the potential energy of an electron outside the well is not infinitely great but has a finite positive value E_{pot}^*, called the **well depth.** The analogy between waves on a stretched string and matter waves fails us for wells of finite depth because we can no longer be sure that matter wave nodes exist at $x = 0$ and at $x = L$. (As we shall see, they don't.)

To find the wave functions describing the quantum states of an electron in the finite well of Fig. 40-5, we *must* resort to Schrödinger's equation, the basic equation of quantum mechanics. From Section 39-7 recall that, for motion in one dimension, we use Schrödinger's equation in the form of Eq. 39-15:

$$\frac{d^2\psi}{dx^2}+\frac{8\pi^2m}{h^2}[E-E_{pot}(x)]\psi=0. \quad \text{(40-12)}$$

Rather than attempting to solve this equation for the finite well, we simply state the results for particular numerical values of E_{pot}^* and L. Figure 40-6 shows these results as

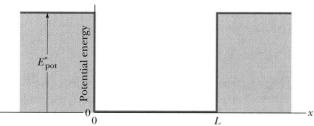

FIGURE 40-5 A *finite* potential energy well. The depth of the well is E_{pot}^* and its width is L. As in the infinite well of Fig. 40-2, the motion of the trapped electron is restricted to the x direction.

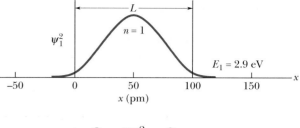
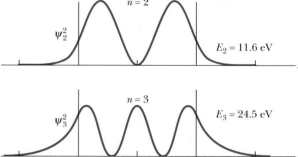

FIGURE 40-6 The probability densities $\psi_n^2(x)$ for an electron confined to the finite well of Fig. 40-5 for the states with $n = 1, 2,$ and 3. The depth of the well is 30 eV, and its width is 100 pm. No other quantum states exist for this trapped electron.

graphs of $\psi_n^2(x)$, the probability density, for a well with $E_{pot}^* = 30$ eV and $L = 100$ pm.

The probability density $\psi_n^2(x)$ for each graph in Fig. 40-6 satisfies Eq. 40-8, the normalization equation. So we know that the areas under all three probability density plots are numerically equal to 1.

If you compare Fig. 40-6, for a finite well, with Fig. 40-4, for an infinite well, you will see one striking difference: for a finite well, there is a finite probability that the electron matter wave (and thus the electron itself) can penetrate the walls of the well—in a region in which Newtonian mechanics says the electron cannot exist. This possibility should not be surprising, because we saw in Section 39-9 that an electron can tunnel through a potential energy barrier. "Leaking" into the walls of a finite potential energy well is a similar phenomenon.

Although you can't tell from Fig. 40-6, the three states shown are the *only* quantum states that can exist with energies less than the well depth, which is 30 eV for this particular finite well. Electrons with $E > 30$ eV are not confined to the well and have energies that are not quantized. Figure 40-7 shows the energy levels for an electron trapped in this well.

SAMPLE PROBLEM 40-4

Suppose a finite well with $E_{pot}^* = 30.0$ eV and $L = 100$ pm confines a single electron in its ground state.

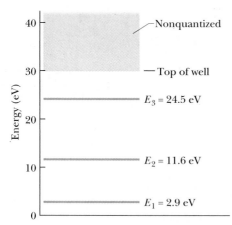

FIGURE 40-7 The energy level diagram for an electron confined to a finite well 30 eV deep and 100 pm wide. Only three discrete quantum states are possible for an electron in this well. States with $E > 30$ eV have a continuous range of energies.

(a) The electron can be raised to quantum states of higher energy by illuminating the well with light of the appropriate wavelength. What discrete wavelengths of incident light would the electron absorb? In what region of the electromagnetic spectrum would these wavelengths (said to be *absorption spectrum lines*) lie?

SOLUTION: The energy imparted by the incident light could raise the electron from its ground state ($n = 1$) to the state with $n = 2$ or to the state with $n = 3$. No other discrete states are possible. The energy difference for the smaller of these energy jumps is $\Delta E = E_2 - E_1$. This energy difference must be contributed by an absorbed photon, of energy $hf = hc/\lambda$. Equating the two energies, we get

$$E_2 - E_1 = \frac{hc}{\lambda}.$$

Solving for λ and substituting energy values from Fig. 40-7 yield

$$\lambda = \frac{hc}{E_2 - E_1}$$

$$= \frac{(6.63 \times 10^{-34} \text{ J} \cdot \text{s})(3.00 \times 10^8 \text{ m/s})}{(11.6 \text{ eV} - 2.9 \text{ eV})(1.60 \times 10^{-19} \text{ J/eV})}$$

$$= 1.43 \times 10^{-7} \text{ m} = 143 \text{ nm}. \quad \text{(Answer)}$$

This wavelength lies in the ultraviolet region of the spectrum.
    The jump from the electron's ground state to the state with $n = 3$ requires an energy difference of

$$\Delta E = E_3 - E_1 = 24.5 \text{ eV} - 2.9 \text{ eV} = 21.6 \text{ eV}.$$

Repeating the calculation above with this energy difference leads to

$$\lambda = 57.6 \text{ nm}, \quad \text{(Answer)}$$

which is also in the ultraviolet region of the spectrum.
    If the electron is initially in its ground state, as we have assumed, no other discrete spectral absorption lines will occur

because the three discrete states shown in Fig. 40-7 are the only ones that exist in this particular finite well.

(b) Can the electron, initially in the ground state, absorb a photon with a wavelength $\lambda = 100$ nm?

SOLUTION: This wavelength is intermediate between the wavelength of 143 nm (required for the jump to the first excited state) and the wavelength of 57.6 nm (required for the jump to the second excited state). To absorb a photon at the intermediate wavelength 100 nm would require that the electron jump to an intermediate quantum state, but there is none. Thus, the electron cannot absorb light at this wavelength (or any other intermediate wavelength).

(c) With the electron in the ground state, what wavelength of light is needed to barely free the electron from the potential well by a single photon absorption?

SOLUTION: To be free of the potential well, the electron must receive an energy that puts it into the nonquantized energy region of Fig. 40-7. So, it must then have an energy of at least E_{pot}^* ($= 30.0$ eV). As in (a), we can write

$$E_{\text{pot}}^* - E_1 = \frac{hc}{\lambda},$$

from which we find

$$\lambda = \frac{hc}{E_{\text{pot}}^* - E_1}$$

$$= \frac{(6.63 \times 10^{-34} \text{ J} \cdot \text{s})(3.00 \times 10^8 \text{ m/s})}{(30.0 \text{ eV} - 2.9 \text{ eV})(1.60 \times 10^{-19} \text{ J/eV})}$$

$$= 4.59 \times 10^{-8} \text{ m} = 45.9 \text{ nm}. \quad \text{(Answer)}$$

(d) Can the electron, initially in the ground state, absorb a photon with an associated wavelength of 20.2 nm? If so, in what state is the electron after the absorption?

SOLUTION: The photon energy hf at this wavelength is

$$hf = h\frac{c}{\lambda} = \frac{(6.63 \times 10^{-34} \text{ J} \cdot \text{s})(3.00 \times 10^8 \text{ m/s})}{20.2 \times 10^{-9} \text{ m}}$$

$$= 9.847 \times 10^{-18} \text{ J} = 61.5 \text{ eV}.$$

This energy exceeds the 30.0 eV depth of the potential well. Thus, the electron can absorb a photon of this energy; the absorption allows the electron to escape from the well. It is then a free particle with a kinetic energy of

$$K = hf - E_{\text{pot}}^* = 61.5 \text{ eV} - 30.0 \text{ eV} = 31.5 \text{ eV}$$

and is no longer in a quantum state.

CHECKPOINT 4: Figure 40-6 shows the three quantum states of an electron trapped in a 30 eV finite well. (a) In which state is the electron most likely to be found near the midpoint of the well? (b) Rank the three states according to the probability of the electron being outside the well, greatest first.

40-5 MORE ELECTRON TRAPS

Here we discuss three types of artificial electron traps.

Nanocrystallites

Perhaps the most direct way to construct a potential energy well in the laboratory is to prepare a sample of a semiconducting material in the form of a powder whose granules are small—in the nanometer range—and of uniform size. Each such **nanocrystallite** acts as a potential well for the electrons trapped within it.

Equation 40-4 shows that we can increase the energy of the least energetic quantum state of an electron trapped in an infinite well by reducing the width L of that well. This is also true for the wells formed by individual nanocrystallites. Thus, the smaller the nanocrystallite, the higher its lowest available level, that is, the higher the threshold energy for the photons of light that it can absorb.

If we shine sunlight on a powder of nanocrystallites, the crystallites can absorb all photons with energies above a certain threshold energy E_t ($= hf_t$). That is, they can absorb all light whose wavelength is *below* a certain threshold λ_t, where

$$\lambda_t = \frac{c}{f_t} = \frac{ch}{E_t}. \qquad (40\text{-}13)$$

Since light not absorbed is scattered, our powder of nanocrystallites will scatter all wavelengths above λ_t.

We see the powder sample by the light it scatters back to our eyes. Thus, by controlling the size of the nanocrystallites in a sample, we can control the wavelengths of the light scattered by the sample, hence the sample's color.

Figure 40-8 shows two samples of the semiconductor cadmium selenide, each consisting of a powder of nanocrystallites of uniform size. The upper sample scatters light at the red end of the spectrum. The lower sample differs from the upper sample *only* in that the lower sample is composed of smaller nanocrystallites. For this reason its threshold energy E_t is larger and, from Eq. 40-13, its threshold wavelength λ_t is smaller. The sample takes on a color of lower wavelength—in this case yellow.

The striking contrast in color between the two samples is compelling evidence of the quantization of the energies of trapped electrons and the dependence of these energies on the size of the electron trap. We remark again that the two samples in Fig. 40-8 are chemically identical; they differ only in the size of the nanocrystallites of which they are composed.

Quantum Dots

The highly developed techniques used to fabricate computer chips can be used to construct, atom by atom, indi-

FIGURE 40-8 Two samples of powdered cadmium selenide, a semiconductor, differing only in the size of their granules. Each granule serves as an electron trap. The upper sample has the larger granules and consequently the smaller spacing between energy levels and the smaller photon energy threshold for the absorption of light. Light not absorbed is scattered, causing the sample to appear red. The lower sample, because of its smaller granules, and consequently its larger level spacing and its larger energy threshold for absorption, appears yellow.

vidual potential energy wells that behave, in many respects, like artificial atoms. These **quantum dots,** as they are usually called, have promising applications in electron optics and computer technology.

In one such arrangement, a "sandwich" is fabricated in which a thin layer of a semiconducting material, shown in purple in Fig. 40-9a, is deposited between two insulating layers, one of which is much thinner than the other. Metal end caps with conducting leads are added at both ends. The materials are chosen to ensure that the potential energy of an electron in the central layer is less than it is in the two insulating layers, causing the central layer to act as a potential energy well. Figure 40-9b is a photograph of an actual quantum dot; the well in which individual electrons can be trapped is the purple region.

The lower (but not the upper) insulating layer in Fig. 40-9a is thin enough to permit electrons to tunnel through it if an appropriate potential difference is applied between the leads. In this way the number of electrons confined to the well can be controlled. The arrangement does indeed behave like an artificial atom with the property that the number of electrons it contains can be controlled. Quantum dots can be constructed in two-dimensional arrays that could well form the basis for computing systems of great speed and storage capacity.

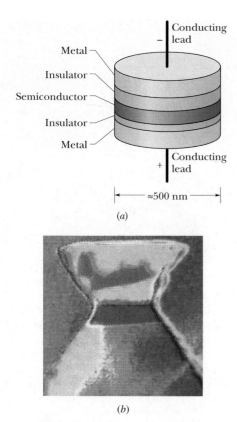

(a)

(b)

FIGURE 40-9 A quantum dot, or "artificial atom." (a) A central semiconducting layer forms a potential energy well in which electrons are trapped. The lower insulating layer is thin enough to allow electrons to be added to or removed from the central layer by barrier tunneling if an appropriate voltage is applied between the leads. (b) A photograph of an actual quantum dot. The central purple band is the electron confinement region.

Quantum Corrals

When a scanning tunneling microscope (described in Section 39-9 and Fig. 39-15) is in operation, its tip exerts a small force on isolated atoms that may be located on an otherwise smooth surface. By careful manipulation of the position of the tip, such isolated atoms can be "dragged" across the surface and deposited at another location. Using this technique, scientists at IBM's Almaden Research Center moved iron atoms across a carefully prepared copper surface, forming the atoms into a circle, which they named a **quantum corral.** The result is shown in the photograph that opens this chapter. Each iron atom in the circle is nestled in a hollow in the copper surface, equidistant from three nearest-neighbor copper atoms. The corral was fabricated at a low temperature (about 4 K) to minimize the tendency of the iron atoms to move randomly about on the surface because of their thermal energies.

The ripples within the corral are due to matter waves associated with electrons that can move over the copper surface but are largely trapped in the potential well of the corral. The dimensions of the ripples are in excellent agreement with the predictions of quantum mechanics.

40-6 THE HYDROGEN ATOM

We now move from artificial atoms to real ones, using the simplest atom—hydrogen—as our example. This atom consists of a single electron (charge $-e$) bound to its central nucleus, a single proton (charge $+e$), by the attractive Coulomb force that acts between them. The hydrogen atom, like all atoms, is an electron trap; it confines its single electron to a region of space. From the confinement principle, we then expect that the electron can exist only in a discrete set of quantum states, each with a well-defined energy. We wish to identify the energies and the wave functions of these states.

The Energies of the Hydrogen Atom States

In Chapter 25 we wrote Eq. 25-43 for the (electric) potential energy of a two-particle system with charges q_1 and q_2:

$$U = \frac{1}{4\pi\epsilon_0}\frac{q_1 q_2}{r},$$

where r is the distance between the particles. For the two-particle system of a hydrogen atom, we change notation a little and write the potential energy as

$$E_{\text{pot}} = \frac{1}{4\pi\epsilon_0}\frac{(e)(-e)}{r} = -\frac{1}{4\pi\epsilon_0}\frac{e^2}{r}. \quad (40\text{-}14)$$

The plot of Fig. 40-10 suggests the three-dimensional potential well in which the hydrogen atom's electron is trapped. This well differs from the finite potential well of Fig. 40-5 in that, for the hydrogen atom, E_{pot} is negative for all values of r because we have (arbitrarily) chosen our zero of potential energy to correspond to $r = \infty$. For the finite well of Fig. 40-5, however, we (equally arbitrarily) chose to assign the zero of potential energy to the region inside the well.

To find the wave functions that define the discrete quantum states of the hydrogen atom and the quantized energies of those states, we must solve Schrödinger's equation, with Eq. 40-14 substituted for E_{pot} in that equation. However, we cannot use the form of Schrödinger's equation given by Eq. 40-12 because that equation holds only for an electron moving in one dimension. In the hydrogen atom, the electron is free to move in three dimensions, so we must use the three-dimensional form of Schrödinger's equation.

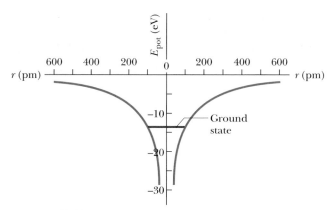

FIGURE 40-10 A plot of Eq. 40-14, which gives the potential energy E_{pot} of a hydrogen atom as a function of the separation r between the electron and the central proton. The plot is shown twice (on the left and on the right) to suggest the three-dimensional spherically symmetric trap to which the electron is confined. Note that r is always a positive quantity.

Solving that equation reveals that the energies of the allowed states are given by

$$E_n = -\frac{me^4}{8\epsilon_0^2 h^2}\frac{1}{n^2} = -\frac{13.6 \text{ eV}}{n^2}, \quad (40\text{-}15)$$

$$\text{for } n = 1, 2, 3, \cdots ,$$

where n is a quantum number and m is the mass of an electron. The lowest energy, which is for the ground state with $n = 1$, is indicated in Fig. 40-10. Figure 40-11 shows the energy levels of the ground state and five excited states, each labeled with its quantum number n. It also shows the energy level for the greatest value of n, namely, $n = \infty$, for which $E_n = 0$. For any greater energy, the electron and proton are not bound together (there is no hydrogen atom), and the corresponding region in Fig. 40-11 is like the non-quantized region for the finite well of Fig. 40-7.

The quantized energy values given by Eq. 40-15 are actually those of the hydrogen atom, that is, of the *electron + proton* system. However, we can usually attribute the energy to the electron alone because its mass is much less than that of the proton. (Similarly, we can attribute the energy of a *ball + Earth* system to the ball alone.) Thus, we can say that when an electron is trapped in a hydrogen atom, the *electron* can have only energy values given by Eq. 40-15.

As with the other potential wells we have discussed, the electron tends to be in the ground state but can jump to an excited state if given the proper amount of energy. One way the electron can gain the energy to make an upward jump between energy levels is to absorb a photon. The energy hf of the photon must then equal the energy differ-

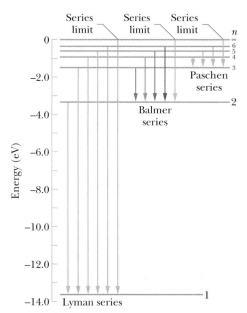

FIGURE 40-11 A plot of Eq. 40-15, showing a few of the energy levels of the hydrogen atom. The downward transitions between these levels, corresponding to the emission of light from the atom, are also shown. The transitions are grouped into series, each labeled with the name of a person associated with the study of the series spectrum.

ence between the initial energy level of the electron and the higher energy level. When the electron reaches a higher energy level, it does not stay there but quickly de-excites to a lower energy level. One way it can de-excite is by emitting a photon. In that case the energy hf of the photon equals the energy difference between the initial higher level and the lower level.

All the possible jumps can be grouped into *series*, each series consisting of the upward jumps that start on, or downward jumps that end on, a particular (home-base) level. Figure 40-11 shows some of the downward jumps for three series. The *Lyman series*, for example, has the ground state as the home-base level. Each series has a *series limit* corresponding to a jump between the home-base level and $n = \infty$. This is the greatest possible jump between quantized levels and thus corresponds to the greatest change in energy of the atom for the given home base.

Figure 40-12 shows the spectrum of the *Balmer series* of the hydrogen atom, as photographed (in one order) with a spectroscope. (The spectral lines are like those shown in Figs. 37-23 and 37-24.) The Balmer series, whose home-base level is $n = 2$, has four spectral lines that are in the visible range, as indicated in Fig. 40-12 and also by the colors used in the Balmer series of Fig. 40-11. The small triangle shown at $\lambda = 364.6$ nm in Fig. 40-12 marks the series limit.

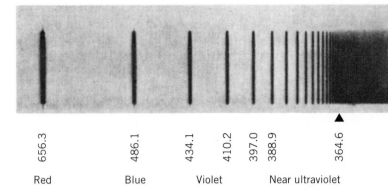

FIGURE 40-12 The spectrum lines of the Balmer series of the hydrogen atom. Whereas Fig. 40-11 shows four transitions of this series, along with the series limit, this figure shows about a dozen lines of this series; note how they are progressively closer toward the series limit, which is marked with a triangle.

λ(nm) 656.3   486.1 434.1 410.2 397.0 388.9   364.6

Red   Blue   Violet   Near ultraviolet

Bohr's Theory of the Hydrogen Atom

In 1913, some 13 years before the formulation of Schrödinger's equation, Bohr proposed a model of the hydrogen atom based on a clever combination of classical and early quantum concepts. His basic assumption—that atoms exist in discrete quantum states of well-defined energy—was a bold break with classical ideas; it carries over today as an indispensable concept in modern quantum mechanics. With this assumption, Bohr made skillful use of the correspondence principle (see Section 40-3), not only to derive Eq. 40-15 for the energies of the quantum states of the hydrogen atom but also to derive a numerical value (the *Bohr radius*) for the effective radius of that atom. In spite of its successes, Bohr's specific model of the hydrogen atom, based on the assumption that the electron moves in planet-like orbits around the nucleus, is inconsistent with the uncertainty principle and has been replaced by the modern probability density model. For his brilliant achievements relating to atomic structure, which greatly stimulated progress toward the modern quantum theory, Bohr was awarded the Nobel prize in 1922.

Quantum Numbers for the Hydrogen Atom

Although the energies of the hydrogen atom states can be described by the single quantum number n, the wave functions describing these states require three quantum numbers, corresponding to the three dimensions in which the electron can move. The three quantum numbers, along with their names and the values that they may have, are shown in Table 40-1.

Each set of quantum numbers (n, l, m_l) identifies the wave function of a particular quantum state. The quantum number n, called the **principal quantum number,** appears in Eq. 40-15 and describes the energy of the state. We state without proof that the **orbital quantum number** l is a measure of the magnitude of the angular momentum associated with the quantum state. The **orbital magnetic quantum number** m_l is related to the orientation in space

of this angular momentum vector. The restrictions on the values of the quantum numbers for the hydrogen atom, as listed in Table 40-1, are not arbitrary but emerge naturally in the process of solving Schrödinger's equation. Note that for the ground state ($n = 1$), the restrictions require that $l = 0$ and $m_l = 0$. That is, the hydrogen atom in its ground state has zero angular momentum.

CHECKPOINT 5: (a) A group of quantum states of the hydrogen atom has $n = 5$. How many values of l are possible for states within this group? (b) A subgroup of hydrogen atom states within the $n = 5$ group has $l = 3$. How many values of m_l are possible for states within this subgroup?

The Wave Function of the Hydrogen Atom Ground State

The wave function for the ground state of the hydrogen atom, as obtained by solving the three-dimensional Schrödinger equation and normalizing the result, is

$$\psi(r) = \frac{1}{\sqrt{\pi}a^{3/2}} e^{-r/a}. \qquad (40\text{-}16)$$

Here a is the **Bohr radius**, a constant with the dimension *length*. This radius is loosely taken to be the effective radius of a hydrogen atom and turns out to be a convenient unit of length for other situations involving atomic dimen-

TABLE 40-1 QUANTUM NUMBERS FOR THE HYDROGEN ATOM

SYMBOL	NAME	ALLOWED VALUES
n	Principal quantum number	1, 2, 3, . . .
l	Orbital quantum number	0, 1, 2, . . . , $n - 1$
m_l	Orbital magnetic quantum number	$-l$, $-(l - 1)$, . . . , $+(l - 1)$, $+l$

sions. Its value is

$$a = \frac{h^2 \epsilon_0}{\pi m e^2} = 5.29 \times 10^{-11} \text{ m} = 52.9 \text{ pm}. \quad (40\text{-}17)$$

As with other wave functions, ψ in Eq. 40-16 does not have physical meaning but ψ^2 does. Specifically, $\psi^2(r) \, dV$ is the probability that the electron will be found in any given (infinitesimal) volume element dV. Because $\psi^2(r)$ here depends only on r, it makes sense to choose, as a volume element dV, the volume between two concentric spherical shells whose radii are r and $r + dr$. That is, we take the volume element dV to be

$$dV = (4\pi r^2) \, dr, \quad (40\text{-}18)$$

in which $4\pi r^2$ is the area of the inner shell and dr is the radial distance between the two shells. Then

$$\psi^2(r) \, dV = \frac{4}{a^3} e^{-2r/a} \, r^2 \, dr. \quad (40\text{-}19)$$

We now define a **radial probability density** $P(r)$ such that $P(r) \, dr$ gives the probability that the electron will be found in the volume element defined by Eq. 40-18. In other words, we define $P(r)$ so that $P(r) \, dr = \psi^2(r) \, dV$. Thus, from Eq. 40-19,

$$P(r) = \frac{4}{a^3} r^2 e^{-2r/a} \quad \substack{\text{(radial probability density,} \\ \text{hydrogen atom ground state).}} \quad (40\text{-}20)$$

Figure 40-13 is a plot of Eq. 40-20. The area under the plot is unity; that is,

$$\int_0^\infty P(r) \, dr = 1. \quad (40\text{-}21)$$

This equation simply states that in a normal hydrogen atom, the electron must be *somewhere* in the space surrounding the nucleus.

The triangular marker on the horizontal axis of Fig. 40-13 is located one Bohr radius from the origin. The

graph tells us that in the ground state of the hydrogen atom, the electron is most likely to be found near this radius.

Figure 40-13 conflicts sharply with the popular view that electrons in atoms follow well-defined orbits like planets moving around the Sun. *This popular view, however familiar, is incorrect.* Figure 40-13 shows us all that we can ever know about the location of the electron in the ground state of the hydrogen atom. The appropriate question is not "When will the electron arrive at such-and-such a point?" but "What are the odds that the electron will be found in a small volume centered on such-and-such a point?" Figure 40-14, which we call a dot plot, suggests the probabilistic nature of the wave function and provides a useful mental model of the hydrogen atom in its ground state. Think of the atom in this state as a fuzzy ball with no sharply defined boundary and no hint of orbits.

It is not easy for a beginner to envision subatomic particles in this probabilistic way. The difficulty is our natural impulse to regard an electron as something like a tiny jelly bean, located at certain places at certain times and following a well-defined path. Electrons and other subatomic particles simply do not behave in this way. Do your best to avoid this *jelly bean fallacy,* as we may call it.

The energy of the ground state, found by putting $n = 1$ in Eq. 40-15, is $E_1 = -13.6$ eV. The wave function of Eq. 40-16 results if you solve Schrödinger's equation with this value of the energy. Actually, you can find a solution of this equation for *any* value of the energy, say $E = -11.6$ eV or -14.3 eV. This may suggest that the energies

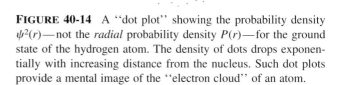

FIGURE 40-14 A "dot plot" showing the probability density $\psi^2(r)$—not the *radial* probability density $P(r)$—for the ground state of the hydrogen atom. The density of dots drops exponentially with increasing distance from the nucleus. Such dot plots provide a mental image of the "electron cloud" of an atom.

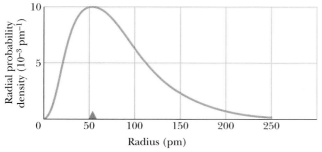

FIGURE 40-13 A plot of the radial probability density $P(r)$ for the ground state of the hydrogen atom. The triangular marker is located at one Bohr radius from the origin, and the origin represents the center of the atom.

of the hydrogen atom states are not quantized. But we know that they are.

The puzzle is solved when we realize that such solutions of Schrödinger's equation are not physically acceptable because they have increasingly large values as $r \rightarrow \infty$. Such "wave functions" tell us that the electron is more likely to be found very far from the nucleus than closer to it, which makes no sense. We get rid of these unwanted solutions by imposing a so-called **boundary condition,** in which we agree to accept only solutions of Schrödinger's equation for which $\psi(r) \rightarrow 0$ as $r \rightarrow \infty$. That is, we agree to deal only with *confined* electrons. With this restriction, the solutions of this equation now form a discrete set, with quantized energies given by Eq. 40-15.

SAMPLE PROBLEM 40-5

(a) What is the wavelength of the least energetic photon emitted in the Lyman series of the hydrogen atom spectrum lines?

SOLUTION: For any series, the transition that produces the least energetic photon is the transition between the home-base level that defines the series and the level immediately above it. Figure 40-11 shows that for the Lyman series, the transition with the least energetic photon is the transition from the level with $n = 2$ to that with $n = 1$. From Eq. 40-15 the energy difference for this transition is

$$\Delta E = E_2 - E_1 = -(13.6 \text{ eV}) \left(\frac{1}{2^2} - \frac{1}{1^2} \right) = 10.2 \text{ eV}.$$

The corresponding wavelength is found from Eq. 39-2 ($E = hf$), written in the form

$$\Delta E = hf = \frac{hc}{\lambda},$$

where hf is the energy of the emitted photon. Solving for the wavelength λ yields

$$\lambda = \frac{hc}{\Delta E} = \frac{(6.63 \times 10^{-34} \text{ J·s})(3.00 \times 10^8 \text{ m/s})}{(10.2 \text{ eV})(1.60 \times 10^{-19} \text{ J/eV})}$$
$$= 1.22 \times 10^{-7} \text{ m} = 122 \text{ nm}. \qquad \text{(Answer)}$$

Light with this wavelength is in the ultraviolet region of the electromagnetic spectrum.

(b) What is the wavelength corresponding to the series limit for the Lyman series?

SOLUTION: Figure 40-11 shows that the series limit corresponds to a transition from the level with $n = \infty$ to that with $n = 1$, the home base for this series. From Eq. 40-15, the energy difference for this transition is

$$\Delta E = E_\infty - E_1 = -(13.6 \text{ eV}) \left(\frac{1}{\infty^2} - \frac{1}{1^2} \right)$$
$$= -(13.6 \text{ eV})(0 - 1) = 13.6 \text{ eV}.$$

The corresponding wavelength is found as in (a) and is

$$\lambda = \frac{hc}{\Delta E} = \frac{(6.63 \times 10^{-34} \text{ J·s})(3.00 \times 10^8 \text{ m/s})}{(13.6 \text{ eV})(1.60 \times 10^{-19} \text{ J/eV})}$$
$$= 9.14 \times 10^{-8} \text{ m} = 91.4 \text{ nm}. \qquad \text{(Answer)}$$

Light with this wavelength is also in the ultraviolet region of the electromagnetic spectrum.

SAMPLE PROBLEM 40-6

Show that the radial probability density for the ground state of the hydrogen atom has a maximum at $r = a$.

SOLUTION: The radial probability density we want is given by Eq. 40-20,

$$P(r) = \frac{4}{a^3} r^2 e^{-2r/a}.$$

To find the maximum of any function, we must differentiate it and set the result equal to zero. If we differentiate $P(r)$ with respect to r, using derivative 7 of Appendix E and the chain rule for differentiating products, we get

$$\frac{dP}{dr} = \frac{4}{a^3} r^2 \left(\frac{-2}{a} \right) e^{-2r/a} + \frac{4}{a^3} 2r \, e^{-2r/a}$$
$$= \frac{8r}{a^3} e^{-2r/a} - \frac{8r^2}{a^4} e^{-2r/a}$$
$$= \frac{8}{a^4} r(a - r) e^{-2r/a}.$$

If we set the right side equal to zero, the resulting equation is true if $r = a$. In other words, dP/dr is equal to zero when $r = a$. (Note that we also have $dP/dr = 0$ at $r = 0$ and at $r = \infty$. However, these conditions correspond to a *minimum* in $P(r)$, as you can see in Fig. 40-13.)

SAMPLE PROBLEM 40-7

It can be shown that the probability $p(r)$ that the electron in the ground state of the hydrogen atom will be found inside a sphere of radius r is given by

$$p(r) = 1 - e^{-2x}(1 + 2x + 2x^2),$$

in which x, a dimensionless quantity, is equal to r/a. Find r for $p(r) = 0.90$.

SOLUTION: We seek the radius of a sphere for which $p(r) = 0.90$. Substituting that value in the expression above for $p(r)$, we have

$$0.90 = 1 - e^{-2x}(1 + 2x + 2x^2)$$

or

$$10e^{-2x}(1 + 2x + 2x^2) = 1.$$

We must find the value of x that satisfies this equality. It is not possible to solve explicitly for x, but a little trial and error with a pocket calculator (write a small program for it) yields $x = 2.67$. This means that the radius of a sphere such that the electron will be detected inside it 90% of the time is $2.67a$. Mark this position on the horizontal axis of Fig. 40-13 and ask yourself whether it is a reasonable answer.

Hydrogen Atom States with $n = 2$

According to rules given in Table 40-1 there are four states of the hydrogen atom with $n = 2$; their quantum numbers are listed in Table 40-2. Consider first the state with $n = 2$ and $l = m_l = 0$; its probability density is represented by the dot plot of Fig. 40-15. Note that this plot, like the plot for the ground state shown in Fig. 40-14, is spherically symmetric. That is, the probability density is a function of the radial coordinate r only and is independent of the angular coordinates θ and ϕ of Fig. 40-16.

It turns out that all quantum states with $l = 0$ have spherically symmetric wave functions. This is reasonable because the quantum number l is a measure of the angular

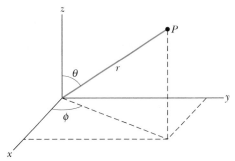

FIGURE 40-16 The relationship between the coordinates x, y, and z of the rectangular coordinate system and the coordinates r, θ, and ϕ of the spherical coordinate system. The latter are more appropriate for analyzing situations involving spherical symmetry, such as the hydrogen atom.

momentum associated with a given state. If $l = 0$, the angular momentum is also zero, which requires that the probability density representing the state have no preferred axis of symmetry.

Dot plots of ψ^2 for the three states with $n = 2$ and $l = 1$ are shown in Fig. 40-17. The probability densities for the states with $m_l = +1$ and $m_l = -1$ are identical. Although these plots are symmetric about the z axis, they are *not* spherically symmetric. That is, the probability densities for these three states are functions of both r and the angular coordinate θ.

Here is a puzzle: What is there about the hydrogen atom that establishes the axis of symmetry that is so obvious in Fig. 40-17? The answer: *absolutely nothing.*

The solution to this puzzle comes about when we realize that all three states shown in Fig. 40-17 have the same

TABLE 40-2 QUANTUM NUMBERS FOR HYDROGEN ATOM STATES WITH $n = 2$

n	l	m_l
2	0	0
2	1	+1
2	1	0
2	1	-1

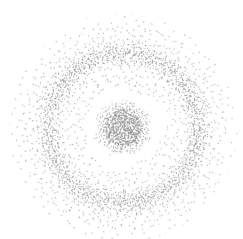

FIGURE 40-15 A dot plot showing the probability density $\psi^2(r)$ for the hydrogen atom in the quantum state with $n = 2$, $l = 0$, and $m_l = 0$. The plot has spherical symmetry about the central nucleus. The gap in the dot density pattern marks a spherical surface over which $\psi^2(r) = 0$.

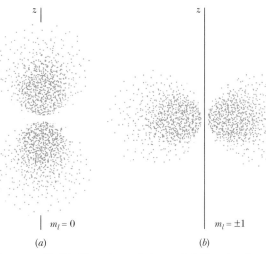

$m_l = 0$

(a)

$m_l = \pm 1$

(b)

FIGURE 40-17 Dot plots of the probability density $\psi^2(r, \theta)$ for the hydrogen atom in states with $n = 2$ and $l = 1$. (a) Plot for $m_l = 0$. (b) Plot for $m_l = +1$ and $m_l = -1$. Both plots show that the probability density is symmetric about the z axis.

energy. Recall that the energy of a state, given by Eq. 40-15, depends only on the principal quantum number n and is independent of l and m_l. In fact, for an *isolated* hydrogen atom there is no way to differentiate experimentally among the three states of Fig. 40-17.

If we add the probability densities for these three states, the combined probability density turns out to be spherically symmetrical, with no unique axis. One can, then, think of the electron as spending one-third of its time in each of the three states of Fig. 40-17, and one can think of the weighted sum of the three independent wave functions as defining a spherically symmetric **subshell,** specified by the quantum numbers $n = 2, l = 1$. The individual states will display their separate existence only if we place the hydrogen atom in an external electric or magnetic field. The three states of the $n = 2, l = 1$ subshell will then have different energies, and the field direction will establish the necessary symmetry axis.

The $n = 2, l = 0$ state, whose probability density is shown in Fig. 40-15, *also* has the same energy as each of the three states of Fig. 40-17. We can view all four states whose quantum numbers are listed in Table 40-2 as forming a spherically symmetric **shell,** specified by the single quantum number n. The importance of shells and subshells will become evident in Chapter 41, where we discuss atoms having more than one electron.

To round out our picture of the hydrogen atom, we display in Fig. 40-18 a dot plot of the probability density for a hydrogen atom state with a relatively large quantum number ($n = 45$) and the largest orbital quantum number that the restrictions of Table 40-1 permit ($l = n - 1 = 44$). The probability density forms a ring that is symmetrical about the z axis and lies very close to the xy plane. The

mean radius of the ring is $n^2 a$, where a is the Bohr radius. This mean radius is more than 2000 times the effective radius of the hydrogen atom in its ground state.

Figure 40-18 suggests the electron orbit of classical physics. Thus we have another illustration of Bohr's correspondence principle, namely, that at large quantum numbers the predictions of quantum mechanics merge smoothly with those of classical physics. Imagine what a dot plot like that of Figure 40-18 would look like for *really* large values of n and l, say $n = 1000$ and $l = 999$.

40-7 QUANTUM WEIRDNESS: AN EXAMPLE

Bohr used to say that if you aren't confused by quantum mechanics, then you don't really understand it. We cannot leave our discussion of quantum matters without examining a prediction of quantum mechanics that seems weird but, as experiment has shown, is undoubtedly correct.

In 1935 Einstein, together with his colleagues Boris Podolsky and Nathan Rosen, explored the quantum mechanics of a two-particle system. They proposed a "thought experiment" (now called the EPR experiment, after their initials) that predicted results so strange that Einstein rejected them, concluding that such predictions indicated a deep flaw in quantum mechanics.

The EPR experiment was carried out in the 1980s and the weird results predicted by quantum mechanics were in fact observed. We shall discuss the EPR experiment in broad outline and then illustrate it by analogy.

In Fig. 40-19 a source S emits two photons, labeled A and B, simultaneously and in opposite directions. Each photon has a certain property X that may have two values, say X_1 and X_2. (The property is actually the polarization direction of the quantum probability wave associated with the photon, but that detail need not concern us.) Because of the way the two photons were generated (simultaneously, in a coordinated emission), it is always true that if photon A

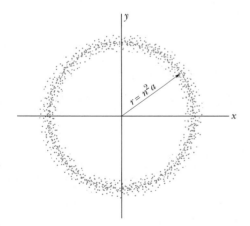

FIGURE 40-18 A dot plot of the probability density $P(r)$ for the hydrogen atom in a quantum state with a relatively large principal quantum number, namely, $n = 45$, and angular momentum quantum number $l = n - 1 = 44$. The dots lie close to the xy plane, the ring of dots suggesting a classical electron orbit.

FIGURE 40-19 A source S emits two photons, simultaneously and in opposite directions. An experimenter A may choose, arbitrarily, to reveal either of two possible properties of photon A. Similarly, a second experimenter B may choose, arbitrarily, to reveal either of the same two possible properties of photon B. However, once experimenter A has made her choice, all choice is removed from experimenter B. The result of his measurement is quite predictable, even though the photons may be very far apart and no information has passed between the experimenters.

has value X_1 then photon B will have value X_2, and conversely. There is nothing weird about that.

These two photons, taken together, constitute a single quantum system that can exist in two states; we can call them state (AX_1, BX_2) and state (AX_2, BX_1). Before any measurement is made, quantum mechanics predicts that the *actual* state of this two-photon system is an intimate equal-parts mixture of *both* states. You can imagine the two-particle system oscillating between the states, spending equal time in both.

By making a suitable measurement on photon A, an experimenter can choose to reveal *either* value X_1 or value X_2 for this photon. Let us say that the experimenter chooses to reveal X_1. It then follows that the two-particle system is no longer a mixture of states (AX_1, BX_2) and (AX_2, BX_1). The act of measurement has caused the system to "collapse" into state (AX_1, BX_2) alone. A measurement made on photon B must reveal only the value X_2. In short, the kind of measurement one conducts on A (a matter of arbitrary choice) automatically removes any choice for the state of photon B. Quantum mechanics predicts this to be true even if the photons are far apart (even kilometers apart) when the first measurement is made; no wonder Einstein called this prediction "spooky actions at a distance." Nevertheless, the 1980s experiments show that that is exactly what happens. Most physicists accept the results of these experiments as an impressive endorsement of the validity of quantum mechanics.

Now for a loose analogy. Suppose that a jelly bean can exist in either of two states, red or green. Let Sally and Sam meet in Chicago. Then let Sally move to Boston, taking with her a jelly bean of each color. Sam moves to Los Angeles, with a jelly bean of each color in his pocket. At a certain time let Sally, without communicating in any way with Sam, decide to eat one of her jelly beans and let her deliberately choose the red one. After this time let Sam, without looking, pull a jelly bean from his pocket; *he will always find it to be green.* Furthermore, Sally's green jelly bean and Sam's red jelly bean will simply disappear: the system has collapsed into its Sally-red, Sam-green state.

If Sally had chosen to eat her green jelly bean, the two-bean system would have collapsed into its Sally-green, Sam-red state, and the two other jelly beans would have vanished. Thus, in our analogy, Sally's arbitrary choice in Boston determines the color of the jelly bean Sam pulls out of his pocket in Los Angeles. Spooky indeed!

If you actually tried the Sally–Sam experiment, it would of course not turn out as we have discussed; our story is just an analogy. To make the analogy exact, we would have to give both Sally and Sam single "quantum jelly beans" that were each red and green at the same time, each jelly bean alternating rapidly between the two states in a correlated way. Such quantum behavior is so small for objects as big as jelly beans that it is hopeless to try to detect such quantum behavior. At the quantum level, however, such events really occur. It may seem weird, but that is the way the world is!

REVIEW & SUMMARY

The Confinement Principle

The **confinement principle** applies to waves of all kinds, including waves on a string and the matter of waves of quantum mechanics. It states that confinement leads to quantization, that is, to the existence of discrete states with discrete energies.

An Electron in an Infinite Well

An infinite well is a device for confining an electron. From the confinement principle we expect that the matter wave representing a trapped electron can exist only in a set of discrete states. The energies associated with these states are

$$E_n = \left(\frac{h^2}{8mL^2}\right)n^2, \quad \text{for } n = 1, 2, 3, \ldots, \quad (40\text{-}4)$$

in which L is the width of the well and n is a **quantum number.** The **wave functions** associated with these states are

$$\psi_n(x) = A \sin\left(\frac{n\pi}{L}\right)x, \quad \text{for } n = 1, 2, 3, \ldots \quad (40\text{-}6)$$

The **probability density** $\psi_n^2(x)$ for an allowed state has the physical meaning that $\psi_n^2(x)\,dx$ is the probability that the electron will be found in the interval between x and $x + dx$. For an electron in an infinite well, the probability densities are

$$\psi_n^2(x) = A^2 \sin^2\left(\frac{n\pi}{L}\right)x, \quad \text{for } n = 1, 2, 3, \ldots \quad (40\text{-}7)$$

At high quantum numbers n, the electron tends toward classical behavior in that it tends to occupy all parts of the well with equal probability. This fact leads to the **correspondence principle**: At large enough quantum numbers, the predictions of quantum mechanics merge smoothly with those of classical physics.

Normalization and Zero-Point Energy

The amplitude A^2 in Eq. 40-7 can be found from the **normalizing equation,**

$$\int_{-\infty}^{+\infty} \psi_n^2(x)\,dx = 1, \quad (40\text{-}8)$$

which asserts that the electron must be *somewhere* within the well, because the probability 1 implies certainty.

From Eq. 40-4 we see that the lowest permitted energy for the electron is not zero but the energy that corresponds to $n = 1$. This lowest energy is called the **zero-point energy** of the electron–well system.

An Electron in a Finite Well

A finite potential energy well is one for which the potential energy of an electron inside the well is less than that for one outside the well by a finite amount E_{pot}^*. There is a finite probability that an electron trapped in such a well can, nevertheless, be outside the well (in the wall).

The Hydrogen Atom

The potential energy function for the hydrogen atom is

$$E_{pot} = -\frac{1}{4\pi\epsilon_0}\frac{e^2}{r}. \qquad (40\text{-}14)$$

The energies of the quantum states of the hydrogen atom are found from the three-dimensional form of Schrödinger's equation to be

$$E_n = -\frac{me^4}{8\epsilon_0^2 h^2}\frac{1}{n^2} = -\frac{13.6 \text{ eV}}{n^2} \quad n = 1, 2, 3, \ldots, \qquad (40\text{-}15)$$

in which n is the **principal quantum number.** The hydrogen atom requires three quantum numbers for its complete description; their names and allowed values are shown in Table 40-1.

The **radial probability density** $P(r)$ for a hydrogen atom state is defined so that $P(r) \, dr$ is the probability that the electron will be found between two concentric shells, centered on the atom's nucleus, whose radii are r and $r + dr$. For the hydrogen atom's ground state,

$$P(r) = \frac{4}{a^3} r^2 e^{-2r/a}, \qquad (40\text{-}20)$$

in which a, the **Bohr radius,** is a length unit whose value is 52.9 pm. Figure 40-13 is a plot of $P(r)$ for the ground state.

Figures 40-15 and 40-17 represent the probability densities (not the *radial* probability densities) for the four hydrogen atom states with $n = 2$. The plot of Fig. 40-15 ($n = 2, l = 0, m_l = 0$) is spherically symmetric. The plots of Fig. 40-17 ($n = 2, l = 1$, $m_l = 0, +1, -1$) are symmetric about the z axis but, when added together, are also spherically symmetric.

All four states with $n = 2$ have the same energy and may be usefully regarded as a **shell,** identified as the $n = 2$ shell. The three states of Fig. 40-17, taken together, may be regarded as the $n = 2, l = 1$ **subshell.** It is not possible to separate the four $n = 2$ states experimentally unless the hydrogen atom is placed in an electric or a magnetic field, to permit the establishment of a definite symmetry axis.

Quantum Weirdness

In a two-particle quantum mechanical system, an arbitrary choice of the kind of measurement an experimenter makes on one of the particles can completely fix the results that a second experimenter finds for the other particle. That is, the first experimenter to make a measurement has an arbitrary choice; the second has no choice.

QUESTIONS

1. If you double the width of an infinite potential well, (a) is the energy of the ground state of the trapped electron multiplied by 4, 2, $\frac{1}{2}$, $\frac{1}{4}$, or some other number? (b) Are the energies of the higher energy states multiplied by this factor or by some other factor, depending on their quantum number?

2. Three electrons are trapped in three different infinite potential wells of widths (a) 50 pm, (b) 200 pm, and (c) 100 pm. Rank the electrons according to their zero-point energies, greatest first.

3. If you wanted to use the idealized trap of Fig. 40-1 to trap a positron, would you need to change (a) the geometry of the trap, (b) the electric potential of the central cylinder, or (c) the electric potentials of the two semi-infinite end cylinders? (A positron has the same mass as an electron but is positively charged.)

4. An electron is trapped in an infinite potential well in a state with $n = 17$. How many (a) nodes and (b) probability maxima does its matter wave have?

5. Figure 40-20 shows three infinite potential wells, each on an x axis. Without written calculation, determine the wave function ψ for a ground-state electron trapped in each well.

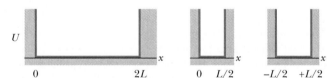

FIGURE 40-20 Question 5.

6. Figure 40-21 indicates the lowest energy levels (in electron-volts) for five situations in which an electron is trapped in an infinite potential well. In wells B, C, D, and E, the electron is in the ground state. We shall excite the electron in well A to the fourth excited state (at 25 eV). The electron can then de-excite to the ground state by emitting one or more photons, corresponding to one long jump or several short jumps. What photon *emission* energies of this de-excitation match a photon *absorption* energy (from the ground state) of the other four wells? Give the corresponding quantum numbers.

7. Is the zero-point energy of a proton trapped in an infinite potential well greater than, less than, or equal to that of an electron trapped in the same potential well?

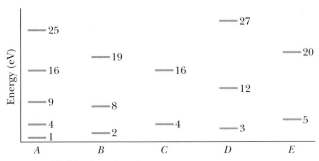

FIGURE 40-21 Question 6.

8. A proton and an electron are trapped in identical infinite potential wells; both particles are in the ground state. At the center of the wells, is the probability density for the proton greater than, less than, or equal to that of the electron?

9. You want to modify the finite potential well of Fig. 40-5 to allow its trapped electron to exist in more than three quantum states. Could you do so by making the well (a) wider or narrower, (b) deeper or shallower?

10. An electron is trapped in a finite potential well that is deep enough to allow the electron to exist in a state with $n = 4$. How many (a) nodes and (b) probability maxima does its associated matter wave have (within the well)?

11. From a visual inspection of Fig. 40-6, rank the quantum numbers of the three quantum states according to the de Broglie wavelength of the electron, greatest first.

12. From a visual inspection of Fig. 40-6, rank the quantum numbers of the three quantum states according to the probability that the electron will be found outside the region given by $0 < x < L$, greatest first.

13. An electron, trapped in a finite potential energy well such as that of Fig. 40-5, is in its state of lowest energy. Are (a) its de Broglie wavelength, (b) the magnitude of its momentum, and (c) its energy greater than, the same as, or less than they would be if the potential well were infinite, as in Fig. 40-2?

14. The table lists the quantum numbers for five proposed hydrogen atom states. Which of them are not possible?

	n	l	m_l
(a)	3	2	0
(b)	2	3	1
(c)	4	3	−4
(d)	5	5	0
(e)	5	3	−2

15. In 1996 physicists working at an accelerator laboratory succeeded in producing atoms of antihydrogen. Such atoms consist of a positron moving in the electric field of an antiproton. A positron has the same mass but opposite charge of an electron. An antiproton has the same mass but opposite charge of a proton. Would you expect the spectrum of antihydrogen be the same as that of normal hydrogen or different?

16. (a) From Fig. 40-11, the energy level diagram for the hydrogen atom, you can show that the photon energy of the second spectral line of the Lyman series is equal to the sum of the photon energies of two other lines. What are those lines? (b) The photon energy of the second spectral line of the Lyman series is also equal to the *difference* between the photon energies of two other lines. What are *those* lines?

17. A hydrogen atom is in the third excited state. To what state (give the quantum number n) should it jump to (a) emit light with the longest possible wavelength, (b) emit light with the shortest possible wavelength, and (c) absorb light with the longest possible wavelength?

EXERCISES & PROBLEMS

SECTION 40-3 Trapping an Electron

1E. You wish to reduce by one-half the zero-point energy of an electron trapped in an infinite potential well. By what factor must you change the width of the potential well?

2E. What is the ground state energy of (a) an electron and (b) a proton if each is trapped in an infinite potential well that is 100 pm wide?

3E. What must be the width of an infinite potential well if an electron trapped in it in the $n = 3$ state is to have an energy of 4.7 eV?

4E. Consider an atomic nucleus to be equivalent to an infinite potential well with $L = 1.4 \times 10^{-14}$ m, a typical nuclear diameter. What would be the ground-state energy of an electron if it were trapped in such a potential well? (*Note:* Nuclei do not contain electrons.)

5E. The ground-state energy of an electron trapped in an infinite potential well is 2.6 eV. What will this quantity be if the width of the potential well is doubled?

6E. An electron, trapped in an infinite potential well 250 pm wide, is in its ground state. How much energy must it absorb if it is to jump up to the state with $n = 4$?

7E. What is the SI unit for the probability density of an electron trapped in an infinite potential well?

8E. A proton is confined to an infinite potential well 100 pm wide. What is its zero-point energy?

9E. Show that $\Delta E/E$ for an electron in an infinite potential well approaches the value $2/n$ at large quantum numbers, where ΔE is defined in Sample Problem 40-1. (Note that although ΔE does not approach zero at large quantum numbers, $\Delta E/E$ does, in accordance with the correspondence principle.)

10P. An electron is trapped in an infinite potential well. (a) What pair of adjacent energy levels (if any) will have three times the energy difference that exists between levels $n = 3$ and $n = 4$? (b) What pair (if any) will have twice that energy difference?

11P. An electron is trapped in an infinite potential well. Show that the energy difference ΔE between its quantum levels n and $n + 2$ is $(h^2/2mL^2)(n + 1)$.

12P. An electron is trapped in an infinite potential well. (a) What pair of adjacent energy levels (if any) has an energy difference equal to the energy of the electron in the state with $n = 5$? (b) With $n = 6$?

13P. An electron is trapped in an infinite potential well that is 100 pm wide; the electron is in ground state. What is the probability that you can detect the electron in an interval of width $\Delta x = 5.0$ pm centered at $x =$ (a) 25 pm, (b) 50 pm, and (c) 90 pm? (*Hint:* The interval Δx is so narrow that you can take the probability density to be constant within it.)

14P. Sample Problem 40-1b deals with an electron confined to move parallel to the axis of an evacuated cylinder 3.0 m long. (a) At what quantum number would the energy between adjacent levels be 1.0 eV, a measurable quantity? (b) What would be the energy of the electron at this quantum number? (c) Is this energy in the relativistic range?

15P. A particle is confined to an infinite potential well of width L. If the particle is in its ground state, what is the probability that it will be found between (a) $x = 0$ and $x = L/3$, (b) $x = L/3$ and $x = 2L/3$, and (c) $x = 2L/3$ and $x = L$?

SECTION 40-4 An Electron in a Finite Well

16E. Figure 40-7 gives the energy levels for an electron trapped in a finite potential energy well 30 eV deep. If the electron is in the $n = 3$ state, what is its kinetic energy?

17E. An electron in the $n = 2$ state in the finite potential well of Fig. 40-5 absorbs 31.7 eV of energy from an external source. What is its kinetic energy after this absorption, assuming that the electron moves to a position for which $x > L$?

18E. (a) Show that each term in Schrödinger's equation (Eq. 40-12) has the same dimensions. (b) What is the common SI unit for each of these terms?

19P. As Fig. 40-6 suggests, the probability density for the region $x > L$ in the finite potential well of Fig. 40-5 drops off exponentially according to

$$\psi^2(x) = Ce^{-2kx},$$

where C is a constant. (a) Show that the wave function $\psi(x)$ that may be found from the equation above is a solution of Schrödinger's equation in its one-dimensional form. (b) What must be the value of k for this to be true?

20P. Show that for the region $x > L$ in the finite potential well of Fig. 40-5, $\psi(x) = De^{2kx}$ is a solution of Schrödinger's equation in its one-dimensional form, where D is a constant. On what basis do we find this mathematically acceptable solution to be physically unacceptable?

21P. As Fig. 40-6 suggests, the probability density for an electron in the region $0 < x < L$ for the finite potential well of Fig. 40-5 is sinusoidal, being given by

$$\psi^2(x) = B \sin^2 kx,$$

in which B is a constant. (a) Show that the wave function $\psi(x)$ that may be found from the equation above is a solution of Schrödinger's equation in its one-dimensional form. (b) What must be the value of k for this to be true?

SECTION 40-6 The Hydrogen Atom

22E. Verify that the constant appearing in Eq. 40-15 is 13.6 eV.

23E. An atom (not a hydrogen atom) absorbs a photon whose associated frequency is 6.2×10^{14} Hz. By what amount does the energy of the atom increase?

24E. An atom (not a hydrogen atom) absorbs a photon whose associated wavelength is 375 nm and then immediately emits photon whose associated wavelength is 580 nm. How much net energy is absorbed by the atom in this process?

25E. Repeat Sample Problem 40-5 for the Balmer series of the hydrogen atom.

26E. (a) What is the energy of the hydrogen atom electron whose probability density is represented by the dot plot of Fig. 40-15? (b) What minimum energy is needed to remove this electron from the atom?

27E. What are (a) the energy, (b) the magnitude of the momentum, and (c) the wavelength of a photon emitted when a hydrogen atom undergoes a transition from a state with $n = 3$ to a state with $n = 1$?

28E. What is the ratio of the shortest wavelength of the Balmer series to the shortest wavelength of the Lyman series?

29E. A neutron, with a kinetic energy of 6.0 eV, collides with a stationary hydrogen atom in its ground state. Explain why the collision must be elastic—that is, why kinetic energy must be conserved. (*Hint:* Show that the hydrogen atom cannot be raised to a higher excitation state as a result of the collision.)

30E. A hydrogen atom is excited from its ground state to the state with $n = 4$. (a) How much energy must be absorbed by the atom? (b) Calculate and display on an energy level diagram the different photon energies that may be emitted as the atom returns to its ground state.

31E. Calculate the radial probability density $P(r)$ for the hydrogen atom in its ground state at (a) $r = 0$, (b) $r = a$, and (c) $r = 2a$, where a is the Bohr radius.

32E. For the hydrogen atom in its ground state, calculate (a) the probability density $\psi^2(r)$ and (b) the radial probability density $P(r)$ for $r = a$, where a is the Bohr radius.

33P. How much work must be done to pull apart the electron and the proton that make up the hydrogen atom if the atom is initially in (a) its ground state and (b) the state with $n = 2$?

34P. What are the widths of the wavelength intervals over which (a) the Lyman series and (b) the Balmer series extend? (Each width begins at the longest wavelength and ends at the series limit.) (c) What are the widths of the corresponding frequency intervals? Express the frequency intervals in terahertz (1 THz = 10^{12} Hz).

35P. In the ground state of the hydrogen atom, the electron has a total energy of -13.6 eV. What are (a) its kinetic energy and (b) its potential energy if the electron is one Bohr radius from the central nucleus?

36P. A hydrogen atom, initially at rest in the $n = 4$ quantum state, undergoes a transition to the ground state, emitting a photon in the process. What is the speed of the recoiling hydrogen atom?

37P. Light of wavelength 486.1 nm is emitted by a hydrogen atom. (a) What transition of the atom is responsible for this radiation? (b) To what series does this transition belong?

38P. (a) Find, using the energy level diagram of Fig. 40-11, the quantum numbers corresponding to a transition in which the wavelength of the emitted radiation is 121.6 nm. (b) To what series does this transmission belong?

39P. A hydrogen atom in a state having a *binding energy* (the energy required to remove an electron) of 0.85 eV makes a transition to a state with an *excitation energy* (the difference between the energy of the state and that of the ground state) of 10.2 eV. (a) What is the energy of the photon emitted as a result of the transition? (b) Identify this transition, using the energy level diagram of Fig. 40-11.

40P. Verify the wavelengths given in Fig. 40-12 for the visible spectral lines of the Balmer series.

41P. A hydrogen atom emits light of wavelength 102.6 nm. What are the initial and final quantum numbers for this transition?

42P. What is the probability that in the ground state of the hydrogen atom, the electron will be found at a radius greater than the Bohr radius? (*Hint:* See Sample Problem 40-7.)

43P. Calculate the probability that the electron in the hydrogen atom, in its ground state, will be found between spherical shells whose radii are a and $2a$, where a is the Bohr radius. (*Hint:* See Sample Problem 40-7.)

44P. Schrödinger's equation for states of the hydrogen atom for which the orbital quantum number l is zero is

$$\frac{1}{r^2}\frac{d}{dr}\left(r^2\frac{d\psi}{dr}\right) + \frac{8\pi^2 m}{h^2}[E - E_{pot}]\psi = 0.$$

Verify that Eq. 40-16, which describes the ground state of the hydrogen atom, is a solution of this equation.

45P. Verify that Eq. 40-20, the radial probability density for the ground state of the hydrogen atom, is normalized. That is, verify that

$$\int_0^\infty P(r)\, dr = 1.$$

46P. (a) For a given value of the principal quantum number n, how many values of the orbital quantum number l are possible? (b) For a given value of l, how many values of the orbital magnetic quantum number m_l are possible? (c) For a given value of n, how many values of m_l are possible?

47P. For what value of the principal quantum number n would the effective radius of the probability density dot plot for the electron in the hydrogen atom be 1.0 mm? Assume that l has its maximum value of $n - 1$. (*Hint:* Be guided by Fig. 40-18.)

48P. What is the probability that an electron in the ground state of the hydrogen atom will be found between two spherical shells whose radii are r and $r + \Delta r$, (a) if $r = 0.500a$ and $\Delta r = 0.010a$ and (b) if $r = 1.00a$ and $\Delta r = 0.01a$, where a is the Bohr radius? (*Hint:* Δr is small enough to permit the radial probability density to be taken to be constant between r and $r + dr$.)

49P*. In Sample Problem 40-6 we showed that the radial probability density for the ground state of the hydrogen atom is a maximum when $r = a$, where a is the Bohr radius. Show that the *average* value of r, defined as

$$\bar{r} = \int P(r)\, r\, dr,$$

has the value $1.5a$. In this expression for $\bar{r}$, each value of $P(r)$ is weighted with the value of r at which it occurs. Note that the average value of r is greater than the value of r for which $P(r)$ is a maximum.

50P*. The wave function for the hydrogen atom quantum state shown in Fig. 40-15, which has $n = 2$ and $l = m_l = 0$, is

$$\psi_{200}(r) = \frac{1}{4\sqrt{2\pi}}a^{-3/2}\left(2 - \frac{r}{a}\right)e^{-r/2a},$$

in which a is the Bohr radius and the subscript on $\psi(r)$ gives the values of the quantum numbers n, l, m_l. (a) Plot $\psi_{200}^2(r)$ and show that your plot is consistent with the dot plot of Fig. 40-15. (b) Show analytically that $\psi_{200}^2(r)$ has a maximum at $r = 4a$. (c) Find the radial probability density $P_{200}(r)$ for this state. (d) Show that

$$\int_0^\infty P_{200}(r)\, dr = 1,$$

and thus that the expression above for the wave function $\psi_{200}(r)$ has been properly normalized.

51P. The wave functions for the three states shown in Fig. 40-17, which have $n = 2$, $l = 1$ and $m_l = 0$, $+1$, and -1, are

$$\psi_{210}(r, \theta) = (1/4\sqrt{2\pi})(a^{-3/2})(r/a)e^{-r/2a}\cos\theta,$$
$$\psi_{21+1}(r, \theta) = (1/8\sqrt{\pi})(a^{-3/2})(r/a)e^{-r/2a}(\sin\theta)\,e^{+i\phi},$$
$$\psi_{21-1}(r, \theta) = (1/8\sqrt{\pi})(a^{-3/2})(r/a)e^{-r/2a}(\sin\theta)\,e^{-i\phi},$$

in which the subscripts on $\psi(r, \theta)$ give the values of the quantum numbers n, l, m_l and the angles θ and ϕ are defined in Fig. 40-16. Note that the first wave function is real but the others, which involve the imaginary number i, are complex. (a) Find the probability density for each wave function and show that each is consistent with its dot plot in Fig. 40-17. (b) Add the three probability densities derived in (a) and show that their sum is spherically symmetric, depending only on the radial coordinate r.

41
All About Atoms

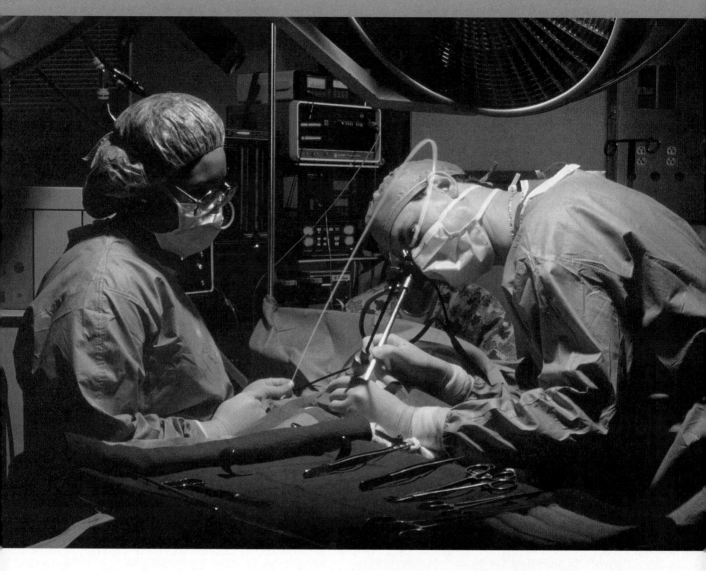

Soon after lasers were invented in the 1960s, they became novel sources of light in uncountable research laboratories. But today, lasers are ubiquitous, being found in such diverse applications as voice and data transmission, surveying, welding, and grocery-store price scanning. The photograph shows surgery being performed with laser light transmitted via optical fibers. Light from a laser and light from any other source are both due to emissions by atoms. What, then, is so different about the light from a laser?

41-1 ATOMS AND THE WORLD AROUND US

In the early years of this century quite a few prominent scientists doubted the very existence of atoms. Today, however, every well-informed person believes that atoms exist and are the building blocks of the material world. Today, we can even pick up individual atoms and move them around. That's how the quantum corral on the opening page of Chapter 40 was formed. You can easily count the 48 iron atoms that make up the circle in that image. We can even photograph single atoms by the light they emit. For example, the faint blue dot at the center of Figure 41-1 is due to light emitted by a single barium atom (actually, an ion) held in a trap at the University of Washington.

41-2 SOME PROPERTIES OF ATOMS

You may think the details of atomic physics are remote from your daily life. However, consider how the following properties of atoms—so basic that we rarely think about them—affect the way we live in our world.

> *Atoms are stable.* Essentially all the atoms that form our tangible world have existed without change for billions of years. What would the world be like if all atoms changed into other forms, perhaps after a few weeks or a few years?

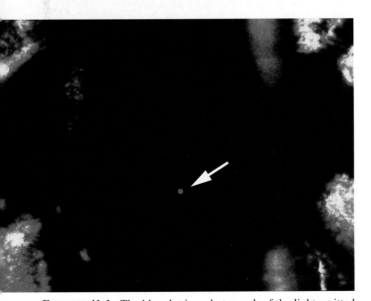

FIGURE 41-1 The blue dot is a photograph of the light emitted from a single barium atom (actually, an ion) held for a long time in a trap at the University of Washington. Special techniques caused the ion to emit light over and over again as it underwent transitions between the same pair of energy levels. The dot represents the cumulative emission of many photons.

> *Atoms combine with each other.* They stick together to form stable molecules and stack up to form rigid solids. An atom is mostly empty space, but you can stand on a floor—made up of atoms—without falling through it.

These basic properties of atoms can be explained by quantum mechanics, as can the three less apparent properties that follow.

Atoms Are Put Together Systematically

Figure 41-2 shows an example of a repetitive property of the elements as a function of their position in the periodic table (Appendix G). The figure is a plot of the **ionization energy** of the elements: the energy required to remove the most loosely bound electron from a neutral atom is plotted as a function of the position in the periodic table of the element to which the atom belongs. The remarkable similarities in the chemical and physical properties of the elements in each vertical column of the periodic table are evidence enough that the atoms are constructed according to systematic rules.

The elements are arranged in the periodic table in six horizontal **periods**; except for the first, each period starts at the left with a highly reactive alkali metal (lithium, sodium, potassium, and so on) and ends at the right with a chemically inert noble gas (neon, argon, krypton, and so on). Quantum mechanics accounts for the chemical properties of these elements. The numbers of elements in the six periods are

$$2, 8, 8, 18, 18, \text{ and } 32.$$

Quantum mechanics predicts these numbers.

Atoms Emit and Absorb Light

We have already seen that atoms can exist only in discrete quantum states, each state having a certain energy. An atom can make a transition from one state to another by emitting light (to jump to a lower energy state) or by absorbing light (to jump to a higher energy state). The frequency f of the light is given by the **Bohr frequency condition**, so called because it was postulated by Bohr well before the advent of modern quantum mechanics:

$$hf = E_{\text{high}} - E_{\text{low}} \quad \text{(Bohr frequency condition)}. \quad (41\text{-}1)$$

Here E_{high} is the higher energy and E_{low} is the lower energy of the pair of quantum states involved in the transition, and hf is the photon energy of the emitted or absorbed light.

Thus the problem of finding the frequencies of the light emitted or absorbed by an atom reduces to the prob-

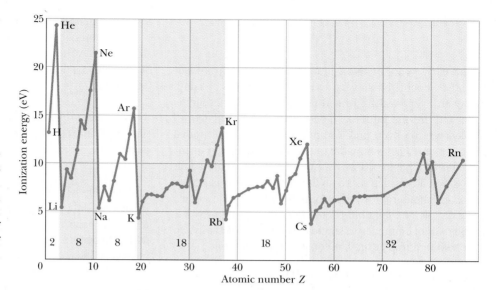

FIGURE 41-2 A plot of the ionization energies of the elements as a function of atomic number, showing the periodic repetition of properties through the six complete horizontal periods of the periodic table. The number of elements in each of these periods is indicated.

lem of finding the energies of the quantum states of that atom. Quantum mechanics allows us—in principle at least—to calculate these energies.

Atoms Have Angular Momentum and Magnetism

Figure 41-3 shows a negatively charged particle moving in a circular orbit around a fixed center. As we discussed in Section 32-4, the orbiting particle has both an angular momentum **L** and (since it is equivalent to a tiny current loop) a magnetic dipole moment $\boldsymbol{\mu}$. (Here, for brevity, we drop the subscript orb that we used in Chapter 32.) As Fig. 41-3 shows, **L** and $\boldsymbol{\mu}$ are both perpendicular to the plane of the orbit but, because of the negative sign of the charge, they point in opposite directions.

The model of Fig. 41-3 is strictly classical and does not accurately represent an electron in an atom. In quantum mechanics, the rigid orbit model has been replaced by the probability density model, best visualized as a dot plot. In quantum mechanics, however, it is still true that in general,

FIGURE 41-3 A classical model showing a particle of mass m and charge $-e$ moving with speed v in a circle of radius r. The moving particle has an angular momentum **L** given by $\mathbf{r} \times \mathbf{p}$, where **p** is its linear momentum $m\mathbf{v}$. The particle's motion is equivalent to a current loop that has an associated magnetic momentum $\boldsymbol{\mu}$ which is directed opposite **L**.

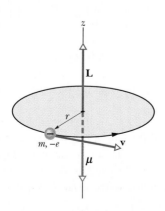

each quantum state of an electron in an atom involves an angular momentum **L** and a magnetic dipole moment $\boldsymbol{\mu}$ that point in opposite directions.

The Einstein–de Haas Experiment

In 1915, well before the discovery of quantum mechanics, Albert Einstein and Dutch physicist W. J. de Haas carried out a clever experiment designed to verify the coupling of the angular momentum and the magnetic moment of individual atoms.

Einstein and de Haas suspended an iron cylinder from a thin fiber, as shown in Fig. 41-4a. A solenoid was placed around the cylinder but not touching it. Initially, the magnetic dipole moments $\boldsymbol{\mu}$ of the atoms of the cylinder point in random directions, so their external magnetic effects cancel (Fig. 41-4a). However, when a current is switched on in the solenoid (Fig. 41-4b) so that a magnetic field **B** is set up parallel to the axis of the cylinder, the magnetic dipole moments of the atoms of the cylinder reorient themselves, lining up with that field. If the angular momentum **L** of each atom is coupled to its magnetic moment $\boldsymbol{\mu}$, then this alignment of the atomic magnetic moments must cause an alignment of the atomic angular momenta opposite the magnetic field.

No external torques initially act on the cylinder; thus its angular momentum must remain at its initial zero value. However, when **B** is turned on and the atomic angular momenta line up antiparallel to **B**, they tend to give a net angular momentum to the cylinder as a whole (directed downward in Fig. 41-4b). To maintain zero angular momentum, the cylinder begins to rotate around its central axis to produce an angular momentum in the opposite direction (upward in Fig. 41-4b).

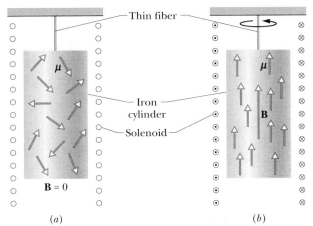

FIGURE 41-4 The Einstein–de Haas experimental setup. (*a*) Initially, the magnetic field in the iron cylinder is zero and the magnetic dipole moment vectors **μ** of its atoms are randomly oriented. The atomic angular momentum vectors (not shown) are directed opposite the magnetic dipole moment vectors and thus are also randomly oriented. (*b*) When a magnetic field **B** is applied along the cylinder's axis, the magnetic dipole moment vectors line up parallel to **B**, which means that the angular momentum vectors line up opposite **B**. Because the cylinder is initially isolated from external torques, its angular momentum is conserved and the cylinder as a whole must begin to rotate as shown.

Were it not for the fiber, the cylinder would continue to rotate for as long as the magnetic field is present. However, the twisting of the fiber quickly produces a torque that momentarily stops the cylinder's rotation and then sends the cylinder rotating in the opposite direction as the twisting is undone. Thereafter, the fiber will twist and untwist as the cylinder oscillates about its initial orientation in angular simple harmonic motion.

The observation of the cylinder's rotation verified that the angular momentum and the magnetic dipole moment of an atom are coupled in opposite directions. Moreover, it

demonstrated that the angular momentum associated with the microscopic systems of atoms can result in visible rotation of an object of everyday size.

41-3 ELECTRON SPIN

As we discussed in Section 32-4, whether an electron is trapped in an atom or is free, it has an intrinsic **spin angular momentum S**, often called simply **spin**. (Recall that *intrinsic* means that **S** is a basic characteristic of an electron, like its mass and electric charge.) As we shall discuss in the next section, the magnitude of **S** is quantized and depends on a **spin quantum number** s, which is always $\frac{1}{2}$ for electrons (and also for protons and neutrons). In addition, the component of **S** measured along any axis is quantized and depends on a **spin magnetic quantum number** m_s, which can have only the value $+\frac{1}{2}$ or $-\frac{1}{2}$.

The existence of electron spin was postulated on an empirical basis by two Dutch graduate students, George Uhlenbeck and Samuel Goudsmit, from their studies of atomic spectra. The quantum mechanical basis for electron spin was provided a few years later, by British physicist P. A. M. Dirac, who developed (in 1929) a relativistic quantum theory of the electron.

It is tempting to account for electron spin by thinking of the electron as a tiny sphere spinning about an axis. However, that classical model, like the classical model of orbits, does not hold up. In quantum mechanics, spin angular momentum is best thought of as a measurable intrinsic property of the electron; you simply can't visualize it by a mechanical model.

Table 41-1 shows the four quantum numbers n, l, m_l, and m_s that completely specify the quantum states of the electron in a hydrogen atom. The same quantum numbers also specify the allowed states of any single electron in a multielectron atom.

TABLE 41-1 ELECTRON STATES FOR AN ATOM

QUANTUM NUMBER	SYMBOL	ALLOWED VALUES	RELATED TO
Principal	n	1, 2, 3, . . .	Distance from the nucleus
Orbital	l	0, 1, 2, . . . , $(n-1)$	Orbital angular momentum
Orbital magnetic	m_l	0, ± 1, ± 2, . . . , $\pm l$	Orbital angular momentum (z component)
Spin magnetic	m_s	$\pm 1/2$	Spin angular momentum (z component)

All states with the same value of n form a **shell**.
There are $2n^2$ states in a shell.

All states with the same values of n and l form a **subshell**.
All states in a subshell have the same energy.
There are $2(2l+1)$ states in a subshell.

41-4 ANGULAR MOMENTA AND MAGNETIC DIPOLE MOMENTS

Every quantum state of an electron in an atom has an associated orbital angular momentum and a corresponding orbital magnetic dipole moment. Every electron, whether trapped in an atom or free, has a spin angular momentum and a corresponding spin magnetic dipole moment. We discuss these quantities separately first, and then discuss their combination.

Orbital Angular Momentum and Magnetism

The magnitude L of the orbital angular momentum $\mathbf{L}$ of an electron in an atom is quantized; that is, it can take on only values that belong to a discrete set. These values are

$$L = \sqrt{l(l + 1)}\hbar, \qquad (41\text{-}2)$$

in which l is the orbital quantum number and $\hbar$ is $h/2\pi$. According to Table 41-1, l must be either zero or a positive integer no greater than $n - 1$. For a state with $n = 3$, for example, only $l = 2$, $l = 1$, and $l = 0$ are permitted.

In an isolated atom, there is no preferred direction with respect to which we can discuss the orientation in space of the vector $\mathbf{L}$; all directions are equivalent. However, magnets line up with magnetic fields, and the orbital angular momentum of a quantum state is tightly coupled to its orbital magnetic dipole moment. Thus, if we immerse the atom in a uniform magnetic field we can now use the direction of the field—which we can take as a z axis—to discuss the orientations of the electron's orbital magnetic dipole moment $\boldsymbol{\mu}_{\text{orb}}$ and its orbital angular momentum $\mathbf{L}$.

As we discussed in Section 32-4, $\boldsymbol{\mu}_{\text{orb}}$ cannot itself be measured; only a projection (a component) can be measured, and that projection is quantized. The quantized values are given by Eq. 32-11 as

$$\mu_{\text{orb},z} = -m_l \mu_{\text{B}}. \qquad (41\text{-}3)$$

Here m_l is the orbital magnetic quantum number of Table 41-1 and μ_{B} is the *Bohr magneton* (Eq. 32-5):

$$\mu_{\text{B}} = \frac{eh}{4\pi m} = \frac{e\hbar}{2m} = 9.274 \times 10^{-24} \text{ J/T}$$

$$\text{(Bohr magneton)}, \qquad (41\text{-}4)$$

where m is the electron mass.

In Section 32-4, we also discussed that the orbital angular momentum $\mathbf{L}$ itself cannot be measured; as above, only a projection can be measured, and that projection is quantized. From Eq. 32-9, the quantized values are given by

$$L_z = m_l \hbar. \qquad (41\text{-}5)$$

Figure 41-5 shows the five quantized projections L_z of the orbital angular momentum for an electron with $l = 2$ and also the associated orientations of the angular momentum $\mathbf{L}$. (Do not take the figure literally—we cannot measure or detect $\mathbf{L}$.) Note that for a given value of l, there are $2l + 1$ different values of m_l. The restriction imposed by quantum mechanics on the direction of the projections L_z is called **space quantization**.

Note that Eq. 41-3 has a minus sign and Eq. 41-5 does not, reflecting the fact that the orbital angular momentum and the orbital magnetic dipole moment of an electron in an atom point in opposite directions.

Spin Angular Momentum and Spin Magnetic Dipole Moment

The magnitude S of the spin angular momentum $\mathbf{S}$ of any electron, whether free or trapped, has the single value given by

$$S = \sqrt{s(s + 1)}\hbar$$
$$= \sqrt{(\tfrac{1}{2})(\tfrac{1}{2} + 1)}\hbar = 0.866\hbar, \qquad (41\text{-}6)$$

where $s\ (= \tfrac{1}{2})$ is the spin quantum number of the electron. Spin angular momentum $\mathbf{S}$ cannot itself be measured; again, only a projection can be measured, and that projection is quantized. From Eq. 32-3, the quantized values are given by

$$S_z = m_s \hbar, \qquad (41\text{-}7)$$

in which m_s, the spin magnetic quantum number of Table 41-1, can have only two values: $+\tfrac{1}{2}$ and $-\tfrac{1}{2}$.

Correspondingly, the spin magnetic dipole moment $\boldsymbol{\mu}_s$ of an electron cannot be directly measured, but its projection can be measured and is quantized. From Eq. 32-4, the quantized values are given by

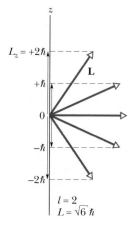

FIGURE 41-5 The allowed values of L_z for an electron in a quantum state with $l = 2$. For every orbital angular momentum vector $\mathbf{L}$ in the figure, there is a vector pointing in the opposite direction, representing the magnitude and direction of the orbital magnetic dipole moment.

$$\mu_{s,z} = -2m_s\mu_B. \qquad (41\text{-}8)$$

Figure 41-6 shows the two quantized projections on the z axis of the spin angular momentum and the spin magnetic dipole moment.

Note that Eq. 41-8, which refers to the spin magnetic dipole moment, differs from Eq. 41-3, which refers to the orbital magnetic dipole moment, by a factor of 2.*

CHECKPOINT 1: An electron is in a quantum state for which the magnitude of the electron's orbital angular momentum $\mathbf{L}$ is $2\sqrt{3}\hbar$. How many projections of the electron's orbital magnetic dipole moment on a z axis are allowed?

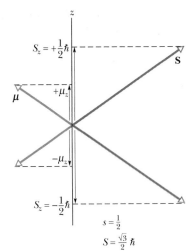

FIGURE 41-6 The allowed values of S_z and μ_z for an electron.

Orbital and Spin Angular Momenta Combined

For an atom that contains more than one electron, we define a total angular momentum $\mathbf{J}$, which is the vector sum of the angular momenta of the individual electrons—both their orbital and their spin angular momenta. The number of electrons (and the number of protons) in a neutral atom is the **atomic number** (or **charge number**) Z. Thus for a neutral atom,

$$\mathbf{J} = (\mathbf{L}_1 + \mathbf{L}_2 + \mathbf{L}_3 + \cdots + \mathbf{L}_Z) +$$
$$(\mathbf{S}_1 + \mathbf{S}_2 + \mathbf{S}_3 + \cdots + \mathbf{S}_Z). \quad (41\text{-}9)$$

Similarly, the total magnetic dipole moment of the multielectron atom is obtained by vectorially adding the magnetic dipole moments (both orbital and spin) of its individual electrons. However, because of the factor of 2 in Eq. 41-8, the resultant magnetic dipole moment for the atom will not point in the direction of the vector $-\mathbf{J}$; instead, it will make a certain angle with that vector. The **effective magnetic dipole moment** $\boldsymbol{\mu}_{\text{eff}}$ for the atom is the (vector) component of the (vector) sum of the individual magnetic dipole moments in the direction of $-\mathbf{J}$.

As you will see in the next section, in typical atoms the orbital angular momenta and the spin angular momenta of most of the electrons add vectorially to zero. Then $\mathbf{J}$ and $\boldsymbol{\mu}_{\text{eff}}$ turn out to be associated with a relatively small number of electrons, often with a single valence electron.

Figure 41-7 suggests a classical model that helps us to visualize the space quantization of the total angular mo-

mentum vector $\mathbf{J}$ and the effective magnetic moment vector $\boldsymbol{\mu}_{\text{eff}}$. It shows these coupled vectors rotating about the z axis, with the vectors tracing out cones; the motion is called *precession*. The projections of $\mathbf{J}$ and $\boldsymbol{\mu}_{\text{eff}}$ on the z axis remain constant during the precession.

The more we learn about physics, the more we tend to look at the world differently. Edward Purcell, a Nobel laureate, said in his Nobel prize lecture that his investigations of atomic angular momenta and magnetic dipole moments caused him to look at snow in a new way. He viewed the snow lying on his doorstep as "full of protons quietly precessing in the Earth's magnetic field."

Precession and the Uncertainty Principle

Heisenberg's uncertainty principle suggests a limitation of the classical model of Fig. 41-7. In its angular form, and for components in the z direction, the uncertainty principle is

$$\Delta J_z\, \Delta \phi \approx \hbar \qquad (z \text{ component}), \qquad (41\text{-}10)$$

in which ϕ is the angle of rotation about the z axis in Fig. 41-7. The projection J_z remains constant throughout the

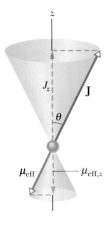

FIGURE 41-7 A classical model showing the total angular momentum vector $\mathbf{J}$ and the effective magnetic moment vector $\boldsymbol{\mu}_{\text{eff}}$ precessing about a z axis that is defined by imposing a weak magnetic field in that direction. Both vectors maintain angle θ with the z axis; hence the projections of $\mathbf{J}$ and $\boldsymbol{\mu}_{\text{eff}}$ on the z axis remain constant during the motion.

---

*An advanced formulation of quantum mechanics, called **quantum electrodynamics**, predicts that the factor "2" in Eq. 41-8 is actually 2.00231930476. This quantity has also been measured experimentally. Within the precision of the experiment, the result agrees with the theoretical prediction.

motion so that $\Delta J_z = 0$. Equation 41-10 then requires that $\Delta \phi$ be infinitely great. This means that, although $J_x^2 + J_y^2$ remains constant, the separate values of J_x and J_y are not measurable quantities. We conclude:

> It is the projections of $\mathbf{J}$ and $\boldsymbol{\mu}_{eff}$ in the direction of an imposed magnetic field that are the important measurable quantities.

41-5 THE STERN–GERLACH EXPERIMENT

In 1922 Otto Stern and Walther Gerlach at the University of Hamburg in Germany verified space quantization experimentally. At that early date quantum mechanics had not been developed, and the concept of electron spin had not been established. It was known, however, that the atoms of many elements have an angular momentum and a magnetic dipole moment and the possibility of space quantization had been proposed.

Figure 41-8 shows the Stern–Gerlach apparatus. Silver is vaporized in an electrically heated oven; the resulting silver atoms escape through a narrow slit in the oven wall into the rest of the apparatus, from which the air has been pumped. Some of the atoms (which are electrically neutral but have a magnetic moment) pass through a slit in a screen (called a *collimator*), forming a narrow beam. The beam passes between the poles of an electromagnet, finally forming a silver deposit on a glass plate.

A Magnetic Dipole in a Nonuniform Magnetic Field

Let us now digress long enough to find out what force acts on a silver atom as it passes between the pole faces of the

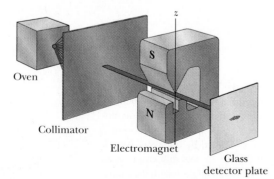

FIGURE 41-8 The apparatus used by Stern and Gerlach in 1922 to demonstrate space quantization. The entire apparatus is contained in an evacuated enclosure.

electromagnet of Fig. 41-8, which are shaped to make the magnetic field as *nonuniform* as possible.

Figure 41-9a shows a dipole of magnetic moment $\boldsymbol{\mu}$, making an angle θ with a *uniform* magnetic field. We can imagine the dipole as having north and south poles, with its magnetic dipole moment vector pointing (by convention) from the south pole to the north pole. For a uniform field, there is no net force on the dipole. The oppositely directed forces $\mathbf{F}_N$ and $\mathbf{F}_S$ on the poles have the same magnitude, and they cancel no matter what the orientation of the dipole. (A magnetic *torque* acts on the dipole of Fig. 41-9a, but that does not concern us here.)

Figures 41-9b and 41-9c show the situation in a nonuniform field. Here the forces $\mathbf{F}_N$ and $\mathbf{F}_S$ do *not* have the same magnitude because the two poles are immersed in fields of different strengths. In this case, there *is* a net force $\mathbf{F}_{net}$ whose magnitude and direction depend on the orientation of the dipole, that is, on the value of θ. In Fig. 41-9b the net force is directed upward, and in Fig. 41-9c it is directed downward. This tells us that a silver atom in the beam of Fig. 41-8 will be deflected as it passes between the pole faces of the electromagnet, the direction and the magnitude of its deflection depending on the orientation of its magnetic dipole moment.

Now let us calculate the deflecting force, that is, the force in the direction of $\mathbf{B}$, which is our z axis. First we note that the magnetic potential energy of a magnetic dipole in a magnetic field $\mathbf{B}$ is, from Eq. 29-36,

$$E_{pot} = -\boldsymbol{\mu} \cdot \mathbf{B} = -(\mu \cos \theta) B, \qquad (41\text{-}11)$$

in which θ is the angle between the directions of $\boldsymbol{\mu}$ and $\mathbf{B}$, as in Fig. 41-9. Then, from Eq. 8-19, the z component F_z of the net force acting on the atom is $-dE_{pot}/dz$; so, from Eq. 41-11,

$$F_z = -\frac{dE_{pot}}{dz} = (\mu \cos \theta) \frac{dB}{dz}. \qquad (41\text{-}12)$$

In Figs. 41-9b and c, B increases as z increases, so the magnetic field *gradient dB/dz* (the field's rate of change) is positive. Thus the sign of the deflecting force in Eq. 41-12 is determined by the angle θ. If $\theta < 90°$ (as in Fig. 41-9b), the atom will be deflected upward; if $\theta > 90°$ (as in Fig. 41-9c), the deflection will be downward. Equation 41-12 also shows why the magnetic field in the Stern–Gerlach apparatus is made as nonuniform as possible; the deflecting force on the silver atoms is directly proportional not to B but to dB/dz.

The Experimental Results

Upon examining the silver deposit on the glass plate, Stern and Gerlach deduced the following: when the electromag-

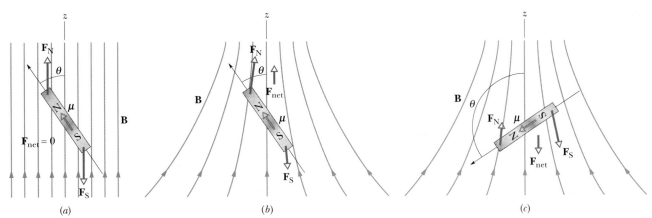

(a) (b) (c)

FIGURE 41-9 A magnetic dipole, represented as a bar magnet with two poles, in (a) a uniform magnetic field and (b, c) a non-uniform magnetic field. The net force $\mathbf{F}_{net}$ acting on the magnet is zero in (a), is directed upward in (b), and is directed downward in (c).

net was turned off, the beam passed through to the glass plate undeflected; when the electromagnet was turned on, the beam of silver atoms was split by the magnetic field into two subbeams, each subbeam corresponding to a different orientation of the magnetic moment of the silver atom. We know now (but it was not known then) that all the spin and orbital magnetic moments of the electrons in a silver atom cancel except for the spin magnetic dipole moment of the atom's single valence electron. From Eq. 41-8 and Fig. 41-6 we expect two subbeams, and not some other number of subbeams, in exact agreement with this experiment. Stern and Gerlach ended the published report of their work with the words: "We view these results as direct experimental evidence of space quantization in a magnetic field." Physicists everywhere agreed.

Figure 41-10 shows, as a graph of beam intensity versus detector position, the results of a more recent repetition of the Stern–Gerlach experiment. Here the experimenters used cesium atoms and a different detection scheme; in all other respects the arrangement was the same as that shown in Fig. 41-8. The separation of the original beam into two subbeams when the magnetic field is turned on is especially clear.

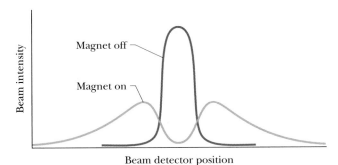

FIGURE 41-10 Results of a modern repetition of the Stern–Gerlach experiment. With the electromagnet turned off, there is only a single beam; with the electromagnet turned on, the original beam splits into two subbeams. The two subbeams correspond to parallel and antiparallel alignment of the magnetic moments of cesium atoms with the external magnetic field.

SAMPLE PROBLEM 41-1

In the magnet in a Stern–Gerlach experiment, the magnetic field gradient dB/dz through which the beam passes is 1.4 T/mm, and the length w of the beam path through the magnet is 3.5 cm. The temperature of the oven in which the silver is evaporated is adjusted so that the most probable speed v for the atoms in the beam is 750 m/s. Find the vertical deflection d of either subbeam as it emerges from the magnet. (The mass M of a silver atom is 1.8×10^{-25} kg and its effective magnetic moment is 1.0 Bohr magneton, or 9.27×10^{-24} J/T.)

SOLUTION: The vertical acceleration of a silver atom as it passes through the magnet is, from Newton's second law and Eq. 41-12,

$$a = \frac{F_z}{M} = \frac{(\mu \cos \theta)(dB/dz)}{M}.$$

Moving horizontally at speed v, each silver atom passes through the length w of the magnet in a time $t = w/v$. The vertical deflection of any atom as it clears the magnet is then

$$d = \tfrac{1}{2}at^2 = (\tfrac{1}{2})\frac{(\mu \cos \theta)(dB/dz)}{M}\left(\frac{w}{v}\right)^2.$$

Setting $\theta = 0°$ for maximum deflection and inserting given data then yield

$$d = \frac{(\mu \cos \theta)(dB/dz)w^2}{2Mv^2}$$

$$= (9.27 \times 10^{-24} \text{ J/T})(1)(1.4 \times 10^3 \text{ T/m})$$

$$\times \frac{(3.5 \times 10^{-2} \text{ m})^2}{(2)(1.8 \times 10^{-25} \text{ kg})(750 \text{ m/s})^2}$$

$$= 7.85 \times 10^{-5} \text{ m} \approx 0.08 \text{ mm}. \qquad \text{(Answer)}$$

The separation between the two subbeams is twice this, or 0.16 mm. This separation is not large but it is easily measured.

41-6 MAGNETIC RESONANCE

As we discussed briefly in Section 32-4, a proton has an intrinsic spin angular momentum **S** and an associated spin magnetic dipole moment $\boldsymbol{\mu}$ that (because the proton is positively charged) is always in the same direction as **S**. If a proton is located in a uniform magnetic field **B** directed along a z axis, the z component μ_z of the spin magnetic dipole moment can have only two quantized orientations: either parallel to **B** or antiparallel to **B**, as shown in Fig. 41-11a. From Eq. 29-37, we know that these two orientations differ in energy by $2\mu_z B$, which is the energy involved in reversing a magnetic dipole in a uniform magnetic field. The lower energy state is with μ_z parallel to **B**, and the higher energy state is with μ_z antiparallel to **B**.

Let us place a drop of water in a uniform magnetic field **B**; then the protons in the hydrogen of the water molecules each have μ_z either parallel or antiparallel to **B**. If we next apply to the drop an alternating electromagnetic field of a certain frequency f, the protons in the lower energy state can undergo reversal in their orientation of μ_z. This process of reversal is called *spin flipping* (because the reversal of a proton's magnetic dipole moment requires a reversal of the proton's spin). The frequency f required for the spin flipping is given by

$$hf = 2\mu_z B, \qquad (41\text{-}13)$$

a condition called **magnetic resonance** (or, as originally, **nuclear magnetic resonance**). In words, if the alternating electromagnetic field is to cause the protons to spin-flip in the magnetic field, the photons associated with that field must have an energy hf equal to the energy difference $2\mu_z B$ between the two possible orientations of μ_z (and thus proton spin) in that field.

Once a proton is spin-flipped to the higher energy state, it can drop back to the lower energy state by emitting a photon of the same energy hf given by Eq. 41-13. Normally more protons are in the lower state than in the higher energy state, as Fig. 41-11b suggests. This means that there will be a detectable net *absorption* of energy from the alternating electromagnetic field.

The constant field **B** in Eq. 41-13 is actually *not* the imposed external field $\mathbf{B}_{\text{ext}}$ in which the water drop is placed; rather, it is that field as modified by the small, local, internal magnetic field $\mathbf{B}_{\text{local}}$ due to the magnetic moments of the atoms and nuclei near a given proton. Thus we can rewrite Eq. 41-13 as

$$hf = 2\mu_z (B_{\text{ext}} + B_{\text{local}}). \qquad (41\text{-}14)$$

To achieve magnetic resonance, it is customary to leave the frequency f of the electromagnetic oscillations fixed and to vary B_{ext} until Eq. 41-14 is satisfied and an absorption peak is recorded.

Nuclear magnetic resonance is a property that is the basis for a valuable analytical tool, particularly for the identification of unknown compounds. Figure 41-12 shows a **nuclear magnetic resonance spectrum**, as it is called, for ethanol, whose formula we may write as CH_3-CH_2-OH. The various resonance peaks all represent spin flips of protons. They occur at different values of B_{ext}, however, because the local environments of the six protons within the ethanol molecule differ from one another. The spectrum of Fig. 41-12 is a unique signature for ethanol.

Spin technology, here called **magnetic resonance imaging** (MRI), has been applied to medical diagnostics with great success. The protons in the various tissues of the human body find themselves in different local magnetic environments. When the body, or part of it, is immersed in a strong external magnetic field, these environmental differences can be detected by spin-flip techniques and translated by computer processing into an image resembling those produced by x rays. Figure 41-13, for example,

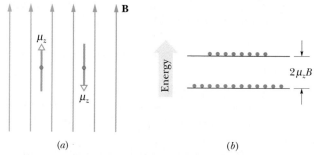

(a) $\qquad\qquad\qquad\qquad$ (b)

FIGURE 41-11 (a) A proton, whose spin component in the direction of an applied magnetic field is $\frac{1}{2}\hbar$, can occupy either of two quantized orientations in an external magnetic field. If Eq. 41-13 is satisfied, the protons in the sample can be induced to flip from one orientation to the other. (b) Normally, there are more protons in the lower energy state than in the higher energy state.

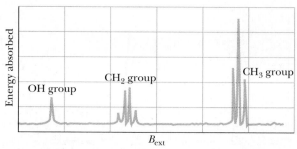

FIGURE 41-12 A nuclear magnetic resonance spectrum for ethanol. The spectral lines represent the absorption of energy associated with spin flips of protons. The three groups of lines correspond, as indicated, to protons in the OH group, the CH_2 group, and the CH_3 group of the ethanol molecule. Note that the two protons in the CH_2 group occupy four different local environments. The entire horizontal axis covers less than 10^{-4} T.

shows a cross section of a human head imaged by this method.

SAMPLE PROBLEM 41-2

A drop of water is suspended in a magnetic field **B** of magnitude 1.80 T and an alternating electromagnetic field is applied, its frequency adjusted to produce spin flips of the protons in the water. The component μ_z of the magnetic dipole moment of a proton, measured along the direction of **B**, is 1.41×10^{-26} J/T. Assume that the local magnetic fields are negligible compared to **B**. What are the frequency f and wavelength λ of the alternating field?

SOLUTION: From Eq. 41-13, we have

$$f = \frac{2\mu_z B}{h} = \frac{(2)(1.41 \times 10^{-26} \text{ J/T})(1.80 \text{ T})}{6.63 \times 10^{-34} \text{ J} \cdot \text{s}}$$

$$= 7.66 \times 10^7 \text{ Hz} = 76.6 \text{ MHz}. \qquad \text{(Answer)}$$

The corresponding wavelength is

$$\lambda = \frac{c}{f} = \frac{3.00 \times 10^8 \text{ m/s}}{7.66 \times 10^7 \text{ Hz}} = 3.92 \text{ m}. \qquad \text{(Answer)}$$

This frequency and wavelength are in the short radio wave region of the electromagnetic spectrum.

41-7 BUILDING THE PERIODIC TABLE

The four quantum numbers of Table 41-1 identify the quantum states of individual electrons in a multielectron

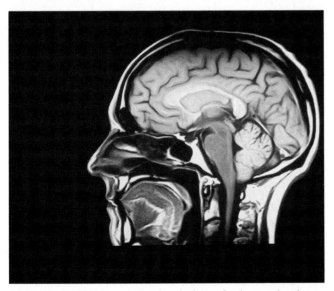

FIGURE 41-13   A cross-sectional view of a human head produced by magnetic resonance imaging. Some of the details visible here would not show up on an x-ray image, even with a modern computerized axial tomography scanner (CAT scanner).

atom. The wave functions for these states, however, are not the same as the wave functions for the corresponding states of the hydrogen atom because, in multielectron atoms, the potential energy associated with a given electron is determined not only by the charge and position of the atom's nucleus but also by the charges and positions of all the other electrons in the atom. Solutions of Schrödinger's equation for multielectron atoms can be carried out numerically—in principle at least—using a computer.

As we discussed in Section 40-6, all states with the same values of the quantum numbers n and l form a subshell. For a given value of l, there are $2l + 1$ possible values of the magnetic quantum number m_l and, for each m_l, there are two possible values for the spin quantum number m_s. Thus, there are $2(2l + 1)$ states in a subshell. It turns out that *all states in a given subshell have the same energy,* its value being determined primarily by the value of n and to a lesser extent by the value of l.

For the purpose of labeling subshells, the values of l are represented by letters:

$$l = 0 \quad 1 \quad 2 \quad 3 \quad 4 \quad 5 \quad \cdots$$
$$s \quad p \quad d \quad f \quad g \quad h \quad \cdots$$

In this notation, for example, the $n = 3$, $l = 2$ subshell would be labeled the $3d$ subshell.

When we assign electrons to states in a multielectron atom, we must be guided by the **Pauli exclusion principle**:

No two electrons in an atom can have the same set of the quantum numbers n, l, m_l, and m_s.

(The principle also holds for protons and neutrons but not for all types of particles.) If this important principle did not hold, all the electrons in an atom would pile up in the state of lowest energy, just as a dozen marbles in a bowl all end up at the bottom of the bowl. Let us examine the atoms of a few elements, to see how the Pauli principle operates in the building up of the periodic table.

Neon

The neon atom has 10 electrons. Only two of them fit into the lowest energy subshell, the $1s$ subshell. These two electrons both have $n = 1$, $l = 0$, and $m_l = 0$, but one has $m_s = +\frac{1}{2}$ and the other has $m_s = -\frac{1}{2}$. The $1s$ subshell, according to Table 41-1, contains $2(2l + 1) = 2$ states. Because this subshell then contains all the electrons permitted by the Pauli principle, it is said to be **closed**.

Two of the remaining eight electrons fill the next lowest energy subshell, the $2s$ subshell. The last six electrons just fill the $2p$ subshell which, with $l = 1$, holds $2(2l + 1) = 6$ states.

In a closed subshell, all allowed z projections of the orbital angular momentum vector **L** are present and, as you can verify from Fig. 41-5, these projections cancel for the subshell as a whole: for every positive projection there is a corresponding negative projection of the same magnitude. Similarly, the z projections of the spin angular momenta also cancel. Thus a closed subshell has no angular momentum and no magnetic moment of any kind. Furthermore, its probability density is spherically symmetric. So neon with its three closed subshells ($1s$, $2s$, and $2p$) has no "loosely dangling electrons" to encourage chemical interaction with other atoms. Neon, like the other **noble gases** that form the right-hand column of the periodic table, is chemically inert.

Sodium

Next after neon in the periodic table comes sodium, with 11 electrons. Ten of them form a closed neonlike core, which, as we have seen, has zero angular momentum. The remaining electron is largely outside this inert core, in the $3s$ subshell—the next lowest energy subshell. Because this **valence electron** of sodium is in a state with $l = 0$ (that is, an s state), the sodium atom's angular momentum and magnetic dipole moment must be due entirely to the spin of this single electron.

Sodium readily combined with other atoms that have a "vacancy" into which sodium's loosely bound valence electron can fit. Sodium, like the other **alkali metals** that form the left-hand column of the periodic table, is chemically active.

Chlorine

The chlorine atom, which has 17 electrons, has a closed 10-electron, neonlike core, with 7 electrons left over. Two of them fill the $3s$ subshell, leaving five to be assigned to the $3p$ subshell, which is the subshell next lowest in energy. This subshell, which has $l = 1$, can hold $2(2l + 1) = 6$ electrons, so there is a vacancy, or a "hole," in this subshell.

Chlorine is receptive to interacting with other atoms that have a valence electron that might fill this hole. Sodium chloride (NaCl), for example, is a very stable compound. Chlorine, like the other **halogens** that form column VIIA of the periodic table, is chemically active.

Iron

The arrangement of the 26 electrons of the iron atom can be represented as follows:

$$\lfloor 1s^2 \quad 2s^2\, 2p^6 \quad 3s^2\, 3p^6\, 3d^6 \quad 4s^2$$

The subshells are listed in numerical order and, following convention, a superscript gives the number of electrons in each subshell. From Table 41-1 we can see that an s-subshell can hold 2 electrons, a p-subshell 6, and a d-subshell 10. Thus iron's first 18 electrons form the five filled subshells that are marked off by the bracket, leaving 8 electrons to be accounted for. Six of the eight go into the $3d$ subshell and the remaining two go into the $4s$ subshell.

The last two electrons do not also go into the $3d$ subshell (which can hold 10 electrons) because the $3d^6\, 4s^2$ configuration results in a lower energy state for the atom as a whole than would the $3d^8$ configuration. An iron atom with 8 electrons (rather than 6) in the $3d$ subshell would quickly make a transition to the $3d^6\, 4s^2$ configuration, emitting electromagnetic radiation in the process. The lesson here is that except for the simplest elements, the states may not be filled in what one we might think of as their "logical" sequence.

SAMPLE PROBLEM 41-3

Account for the number of elements in the six horizontal periods of the periodic table in terms of the populations of the subshells.

SOLUTION: As Appendix G shows, the numbers of elements in the six horizontal rows are 2, 8, 8, 18, 18, and 32. The population of a subshell depends only on the quantum number l and is $2(2l + 1)$. Thus

ORBITAL QUANTUM NUMBER l	SUBSHELL POPULATION $2(2l + 1)$
0	2
1	6
2	10
3	14

We can account for each horizontal period in terms of closed subshells in this way:

PERIOD NUMBERS	ELEMENTS IN THE PERIOD	SUMS OF SUBSHELL POPULATIONS
1	2	2
2, 3	8	$2 + 6 = 8$
4, 5	18	$2 + 6 + 10 = 18$
6	32	$2 + 6 + 10 + 14 = 32$

41-8 X RAYS AND THE NUMBERING OF THE ELEMENTS

When a solid target, such as solid copper or tungsten, is bombarded with electrons whose kinetic energies are in the kiloelectron-volt range, electromagnetic radiations called **x rays** are emitted. Our concern here is what these rays—whose medical, dental, and industrial usefulness is so well known and widespread—can teach us about the atoms that absorb or emit them.

Figure 41-14 shows the wavelength spectrum of the x rays produced when a beam of 35 keV electrons falls on a molybdenum target. We see a broad, continuous spectrum of radiation on which are superimposed two peaks of sharply defined wavelengths. The continuous spectrum and the peaks arise in different ways, which we next discuss separately.

The Continuous X-Ray Spectrum

Here we examine the continuous x-ray spectrum of Fig. 41-14, ignoring for the time being the two prominent peaks that rise from it. Consider an electron of initial kinetic energy K_0 that happens to collide (interact) with one of the target atoms, as in Fig. 41-15. The electron may well lose an amount of energy ΔK, which will appear as the energy of an x-ray photon that is radiated away from the site of the collision. (The energy transferred to the recoiling atom is small because of the relatively large mass of the atom; here we neglect that transfer.)

The scattered electron in Fig. 41-15, whose energy is now less than K_0, may have a second collision with a target atom, generating a second photon, whose energy will in general be different from the energy of the photon pro-

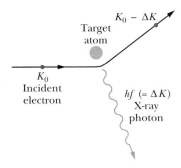

FIGURE 41-15 An electron of kinetic energy K_0 passing near an atom in the target may generate an x-ray photon, the electron losing part of its energy in the process. The continuous x-ray spectrum arises in this way.

duced in the first collision. This electron-scattering process can continue until the electron is approximately stationary. All the photons generated by these collisions form part of the continuous x-ray spectrum.

The prominent feature of that spectrum of Fig. 41-14 is the sharply defined **cutoff wavelength** $\lambda_{\min}$, below which the continuous spectrum does not exist. This minimum wavelength corresponds to a collision in which an incident electron loses *all* its initial kinetic energy K_0 in a single head-on collision with a target atom. Essentially all this energy appears as the energy of a single photon, whose associated wavelength—the minimum possible x-ray wavelength—is found from

$$K_0 = hf = \frac{hc}{\lambda_{\min}},$$

which yields

$$\lambda_{\min} = \frac{hc}{K_0} \quad \text{(cutoff wavelength).} \quad (41\text{-}15)$$

The cutoff wavelength is totally independent of the target material. If we were to switch from a molybdenum target to a copper target, for example, all features of the x-ray spectrum of Fig. 41-14 would change *except* the cutoff wavelength.

CHECKPOINT 2: Does the cutoff wavelength $\lambda_{\min}$ of the continuous x-ray spectrum increase, decrease, or remain the same if you (a) increase the kinetic energy of the electrons that strike the x-ray target, (b) allow the electrons to strike a thin foil rather than a thick block of the target material, (c) change the target to an element of higher atomic number?

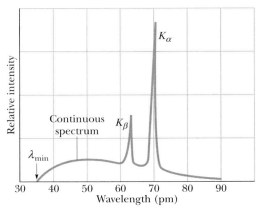

FIGURE 41-14 The distribution by wavelength of the x rays produced when 35 keV electrons strike a molybdenum target. The sharp peaks and the continuous spectrum from which they rise are produced by different mechanisms.

SAMPLE PROBLEM 41-4

A beam of 35.0 keV electrons strikes a molybdenum target, generating the x rays whose spectrum is shown in Fig. 41-14.

(a) What is the cutoff wavelength?

SOLUTION: From Eq. 41-15 we have

$$\lambda_{min} = \frac{hc}{K_0} = \frac{(4.14 \times 10^{-15} \text{ eV} \cdot \text{s})(3.00 \times 10^8 \text{ m/s})}{35.0 \times 10^3 \text{ eV}}$$

$$= 3.55 \times 10^{-11} \text{ m} = 35.5 \text{ pm}. \quad \text{(Answer)}$$

(b) Suppose that one of the incident electrons loses kinetic energy by small amounts until its energy is reduced from 35.0 keV to 20.0 keV. What is the associated wavelength λ of a photon that it would then generate if it lost all this remaining kinetic energy in a single head-on collision with an atom?

SOLUTION: We carry out the calculation as in (a), substituting 20.0 keV for 35.0 keV. The result is

$$\lambda_{min} = 62.1 \text{ pm}. \quad \text{(Answer)}$$

This wavelength is larger than the minimum wavelength calculated in (a) because less energy is involved.

The Characteristic X-Ray Spectrum

We now turn our attention to the two peaks of Fig. 41-14, labeled K_α and K_β. These peaks, together with other peaks that appear at wavelengths beyond the wavelength range displayed in Fig. 41-14, form the **characteristic x-ray spectrum** of the target material.

The peaks arise in a two-part process. (1) An energetic electron strikes an atom in the target and, while it is being scattered, the incident electron knocks out one of the atom's deep-lying (low n value) electrons. If the deep-lying electron is in the shell defined by $n = 1$ (called, for historical reasons, the K shell), there remains a vacancy, or *hole*, in this shell. (2) An electron in one of the shells located farther from the nucleus transfers to the K shell, filling the hole in this shell. During this transfer, the atom emits a characteristic x-ray photon. If the electron that fills the K-shell vacancy transfers from the shell with $n = 2$ (called the L shell), the emitted radiation is the K_α line of Fig. 41-14; if it transfers from the shell with $n = 3$ (called the M shell), it produces the K_β line, and so on. The hole left in either the L or M shell will be filled by an electron from still farther out in the atom.

In studying x rays, it is more convenient to keep track of the hole created deep in the atom's "electron cloud" rather than recording the changes in the quantum state of the electrons that transfer to fill that hole. Figure 41-16 does exactly that; it is an energy level diagram for molybdenum, the element to which Fig. 41-14 refers. The baseline ($E = 0$) represents the neutral atom in its ground state. The level marked K (at $E = 20$ keV) represents the energy of the molybdenum atom with a hole in its K shell. Similarly, the level marked L (at $E = 2.7$ keV) represents the atom with a hole in its L shell, and so on.

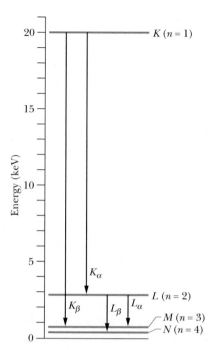

FIGURE 41-16 A simplified atomic energy level diagram for molybdenum, showing the transitions (of holes rather than electrons) that give rise to some of the characteristic x rays of that element. Each horizontal line represents the energy of the atom with a hole (a missing electron) in the shell indicated.

The transitions marked K_α and K_β in Fig. 41-16 are the ones that produce the two x-ray peaks in Fig. 41-14. The K_α spectral line, for example, originates when an electron from the L shell fills a hole in the K shell. This activity corresponds to a downward transition on the energy level diagram of Fig. 41-16 from the K level to the L level.

Numbering the Elements

In 1913 British physicist H. G. J. Moseley generated characteristic x rays for as many elements as he could find—he found 38—by using them as targets for electron bombardment in an evacuated tube of his own design. By means of a trolley manipulated by strings, Moseley was able to move the individual targets into the path of an electron beam. He measured the wavelengths of the x rays by the crystal diffraction method described in Section 37-9.

Moseley then sought (and found) regularities in these spectra as he moved from element to element in the periodic table. In particular, he noted that if, for a given spectral line such as K_α, he plotted for each element the square root of the line frequency f against the position of the element in the periodic table, a straight line resulted. Figure 47-17 shows a portion of his extensive data. Moseley's conclusion was:

We have here a proof that there is in the atom a fundamental quantity, which increases by regular steps as we pass from one element to the next. This quantity can only be the charge on the central nucleus.

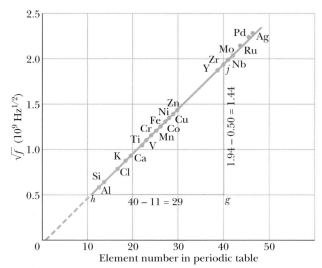

FIGURE 41-17 A Moseley plot of the K_α line of the characteristic x-ray spectra of 21 elements. The frequency is calculated from the measured wavelength. Measurements indicated along the *hgj* triangle are used in Sample Problem 41-6 to determine the slope of the straight-line plot.

Owing to Moseley's work, the characteristic x-ray spectrum became the universally accepted signature of an element, permitting the solution of a number of periodic table puzzles. Prior to that time (1913), the position of an element in the table was assigned in order of atomic *weight*, although there were several pairs of elements in which it was necessary to invert this order because of compelling chemical evidence; Moseley showed that it is the nuclear charge (that is, the atomic *number Z*) that is the real basis for numbering the elements.

In 1913 the periodic table had several empty squares, and a surprising number of claims for new elements had been advanced. The x-ray spectrum provided a conclusive test of such claims. The lanthanide elements, often called the rare earth elements, had been sorted out only imperfectly because of their similar chemical properties. Once Moseley's work was reported, these elements were properly organized in short order. In more recent times, the identities of elements beyond uranium are pinned down beyond dispute when the elements are available in quantities large enough to permit a study of their individual x-ray spectra.

It is not hard to see why the characteristic x-ray spectrum shows such impressive regularities from element to element while the optical spectrum in the visible and near-visible region does not: the key to the identity of an element is the charge on its nucleus. Gold, for example, is what it is because its atoms have a nuclear charge of $+79e$ (that is, $Z = 79$). An atom with one more elementary charge on its nucleus is mercury; one less is platinum. The

K electrons, which play such a large role in the production of the x-ray spectrum, lie very close to the nucleus and are thus sensitive probes of its charge. The optical spectrum, on the other hand, involves transitions of the outermost electrons, which are heavily screened from the nucleus by the remaining electrons of the atom and are thus *not* sensitive probes of nuclear charge.

Accounting for the Moseley Plot

Moseley's experimental data, of which the Moseley plot of Fig. 41-17 is but a part, can be used directly to assign the elements to their proper squares in the periodic table. This can be done even if no theoretical basis for Moseley's results can be established. However, there is such a basis.

According to Eq. 40-15 the energy of the hydrogen atom is

$$E_n = -\frac{me^4}{8\epsilon_0^2 h^2}\frac{1}{n^2} = -\frac{13.6 \text{ eV}}{n^2},$$
$$\text{for } n = 1, 2, 3, \cdots . \quad (41\text{-}16)$$

Consider now one of the two innermost electrons in the K shell of a multielectron atom. Because of the presence of the other K-shell electron, our electron "sees" an effective nuclear charge of approximately $(Z - 1)e$, where e is the elementary charge and Z is the atomic number of the element. The factor e^4 in Eq. 41–16 is the product of e^2—the square of hydrogen's nuclear charge—and $(-e)^2$—the square of an electron's charge. So for a multielectron atom, we can approximate the effective energy of the atom by replacing the factor e^4 in Eq. 41-16 with $(Z - 1)^2 e^2 \times (-e)^2$, or $e^4(Z - 1)^2$. We find

$$E_n = -\frac{(13.6 \text{ eV})(Z - 1)^2}{n^2}. \quad (41\text{-}17)$$

We saw that the K_α x-ray photon (of energy hf) arises when an electron makes a transition from the L shell (with $n = 2$ and energy E_2) to the K shell (with $n = 1$ and energy E_1). Thus, using Eq. 41-17, we may write the energy of the emitted photon as

$$hf = E_2 - E_1$$
$$= \frac{-(13.6 \text{ eV})(Z - 1)^2}{2^2} - \frac{-(13.6 \text{ eV})(Z - 1)^2}{1^2}$$
$$= (10.2 \text{ eV})(Z - 1)^2.$$

Then the frequency f of the K_α line is

$$f = \frac{hf}{h} = \frac{(10.2 \text{ eV})(Z - 1)^2}{(4.14 \times 10^{-15} \text{ eV} \cdot \text{s})}$$
$$= (2.46 \times 10^{15} \text{ Hz})(Z - 1)^2. \quad (41\text{-}18)$$

Taking the square root of both sides yields

$$\sqrt{f} = CZ - C, \qquad (41\text{-}19)$$

in which C is a constant. Equation 41-19 is the equation of a straight line. It shows that if we plot the square root of the frequency of the K_α x-ray spectral line against the atomic number Z, we should obtain a straight line. As Fig. 41-17 shows, that is exactly what Moseley found.

CHECKPOINT **3:** The K_α x rays arising from a cobalt ($Z = 27$) target have a wavelength of about 179 pm. Is the wavelength of the K_α x rays arising from a nickel ($Z = 28$) target greater than or less than 179 pm?

SAMPLE PROBLEM 41-5

A cobalt target is bombarded with electrons, and the wavelengths of its characteristic x-ray spectrum are measured. There is also a second, fainter characteristic spectrum, which is due to an impurity in the cobalt. The wavelengths of the K_α lines are 178.9 pm (cobalt) and 143.5 pm (impurity). What is the impurity?

SOLUTION: Let us apply Eq. 41-19 to both the cobalt (Co) and the impurity (X). Substituting c/λ for f, we obtain

$$\sqrt{\frac{c}{\lambda_{\text{Co}}}} = CZ_{\text{Co}} - C \quad \text{and} \quad \sqrt{\frac{c}{\lambda_{\text{X}}}} = CZ_{\text{X}} - C.$$

Dividing the second equation by the first yields

$$\sqrt{\frac{\lambda_{\text{Co}}}{\lambda_{\text{X}}}} = \frac{Z_{\text{X}} - 1}{Z_{\text{Co}} - 1}.$$

Substituting the given data, and $Z_{\text{Co}} = 27$, yields

$$\sqrt{\frac{178.9 \text{ pm}}{143.5 \text{ pm}}} = \frac{Z_{\text{X}} - 1}{27 - 1}.$$

Solving for the unknown, we find that

$$Z_{\text{X}} = 30.0. \qquad \text{(Answer)}$$

A glance at the periodic table identifies the impurity as zinc.

SAMPLE PROBLEM 41-6

(a) Evaluate the constant C in Eq. 41-19.

SOLUTION: Comparing Eq. 41-18 and Eq. 41-19 reveals that

$$C = \sqrt{2.46 \times 10^{15} \text{ Hz}} = 4.96 \times 10^{7} \text{ Hz}^{1/2}. \quad \text{(Answer)}$$

(b) Verify from the Moseley plot of Fig. 41-17 that C is the slope of the straight line in that figure.

SOLUTION: If we measure the lines hg and gj in Fig. 41-17, we find that

$$C = \frac{gj}{hg} = \frac{(1.94 - 0.50) \times 10^{9} \text{ Hz}^{1/2}}{40 - 11}$$

$$= 4.96 \times 10^{7} \text{ Hz}^{1/2}. \qquad \text{(Answer)}$$

These two results are in full agreement. The agreement is not nearly as good as for lines other than K_α in the x-ray spectrum; for them one must make more careful calculations of the effects of the surrounding electrons on the electron producing a line.

41-9 LASERS AND LASER LIGHT

In the late 1940s and again in the early 1960s, quantum mechanics made two enormous contributions to technology: the **transistor**, which ushered in the computer revolution, and the **laser**. Laser light, like the light from an ordinary lightbulb, is emitted when atoms make a transition from one quantum state to a quantum state of lower energy. In a laser, however—but not in other light sources—the atoms act together to produce light with special characteristics, some of which we now describe.

1. Laser light is highly monochromatic. Light from an ordinary incandescent lightbulb, being spread over a continuous range of wavelengths, cannot even be discussed in terms of monochromaticity. The spectral lines from a fluorescent neon sign *are* monochromatic, to about 1 part in about 10^6. However, the sharpness of definition of laser light can be many times greater, as much as 1 part in 10^{15}.

2. Laser light is highly coherent. Individual long waves (*wave trains*) for laser light can be several hundred kilometers long. When two separated beams that have traveled such distances over separate paths are recombined, they "remember" their common origin and are able to form a pattern of interference fringes. The corresponding *coherence length* for wave trains emitted by a lightbulb is typically less than a meter.

3. Laser light is highly directional. A laser beam spreads very little; it departs from strict parallelism only because of diffraction at the exit aperture of the laser. For example, a laser pulse used to measure the distance to the Moon generates a spot on the Moon's surface whose diameter is only one-millionth of the Moon's diameter. Light from an ordinary bulb can be made into an approximately parallel beam by a lens, but the beam divergence is much greater than for laser light. Each point on a lightbulb's filament forms its own separate beam, and the angular divergence of the overall composite beam is set by the size of the filament.

4. Laser light can be sharply focused. If two light beams transport the same amount of energy, the beam that can be focused to the smaller spot will have the greater intensity at that spot. For laser light, the focused spot can be so small that an intensity of 10^{17} W/cm^2 is readily obtained. An oxyacetylene flame, by contrast, has an intensity of only about 10^3 W/cm^2.

Lasers Have Many Uses

The smallest lasers, used for voice and data transmission over optical fibers, have as their active medium a semiconducting crystal about the size of a pinhead. Small as they are, such lasers can generate about 200 mW of power. The largest lasers, used for nuclear fusion research and for astronomical and military applications, fill a large building. The largest such laser can generate brief pulses of laser light with a power level, during the pulse, of about 10^{14} W. This is a few hundred times greater than the total electric power generating capacity of the United States. To avoid a brief national power blackout during a pulse, the energy required for each pulse is stored up at a steady rate during the relatively long interpulse interval.

Among the many uses of lasers are reading bar codes, manufacturing and reading compact disks, performing surgery of many kinds (see the opening photo of this chapter and Fig. 41-18), surveying, cutting cloth in the garment industry (several hundred layers at a time), welding auto bodies, and generating holograms.

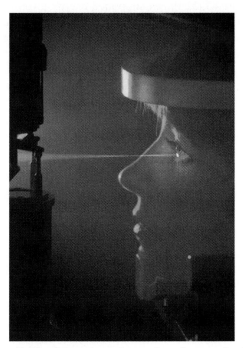

FIGURE 41-18 A laser beam is sent into the eye of a diabetes patient to seal blood vessels in her retina.

41-10 HOW LASERS WORK

The word "laser" is an acronym for "light amplification by the stimulated emission of radiation," so you should not be surprised that **stimulated emission** is the key to laser operation. Einstein introduced this concept in 1917. Although the world had to wait until 1960 to see an operating laser, the groundwork for its development was put in decades earlier.

Consider an isolated atom that can exist either in its state of lowest energy (its ground state), whose energy is E_0, or in a state of higher energy (an excited state), whose energy is E_x. Here are three processes by which the atom can move from one of these states to the other:

1. ***Absorption.*** Figure 41-19a shows the atom initially in its ground state. If the atom is placed in an electromagnetic field that is alternating at frequency f, the atom can absorb an amount of energy hf from that field and move to the higher energy state. From conservation of energy we have

$$hf = E_x - E_0. \qquad (41\text{-}20)$$

We call this process **absorption.**

2. ***Spontaneous emission.*** In Fig. 41-19b the atom is in its excited state and no external radiation is present. After a certain time, the atom will move *of its own accord* to

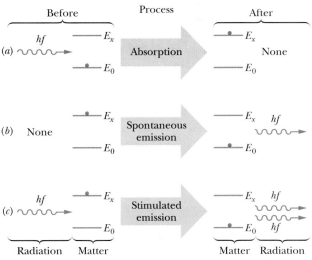

FIGURE 41-19 The interaction of radiation and matter in the processes of (a) absorption, (b) spontaneous emission, and (c) stimulated emission. An atom (matter) is represented by the red dot; the atom is in either a lower quantum state with energy E_0 or a higher quantum state with energy E_x. In (a) the atom absorbs a photon of energy hf from a passing light wave. In (b) it emits a light wave by emitting a photon of energy hf. In (c) a passing light wave with photon energy hf causes the atom to emit a photon of the same energy, increasing the energy of the light wave.

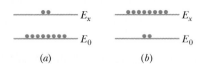

its ground state, emitting a photon of energy hf in the process. We call this process **spontaneous emission**—*spontaneous* because the event was not triggered by any outside influence. The light from the filament of an ordinary lightbulb is generated in this way.

Normally, the mean life of excited atoms before spontaneous emission occurs is about 10^{-8} s. However, for some excited states, this mean life is perhaps as much as 10^5 times longer. We call such long-lived states **metastable**; they play an important role in laser operation.

3. *Stimulated emission.* In Fig. 41-19c the atom is again in its excited state, but this time radiation with a frequency given by Eq. 41-20 is present. A photon of energy hf can stimulate the atom to move to its ground state, during which process the atom emits an additional photon, whose energy is also hf. We call this process **stimulated emission**—*stimulated* because the event is triggered by the external photon.

The emitted photon in Fig. 41-19c is in every way identical to the stimulating photon. Thus the waves associated with the photons have the same energy, phase, polarization, and direction of travel. Under proper conditions, a chain reaction of similar stimulated emission processes can be triggered by a single initial photon of the correct frequency. Laser light is generated in this way.

Note, parenthetically, that the photons associated with a beam of laser light are all in the same quantum state. Photons, unlike electrons in atoms, do *not* obey the Pauli exclusion principle. Photons ''like'' to pile up in the same quantum state; electrons are forbidden to do so.

Figure 41-19c describes stimulated emission for a single atom. Suppose now that a sample contains a large number of atoms in thermal equilibrium at temperature T. Before any radiation is directed at the sample, a number N_0 of these atoms are in their ground state with energy E_0, and a number N_x are in a state of higher energy E_x. Ludwig Boltzmann showed that N_x is given in terms of N_0 by

$$N_x = N_0 \, e^{-(E_x - E_0)/kT}, \qquad (41\text{-}21)$$

in which k is Boltzmann's constant. This equation seems reasonable. The quantity kT is the mean kinetic energy of an atom at temperature T. The higher the temperature, the more atoms—on average—will have been ''bumped up'' by thermal agitation (that is, by atom–atom collisions) to the higher energy state E_x. Also, because $E_x > E_0$, Eq. 41-21 requires that $N_x < N_0$. That is, there will always be fewer atoms in the excited state than in the ground state. This is what we would expect if the level populations are determined only by the action of thermal agitation. Figure 41-20a illustrates this situation.

If we now flood the atoms of Fig. 41-20a with photons

FIGURE 41-20 (a) The equilibrium distribution of atoms between the ground state E_0 and excited state E_x, accounted for by thermal agitation. (b) An inverted population, obtained by special methods. Such an inverted population is essential for laser action.

of energy $E_x - E_0$, photons will disappear via absorption by ground-state atoms, and photons will be generated largely via stimulated emission of excited-state atoms. Einstein showed that the probabilities per atom for these two processes are identical. Thus, because there are more atoms in the ground state, the *net* effect will be the absorption of photons.

To produce laser light, we must have more photons emitted than absorbed. That is, we must have a situation in which stimulated emission dominates. The direct way to bring this about is to start with more atoms in the excited state than in the ground state, as in Fig. 41-20b. Since, however, such a **population inversion** is not consistent with thermal equilibrium, we must think up clever ways to set up and maintain one.

The Helium–Neon Gas Laser

Figure 41-21 shows a type of laser commonly found in student laboratories. It was developed in 1961 by Ali Javan and his coworkers. The glass discharge tube is filled with a $20:80$ mixture of helium and neon gases, neon being the medium in which laser action occurs.

Figure 41-22 shows simplified energy level diagrams for the two atoms. An electric current passed through the helium–neon gas mixture serves—through collisions between helium atoms and electrons of the current—to raise many helium atoms to state E_3, which is metastable.

The energy of helium state E_3 (20.61 eV) is very close to the energy of neon state E_2 (20.66 eV). Thus when a metastable (E_3) helium atom and a ground-state (E_0) neon atom collide, the excitation energy of the helium atom is

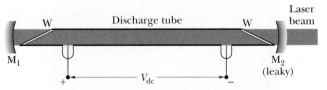

FIGURE 41-21 The elements of a helium–neon gas laser. An applied potential V_{dc} sends electrons through a discharge tube containing a mixture of helium gas and neon gas. Electrons collide with helium atoms, which then collide with neon atoms, which emit light along the length of the tube. The light passes through transparent windows W and reflects back and forth through the tube from mirrors M_1 and M_2 to cause more neon atom emissions. Some of the light leaks through mirror M_2 to form the laser beam.

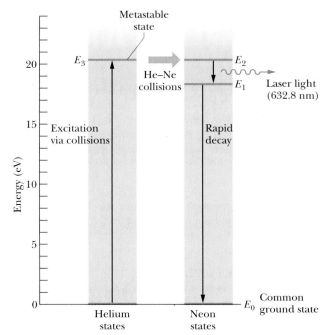

FIGURE 41-22 Four essential energy levels for helium and neon atoms in a helium–neon gas laser. Laser action occurs between levels E_2 and E_1 of neon when more atoms are in the E_2 level than in the E_1 level.

often transferred to the neon atom, which then moves to state E_2. In this way, neon level E_2 in Fig. 41-22 can become more heavily populated than neon level E_1.

This population inversion is relatively easy to set up and maintain because (1) initially there are essentially no neon atoms in state E_1, (2) the metastability of helium level E_3 ensures a ready supply of neon atoms in level E_2, and (3) atoms in level E_1 decay rapidly (through intermediate levels not shown) to the neon ground state E_0.

Suppose now that a single photon is spontaneously emitted as a neon atom transfers from state E_2 to state E_1. Such a photon can trigger a stimulated emission event which, in turn, can trigger other stimulated emission events. Through such a chain reaction, a coherent beam of red laser light, moving parallel to the tube axis, can build up rapidly. This light, of wavelength 632.8 nm, can move back and forth through the discharge tube many times by successive reflections from mirrors M_1 and M_2 (Fig. 41-21), accumulating additional stimulated emission photons with each passage.

Mirror M_1 is coated with an almost totally reflecting film. Mirror M_2, on the other hand, is coated so as to be slightly ''leaky,'' permitting a small fraction of the laser light to escape at each reflection and form a useful external beam of laser light.

CHECKPOINT **4:** The wavelength of light from laser A (a helium–neon gas laser) is 632.8 nm; that from laser

B (a carbon dioxide gas laser) is 10.6 μm. That from laser C (a gallium arsenide semiconductor laser) is 840 nm. Rank these lasers according to the energy interval between the two quantum states responsible for laser action, greatest first.

SAMPLE PROBLEM 41-7

In the helium–neon laser of Fig. 41-21, laser action occurs between two excited states of the neon atom. However, in many lasers, laser action (*lasing*) occurs between the ground state and an excited state, as suggested in Fig. 41-20.

(a) Consider such a laser that emits at a wavelength $\lambda = 550$ nm. If a population inversion had not been generated, what is the ratio of the population of atoms in state E_x to that in the ground state E_0?

SOLUTION: From Eq. 41-21, the ratio is

$$N_x/N_0 = e^{-(E_x - E_0)/kT}. \qquad (41\text{-}22)$$

The separation between the two energy levels must be

$$E_x - E_0 = hf = \frac{hc}{\lambda}$$

$$= \frac{(6.63 \times 10^{-34}\ \text{J·s})(3.00 \times 10^8\ \text{m/s})}{(550 \times 10^{-9}\ \text{m})(1.60 \times 10^{-19}\ \text{J/eV})}$$

$$= 2.26\ \text{eV}.$$

The mean energy of thermal agitation kT for an atom at room temperature (300 K) is

$$kT = (8.62 \times 10^{-5}\ \text{eV/K})\ (300\ \text{K}) = 0.0259\ \text{eV}.$$

Substituting the last two results into Eq. 41-22 yields

$$N_x/N_0 = e^{-(2.26\ \text{eV})/0.0259\ \text{eV}}$$

$$= e^{-87.26} \approx 1.3 \times 10^{-38}. \qquad (\text{Answer})$$

This is an extremely small number. It is not unreasonable, however. An atom whose mean thermal agitation energy is only 0.0259 eV will not often impart an energy of 2.26 eV to another atom in a collision.

(b) For the conditions of (a), at what temperature would the ratio N_x/N_0 be 1/2?

SOLUTION: Making this substitution into Eq. 41-22, taking the natural logarithm of both sides, and solving for T yield

$$T = \frac{E_x - E_0}{k(\ln 2)} = \frac{2.26\ \text{eV}}{(8.62 \times 10^{-5}\ \text{eV/K})\ (\ln 2)}$$

$$= 38,000\ \text{K}. \qquad (\text{Answer})$$

This is much hotter than the surface of the Sun. It is clear that if we are to invert the populations of these two levels, some specific mechanism for bringing this about is needed. No temperature, however high, will generate a population inversion.

REVIEW & SUMMARY

Some Properties of Atoms

The energies of atoms are quantized; that is, the atoms have only certain specific values of energy associated with different quantum states. Atoms can make transitions between different quantum states by emitting or absorbing a photon; the frequency f associated with that light is given by the *Bohr frequency condition*:

$$hf = E_{high} - E_{low}, \qquad (41\text{-}1)$$

where E_{high} is the higher energy and E_{low} is the lower energy of the pair of quantum states involved in the transition. Atoms also have quantized angular momenta and magnetic dipole moments.

Angular Momenta and Magnetic Dipole Moments

An electron trapped in an atom has an *orbital angular momentum* **L** and an associated *orbital magnetic dipole moment* $\boldsymbol{\mu}_{orb}$, which are always in opposite directions. The magnitude of **L** is given by

$$L = \sqrt{l(l + 1)}\hbar, \qquad (41\text{-}2)$$

where l is the *angular momentum quantum number* (which can have the values given by Table 41-1) and $\hbar = h/2\pi$. The projection L_z of **L** on an arbitrary z axis is quantized and measurable and can have the values

$$L_z = m_l \hbar, \qquad (41\text{-}5)$$

where m_l is the *orbital magnetic quantum number* (which can have the values given by Table 41-1).

The projection $\mu_{orb,z}$ of the orbital magnetic dipole moment on the z axis is quantized and measurable and can have the values

$$\mu_{orb,z} = -m_l \mu_B, \qquad (41\text{-}3)$$

where m_l is the *orbital magnetic quantum number* and μ_B is the *Bohr magneton*:

$$\mu_B = \frac{eh}{4\pi m} = 9.274 \times 10^{-24} \text{ J/T}. \qquad (41\text{-}4)$$

An electron, whether trapped or free, has an intrinsic *spin angular momentum* (or just *spin*) **S** and an intrinsic *spin magnetic dipole moment* $\boldsymbol{\mu}_s$, which are always in opposite directions. The magnitude of **S** is given by

$$S = \sqrt{s(s + 1)}\,\hbar, \qquad (41\text{-}6)$$

where s is the *spin quantum number* of the electron, which is always $\frac{1}{2}$. The projection S_z of **S** on an arbitrary z axis is quantized and measurable and can have the values

$$S_z = m_s \hbar, \qquad (41\text{-}7)$$

where m_s is the *spin magnetic quantum number* of the electron, which can be $+\frac{1}{2}$ or $-\frac{1}{2}$. The projection $\mu_{s,z}$ of the spin magnetic dipole moment $\boldsymbol{\mu}_s$ on the arbitrary z axis is quantized and measurable and can have the values

$$\mu_{s,z} = -2m_s \mu_B. \qquad (41\text{-}8)$$

Spin and Magnetic Resonance

A proton has an intrinsic spin angular momentum **S** and an associated spin magnetic dipole moment $\boldsymbol{\mu}$ that is always in the *same*

direction as **S**. If a proton is located in an external magnetic field **B**, the projection μ_z of $\boldsymbol{\mu}$ on an axis z (defined to be along the direction of **B**) can have only two quantized orientations: parallel to **B** or antiparallel to **B**. The associated energy difference between these orientations is $2\mu_z B$. The energy required of a photon to *spin-flip* the proton between the two orientations is

$$hf = 2\mu_z(B_{ext} + B_{local}), \qquad (41\text{-}14)$$

where B_{ext} now represents the external field and B_{local} is the local magnetic field set up by the atoms and nuclei surrounding the proton. Detection of such spin flips can lead to *nuclear magnetic resonance spectra* by which specific substances can be identified.

Building the Periodic Table

Electrons in atoms obey the **Pauli exclusion principle**, which states that *no two electrons in the same atom can have the same set of the quantum numbers* n, l, m_l, and m_s. The elements are listed in the periodic table in order of increasing atomic number Z; the nuclear charge is Ze, and Z is both the number of protons in the nucleus and the number of electrons in the neutral atom.

States with the same value of n form a **shell**, and those with the same values of both n and l form a **subshell**. In *closed* shells and subshells, which are those that contain the maximum number of electrons, the angular momenta and the magnetic moments of the individual electrons add to zero.

X Rays and the Numbering of the Elements

A **continuous spectrum** of x rays arises when high-energy electrons lose some of their energy in a collision with an atomic nucleus. The **cutoff wavelength** λ_{min} results when such electrons lose *all* their initial energy in a single such encounter and is given by

$$\lambda_{min} = \frac{hc}{K_0}, \qquad (41\text{-}15)$$

in which K_0 is the initial kinetic energy of the electrons that strike the target.

Characteristic x rays arise when high-energy electrons eject electrons from deep within the atom; when the resulting "hole" is filled by an electron from farther out in the atom, a photon of the characteristic x-ray spectrum is generated.

In 1913 the British physicist H. G. J. Moseley measured the frequencies of the characteristic x rays from a number of elements. He noted that when the square root of the frequency is plotted against the position of the element in the periodic table, a straight line results, as in the **Moseley plot** of Fig. 41-17. This allowed Moseley to conclude that the property of the atom that determines the position of an element in the periodic table is not its atomic mass but its **atomic number** Z, that is, the number of protons in its nucleus.

Lasers and Laser Light

Laser light arises by **stimulated emission**. That is, when radiation of frequency given by

$$hf = E_x - E_0 \qquad (41\text{-}20)$$

is present, a transition from an upper energy level to a lower energy level of an atom can occur, a photon of frequency f being emitted. The stimulating photon and the emitted photon are identical in every respect and combine to form laser light.

For the emission process to predominate, there must normally be a **population inversion**; that is, there must be more atoms in the upper energy level than in the lower.

QUESTIONS

1. An electron in an atom of gold is in a state with $n = 4$. Which of these values of l are possible for it: $-3, 0, 2, 3, 4, 5$?

2. An atom of silver has closed $3d$ and $4d$ subshells. Which subshell has the greater number of electrons, or do they have the same number?

3. An atom of uranium has closed $6p$ and $7s$ subshells. Which subshell has the greater number of electrons?

4. An electron in a mercury atom is in the $3d$ subshell. Which values of m_l are possible for it: $-3, -1, 0, 1, 2$?

5. (a) How many subshells are there in the $n = 2$ shell? How many electron states? (b) Repeat (a) for the $n = 5$ shell.

6. From which atom of each of the following pairs is it easier to remove an electron? (a) Krypton or bromine? (b) Rubidium or cerium? (c) Helium or hydrogen?

7. On what quantum numbers does the energy of an electron depend in (a) a hydrogen atom and (b) a vanadium atom?

8. Label these statements as true or false: (a) One (and only one) of these subshells cannot exist: $2p, 4f, 3d, 1p$. (b) The number of values of m_l that are allowed depends only on l and not on n. (c) There are four subshells with $n = 4$. (d) The least value of n that can be associated with a given value of l is $l + 1$. (e) All states with $l = 0$ also have $m_l = 0$. (f) There are n subshells for each value of n.

9. Which (if any) of these statements about the Einstein–de Haas experiment or its results are true? (a) Atoms have angular momentum. (b) The angular momentum of atoms is quantized. (c) Atoms have magnetic moments. (d) The magnetic moments of atoms are quantized. (e) The angular momentum of an atom is strongly coupled to its magnetic moment. (f) The experiment relies on the conservation of angular momentum.

10. Consider the elements krypton and rubidium. (a) Which is more suitable for use in a Stern–Gerlach experiment of the kind described in connection with Fig. 41-8? (b) Which, if either, would not work at all?

11. The x-ray spectrum of Fig. 41-14 is for 35.0 keV electrons striking a molybdenum ($Z = 42$) target. If you substitute a silver ($Z = 47$) target for the molybdenum target, will (a) $\lambda_{\min}$, (b) the wavelength for the K_α line, (c) the wavelength for the K_β line increase, decrease, or remain unchanged?

12. The K_α x-ray line for any element arises because of a transition between the K shell ($n = 1$) and the L shell ($n = 2$). Figure 41-14 shows this line (for a molybdenum target) occurring at a single wavelength. With higher resolution, however, the line splits into several wavelength components because the L shell does not have a unique energy. (a) How many components does the K_α line have? (b) Similarly, how many components does the K_β line have?

13. Which (if any) of the following is essential for laser action to occur between two energy levels of an atom? (a) There are more atoms in the upper level than in the lower. (b) The upper level is metastable. (c) The lower level is metastable. (d) The lower level is the ground state of the atom. (e) The lasing medium is a gas.

14. Figure 41-22 shows partial energy level diagrams for the helium and neon atoms that are involved in the operation of a helium–neon laser. It is said that a helium atom in state E_3 can collide with a neon atom in its ground state and raise the neon atom to state E_2. The energy of helium state E_3 (20.61 eV) is close to, but not exactly equal to, the energy of neon state E_2 (20.66 eV). How can the energy transfer take place if these energies are not *exactly* equal?

EXERCISES & PROBLEMS

SECTION 41-4 Angular Momenta and Magnetic Dipole Moments

1E. Show that $\hbar = 1.06 \times 10^{-34}$ J·s $= 6.59 \times 10^{-16}$ eV·s.

2E. How many electron states are there in the following subshells: (a) $n = 4$, $l = 3$; (b) $n = 3$, $l = 1$; (c) $n = 4$, $l = 1$; (d) $n = 2$, $l = 0$?

3E. How many electron states are there in the following shells: (a) $n = 4$, (b) $n = 1$, (c) $n = 3$, (d) $n = 2$?

4E. (a) What is the magnitude of the orbital angular momentum in a state with $l = 3$? (b) What is the magnitude of its largest projection on an imposed z axis?

5E. (a) What number of possible l values are associated with $n = 3$? (b) What number of possible m_l values are associated with $l = 1$?

6E. An electron in a hydrogen atom is in a state with $l = 5$. What is the minimum possible angle between **L** and L_z?

7E. Write down all the quantum numbers for states that form the subshell with $n = 4$ and $l = 3$.

8E. An electron in a multielectron atom is known to have the quantum number $l = 3$. What are the possible n, m_l, and m_s quantum numbers?

9E. An electron in a multielectron atom has a maximum m_l value of $+4$. What can you say about the rest of its quantum numbers?

10E. How many electron states are there in a shell defined by the quantum number $n = 5$?

11E. An electron is in a state with $n = 3$. What are (a) the number of possible values of l, (b) the number of possible values of m_l, (c) the number of possible values of m_s, (d) the number of states in the $n = 3$ shell, and (e) the number of subshells in the $n = 3$ shell?

12P. An electron is in a state with $l = 3$. Calculate and tabulate the allowed values of L_z, μ_z, and θ, where θ is the angle made by the corresponding vector with the positive direction of the z axis. Find also the magnitudes of $\mathbf{L}$ and $\boldsymbol{\mu}$.

13P. (A correspondence principle problem.) Estimate (a) the quantum number l for the orbital motion of Earth around the Sun and (b) the number of allowed orientations of the plane of Earth's orbit, according to the rules of space quantization. (c) Find θ_{min}, the half-angle of the smallest cone that can be swept out by a perpendicular to Earth's orbit as Earth revolves around the Sun.

14P. If $\mathbf{L}$ is measured along, say, the z axis to give a value for L_z, show that the most that can be said about the other two components of $\mathbf{L}$ is

$$(L_x^2 + L_y^2)^{1/2} = [l(l + 1) - m_l^2]^{1/2}\,\hbar.$$

SECTION 41-5 The Stern–Gerlach Experiment

15E. Calculate the two possible angles between the electron spin angular momentum vector and the magnetic field in Sample Problem 41-1. Bear in mind that the orbital angular momentum of the valence electron in the silver atom is zero.

16E. What is the acceleration of the silver atom as it passes through the deflecting magnet in the Stern–Gerlach experiment of Sample Problem 41-1?

17E. Assume that in the Stern–Gerlach experiment described for neutral silver atoms, the magnetic field $\mathbf{B}$ has a magnitude of 0.50 T. (a) What is the energy difference between the orientations of the silver atoms in the two subbeams? (b) What is the frequency of the radiation that would induce a transition between these two states? (c) What is its wavelength, and to what part of the electromagnetic spectrum does it belong? The magnetic moment of a neutral silver atom is 1 Bohr magneton.

18P. Suppose that a hydrogen atom in its ground state moves 80 cm through and perpendicular to a vertical magnetic field that has a magnetic field gradient, dB/dz of 1.6×10^2 T/m. (a) What magnitude of force does the field gradient exert on the atom due to the magnetic moment of its electron, which we take to be 1 Bohr magneton? (b) What is the vertical displacement of the atom in the 80 cm of travel if its speed is 1.2×10^5 m/s?

SECTION 41-6 Magnetic Resonance

19E. What is the wavelength of a photon that will induce a transition of an electron spin from parallel to antiparallel orientation in a magnetic field of magnitude 0.200 T? Assume that $l = 0$.

20E. The proton, like the electron, has a spin quantum number s of $\frac{1}{2}$. In the hydrogen atom in its ground state ($n = 1$ and $l = 0$), there are two energy levels, depending on whether the electron and proton spins are parallel or antiparallel. If an atom has a spin flip from the state of higher energy to that of lower energy, a photon of wavelength 21 cm is emitted. Radio astronomers observe this 21 cm radiation coming from deep space. What is the effective magnetic field (due to the magnetic dipole moment of the proton) experienced by the electron emitting this radiation?

21E. An external oscillating magnetic field of frequency 34 MHz is applied to a sample that contains hydrogen atoms. Resonance is observed when the strength of the constant external magnetic field equals 0.78 T. Calculate the strength of the local magnetic field at the site of the protons that are undergoing spin flips, assuming the external and local fields are parallel there.

22E. Excited sodium atoms emit two closely spaced spectrum lines (the sodium doublet; see Fig. 41-23) with wavelengths 588.995 and 589.592 nm. (a) What is the difference in energy between the two upper energy levels? (b) This energy difference occurs because the electron's spin magnetic moment ($= 1$ Bohr magneton) can be oriented either parallel or antiparallel to the internal magnetic field associated with the electron's orbital motion. Use your result in (a) to find the strength of this internal magnetic field.

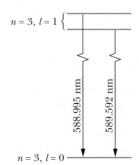

FIGURE 41-23
Exercise 22.

SECTION 41-7 Building the Periodic Table

23P. Show that if the 63 electrons in an atom of europium were assigned to shells according to the "logical" sequence of quantum numbers, this element would have chemical properties similar to those of sodium.

24P. Consider the elements selenium ($Z = 34$), bromine ($Z = 35$), and krypton ($Z = 36$). In their part of the periodic table, the subshells of the electronic states are filled in the sequence

$$1s \quad 2s \quad 2p \quad 3s \quad 3p \quad 3d \quad 4s \quad 4p \cdots$$

For each element, identify the highest occupied subshell and state how many electrons are in it.

25P. Suppose that the electron had no spin and that the Pauli exclusion principle still held. Which, if any, of the present noble gases would remain in that category?

26P. What are the four quantum numbers for the two electrons of the helium atom in its ground state?

27P. Two electrons in lithium ($Z = 3$) have for their quantum numbers $n = 1$, $l = 0$, $m_l = 0$, and $m_s = \pm\frac{1}{2}$. What quantum numbers can the third electron have if the atom is to be in (a) its ground state and (b) its first excited state?

28P. Suppose there are two electrons in the same atom, both of which have $n = 2$ and $l = 1$. (a) If the exclusion principle did not apply, how many combinations of states would conceivably be possible? (b) How many states does the exclusion principle forbid? Which are they?

29P. Show that the number of states with the same quantum number n is given by $2n^2$.

SECTION 41-8 X Rays and the Numbering of the Elements

30E. Show that the cutoff wavelength (in picometers) in the continuous x-ray spectrum from any target is given by $\lambda_{min} = 1240/V$, where V is the potential difference (in kilovolts) through which the electrons are accelerated before they strike the target.

31E. Knowing that the minimum x-ray wavelength produced by 40.0 keV electrons striking a target is 31.1 pm, determine the Planck constant h.

32E. What is the minimum potential difference across an x-ray tube that will produce x rays with a wavelength of 0.100 nm?

33P. A 20 keV electron is brought to rest by undergoing two successive nuclear encounters such as that of Fig. 41-15, thus transferring its kinetic energy to the energy of two photons. The wavelength associated with the second photon is 130 pm greater than the wavelength of the first photon. (a) Find the kinetic energy of the electron after its first encounter. (b) What are the associated wavelengths and energies of the two photons?

34P. X rays are produced in an x-ray tube by a target potential of 50.0 kV. An electron makes three collisions in the target before coming to rest and loses half its remaining kinetic energy in each of the first two collisions. Determine the wavelengths of the resulting photons. (Neglect the recoil of the heavy target atoms.)

35P. Show that a moving electron cannot spontaneously change into an x-ray photon in free space. A third body (atom or nucleus) must be present. Why is it needed? (*Hint:* Examine the conservation of energy and momentum.)

36E. When electrons bombard a molybdenum target, they produce both continuous and characteristic x rays as shown in Fig. 41-14. In that figure the kinetic energy of the incident electrons is 35.0 keV. If the accelerating potential is increased to 50.0 keV, what mean values of (a) λ_{min}, (b) the wavelength of the K_α line, and (c) the wavelength of the K_β line result?

37E. In Fig. 41-14, the x rays shown are produced when 35.0 keV electrons strike a molybdenum ($Z = 42$) target. If the accelerating potential is maintained at this value but a silver ($Z = 47$)

target is used instead, what values of (a) λ_{min}, (b) the wavelength of the K_α, and (c) the wavelength of the K_β line result? The K, L, and M atomic x-ray levels for silver (compare Fig. 41-16) are 25.51, 3.56, and 0.53 keV.

38E. The wavelength of the K_α line from iron is 193 pm. What is the energy difference between the two states of the iron atom that give rise to this transition?

39P. From Fig. 41-14, calculate approximately the energy difference $E_L - E_M$ for molybdenum. Compare it with the value that may be obtained from Fig. 41-16.

40E. Calculate the ratio of the wavelength of the K_α line for niobium (Nb) to that for gallium (Ga). Take needed data from the periodic table of Appendix G.

41P. Here are the K_α wavelengths (pm) of a few elements:

Ti	275	Co	179
V	250	Ni	166
Cr	229	Cu	154
Mn	210	Zn	143
Fe	193	Ga	134

Make a Moseley plot (like that in Fig. 41-17) from these data and verify that its slope agrees with the value calculated in Sample Problem 41-6.

42P. A tungsten ($Z = 74$) target is bombarded by electrons in an x-ray tube. (a) What is the minimum value of the accelerating potential that will permit the production of the characteristic K_α and K_β lines of tungsten? (b) For this same accelerating potential, what is λ_{min}? (c) What are the K_α and K_β wavelengths? The K, L, and M energy levels for tungsten (see Fig. 41-16) have energies 69.5, 11.3, and 2.30 keV, respectively.

43P. A molybdenum ($Z = 42$) target is bombarded with 35.0 keV electrons and the x-ray spectrum of Fig. 41-14 results. Here the K_β and the K_α wavelengths are 63.0 and 71.0 pm, respectively. (a) What are the corresponding photon energies? (b) It is desired to filter these radiations through a material that will absorb the K_β line much more strongly than it will absorb the K_α line. What substance would you use? The K ionization energies for molybdenum and for four neighboring elements are:

	Zr	Nb	Mo	Tc	Ru
Z	40	41	42	43	44
E_K (keV)	18.00	18.99	20.00	21.04	22.12

(*Hint:* A substance will absorb one x radiation more strongly than another if the photons of the first have enough energy to eject a K electron from the atom of the substance but the photons of the second do not.)

44P. The binding energies of K-shell and L-shell electrons in copper are 8.979 and 0.951 keV, respectively. If a K_α x ray from copper is incident on a sodium chloride crystal and gives a first-order Bragg reflection at an angle of 74.1° measured relative to parallel planes of sodium atoms, what is the spacing between these parallel planes?

45P. (a) Using Eq. 41-18, estimate the ratios of photon energies due to K_α transitions in two atoms whose atomic numbers are Z and Z'. (b) What is this ratio for uranium and aluminum? (c) For uranium and lithium?

46P. Determine how close the theoretical K_α x-ray photon energies, as obtained from Eq. 41-19, are to the measured energies of the low-mass elements from lithium to magnesium. To do this, (a) first determine the constant C in Eq. 41-19 to five significant figures by finding C in terms of the fundamental constants in Eq. 41-16 and then using data from Appendix B to evaluate those constants. (b) Next, calculate the percentage deviations of the theoretical from the measured energies. (c) Finally, plot the deviations and comment on the trend. The measured energies (eV) of the K_α photons for these elements are

Li	54.3	O	524.9
Be	108.5	F	676.8
B	183.3	Ne	848.6
C	277	Na	1041
N	392.4	Mg	1254

(There is actually more than one K_α ray because of the splitting of the L energy level, but that effect is negligible for the elements listed here.)

SECTION 41-9   Lasers and Laser Light

47E. Lasers can be used to generate pulses of light whose durations are as short as 10 fs. (a) How many wavelengths of light ($\lambda = 500$ nm) are contained in such a pulse? (b) Supply the missing quantity (in years):

$$\frac{10 \text{ fs}}{1 \text{ s}} = \frac{1 \text{ s}}{X}.$$

48E. For the conditions of Sample Problem 41-7, how many moles of lasing material are needed to put 10 atoms in the excited state E_x?

49E. By measuring the go-and-return time for a laser pulse to travel from an Earth-bound observatory to a reflector on the Moon, it is possible to measure the separation between these bodies. (a) What is the predicted value of this time? (b) The separation can be measured to a precision of about 15 cm. To what uncertainty in travel time does this correspond? (c) The laser beam forms a spot on the Moon 3 km in diameter. What is the angular divergence of the beam?

50E. A hypothetical atom has energy levels evenly separated by 1.2 eV. For a temperature of 2000 K, what is the ratio of the number of atoms in the 13th excited state to the number in the 11th excited state?

51E. A hypothetical atom has only two atomic energy levels, separated by 3.2 eV. In the atmosphere of a star there are $6.1 \times 10^{13}/\text{cm}^3$ of these atoms in the higher energy state and $2.5 \times 10^{15}/\text{cm}^3$ in the lower energy state. What is the temperature of the star's atmosphere?

52E. A population inversion for two energy levels is often de-

scribed by assigning a negative Kelvin temperature to the system. What negative temperature would describe a system in which the population of the upper energy level exceeds that of the lower level by 10% and the energy difference between the two levels is 2.1 eV?

53E. A helium–neon laser emits laser light at a wavelength of 632.8 nm and a power of 2.3 mW. At what rate are photons emitted by this device?

54E. A pulsed laser emits light at a wavelength of 694.4 nm. The pulse duration is 12 ps and the energy per pulse is 0.150 J. (a) What is the length of the pulse? (b) How many photons are emitted in each pulse?

55E. The active volume of a laser constructed of the semiconductor GaAlAs is only 200 μm^3 (smaller than a grain of sand) and yet the laser can continuously deliver 5.0 mW of power at a wavelength of 0.80 μm. At what rate does it generate photons?

56E. Assume that lasers are available whose wavelengths can be precisely "tuned" to anywhere in the visible range, that is, in the range 450 nm $< \lambda <$ 650 nm. If every television channel occupies a bandwidth of 10 MHz, how many channels could be accommodated within this wavelength range?

57E. A high-powered laser beam ($\lambda = 600$ nm) with a beam diameter of 12 cm is aimed at the Moon, 3.8×10^5 km distant. The beam spreads only because of diffraction. The angular location of the edge of the central diffraction disk (see Eq. 37-12) is given by

$$\sin \theta = \frac{1.22\lambda}{d},$$

where d is the diameter of the beam aperture. What is the diameter of the central diffraction disk on the Moon's surface?

58P. The active medium in a particular laser that generates laser light at a wavelength of 694 nm is 6.00 cm long and 1.00 cm in diameter. (a) Treat the medium as an optical resonance cavity analogous to a closed organ pipe. How many standing wave nodes are there along the laser axis? (b) By what amount Δf would the beam frequency have to shift to increase this number by one? (c) Show that Δf is just the inverse of the travel time of laser light for one round trip back and forth along the laser axis. (d) What is the corresponding fractional frequency shift $\Delta f/f$? The appropriate index of refraction of the lasing medium (a ruby crystal) is 1.75.

59P. The mirrors in the laser of Fig. 41-21, which are separated by 8.0 cm, form an optical cavity in which standing waves of laser light can be set up. In the vicinity of $\lambda = 533$ nm, how far apart in wavelength are the adjacent allowed operating modes?

60P. A hypothetical atom has two energy levels, with a transition wavelength between them of 580 nm. In a particular sample at 300 K, 4.0×10^{20} such atoms are in the state of lower energy. (a) How many atoms are in the upper state, assuming conditions of thermal equilibrium? (b) Suppose, instead, that 3.0×10^{20} of these atoms are "pumped" into the upper state by an external process, with 1.0×10^{20} atoms remaining in the lower state. What is the maximum energy that could be released by the atoms in a single laser pulse if each is affected once?

61P. The beam from an argon laser (of wavelength 515 nm) has a diameter d of 3.00 mm and a continuous wave power output of 5.00 W. The beam is focused onto a diffuse surface by a lens whose focal length f is 3.50 cm. A diffraction pattern such as that of Fig. 37-9 is formed, the radius of the central disk being given by

$$R = \frac{1.22 f \lambda}{d}$$

(see Eq. 37-12 and Sample Problem 37-3). The central disk can be shown to contain 84% of the incident power. (a) What is the radius of the central disk? (b) What is the average power flux density in the incident beam? (c) What is the average power flux density in the central disk?

62P. Can an incoming intercontinental ballistic missile be destroyed by an intense laser beam? A beam of intensity 10^8 W/m^2 would probably burn into and destroy a hardened (nonspinning) missile in 1 s. (a) If the laser had 5.0 MW power, 3.0 μm wavelength, and a 4.0 m beam diameter (a very powerful laser indeed), would it destroy a missile at a distance of 3000 km? (b) If the wavelength could be changed, what maximum value would work? Use the equation for the central disk given in Exercise 57, and take the focal length to be the distance to the target.

Additional Problems

63. *Martian* CO_2 *laser.* Where sunlight shines on the atmosphere of Mars, carbon dioxide molecules at an altitude of about 75 km undergo naturally occurring laser action. The energy levels involved in the action are shown in Fig. 41-24; population inversion occurs between energy levels E_2 and E_1. (a) What wavelength of sunlight excites the molecules in the lasing action? (b) At what wavelength does lasing occur? (c) In what region of the electromagnetic spectrum do the excitation and lasing wavelengths lie?

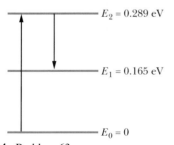

FIGURE 41-24   Problem 63.

64. *Comet stimulated emission.* When a comet approaches the Sun, the increased warmth evaporates water from the frozen ice on the surface of the comet nucleus, producing a thin atmosphere of water vapor around the nucleus. Sunlight can then dissociate the water vapor into H and OH. The sunlight can also excite the OH molecules into higher energy levels, two of which are represented in Fig. 41-25.

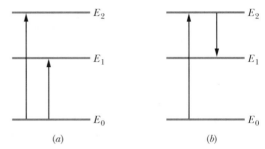

FIGURE 41-25   Problem 64.

When the comet is still relatively far from the Sun, the sunlight causes equal excitation to the E_2 and E_1 levels (Fig. 41-25a). Hence, there is no population inversion between the two levels. However, as the comet approaches the Sun, the excitation to the E_1 level decreases and population inversion occurs. The reason has to do with one of the many wavelengths—said to be *Fraunhofer lines*—that are missing in sunlight because, as the light travels outward through the Sun's atmosphere, those particular wavelengths are absorbed by the atmosphere.

As a comet approaches the Sun, the Doppler effect due to the comet's speed relative to the Sun shifts the Fraunhofer lines in wavelength, apparently overlapping one of them with the wavelength required for the excitation to the E_1 level in the OH molecules. Population inversion then occurs in those molecules, and they radiate stimulated emission (Fig. 41-25b). For example, as comet Kohoutek approached the Sun in December 1973 and January 1974, it radiated stimulated emission at about 1666 MHz during mid-January. (a) What was the energy difference $E_2 - E_1$ for that emission? (b) In what region of the electromagnetic spectrum was the emission?

42
Conduction of Electricity in Solids

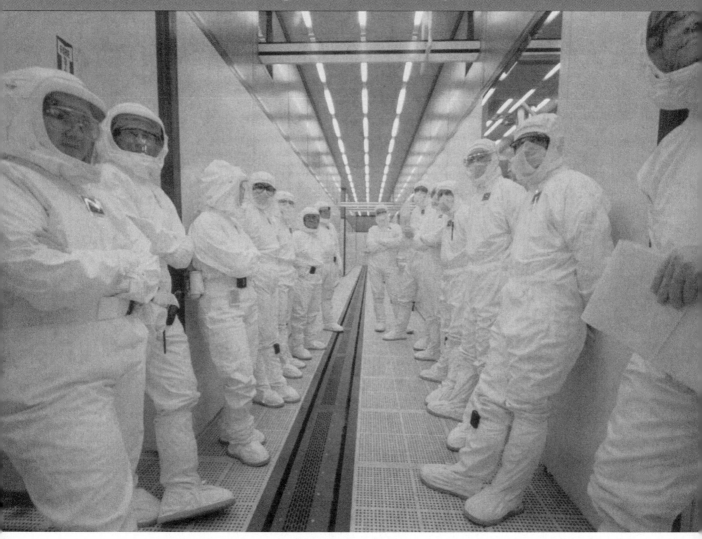

A few of the workers at the Fab 11 factory at Rio Rancho, New Mexico. The plant, which represents an investment of $2.5 billion, has floor space equivalent to about two dozen football fields. According to the New York Times, the plant, "on a high desert mesa in New Mexico is probably the most productive factory in the world, in terms of the value of the goods that it makes." But what do these workers manufacture? Why are they suited up like astronauts? And why is the floor they are standing on perforated ?

42-1 SOLIDS

You have seen how well quantum mechanics works when we apply it to questions involving individual atoms. In this chapter we hope to show, by a single broad example, that this theory works just as well when we apply it to questions involving assemblies of atoms in the form of solids.

Every solid has an enormous range of properties that we can choose to examine. Is it transparent? Can it be hammered out into a thin sheet? At what speeds do sound waves travel through it? Is it magnetic? Is it a good heat conductor? . . . The list goes on and on. However, we choose to focus this entire chapter on a single question: *What are the mechanisms by which a solid conducts, or does not conduct, electricity?* As you will see, quantum mechanics provides the answer.

42-2 THE ELECTRICAL PROPERTIES OF SOLIDS

We shall examine only **crystalline solids**, that is, solids whose atoms are arranged in a repetitive three-dimensional structure called a **lattice**. We shall not consider such solids as wood, plastic, glass, or rubber, whose atoms are not arranged in such repetitive patterns. Figure 42-1 shows the basic repetitive units (the **unit cells**) of the lattice structures of copper, our prototype of a metal, and silicon and diamond, our prototypes of a semiconductor and an insulator, respectively.

We can classify solids electrically according to three basic properties:

1. Their **resistivity** ρ at room temperature, with the SI unit ohm-meter ($\Omega \cdot m$); resistivity is defined in Section 27-4.

2. Their **temperature coefficient of resistivity** α, defined as $\alpha = (1/\rho)(d\rho/dT)$ and having the SI unit inverse kelvin (K^{-1}). We can evaluate α for any solid by measuring ρ over a range of temperatures.

3. Their **number density of charge carriers** n. This quantity, the number of charge carriers per unit volume, can be found from measurements of the Hall effect, as discussed in Section 29-4, and from other measurements. It has the SI unit inverse cubic meter (m^{-3}).

From measurements of room-temperature resistivity alone, we discover that there are some materials—we call them **insulators**—that for all practical purposes do not conduct electricity at all. These are materials with very high resistivity. Diamond, an excellent example, has a resistivity greater than that of copper by the enormous factor of about 10^{24}. Thus we may immediately classify crystalline solids into insulators and noninsulators.

We can then use measurements of ρ, α, and n to divide most noninsulators, at least at low temperatures, into two major categories: **metals** and **semiconductors**.

Semiconductors have a considerably larger resistivity ρ than metals.

Semiconductors have a temperature coefficient of resistivity α that is both large and negative. That is, the resistivity of a semiconductor *decreases* with temperature, whereas that of a metal *increases*.

Semiconductors have a considerably smaller number density of charge carriers n than metals.

Table 42-1 shows values of these quantities for copper, our prototype metal, and silicon, our prototype semiconductor.

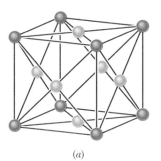 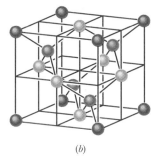

(a)   (b)

FIGURE 42-1 (*a*) The unit cell for copper is a cube. There is one copper atom (darker) at each corner of the cube and one copper atom (lighter) at the center of each face of the cube. The arrangement is called *face-centered cubic*. (*b*) The unit cell for silicon and diamond is also a cube, the atoms being arranged in a so-called *diamond lattice*. There is one atom (darkest) at each corner of the cube and one atom (lightest) at the center of each cube face; in addition, four atoms (medium color) lie within the cube. Every atom is bonded to its four nearest neighbors by a two-electron covalent bond (only the four atoms within the cube show all four *nearest* neighbors).

TABLE 42-1 SOME ELECTRIC PROPERTIES OF TWO MATERIALS[a]

	UNIT	COPPER	SILICON
Type of conductor		Metal	Semiconductor
Number density of charge carriers, n	m^{-3}	9×10^{28}	1×10^{16}
Resistivity, ρ	$\Omega \cdot m$	2×10^{-8}	3×10^{3}
Temperature coefficient of resistivity, α	K^{-1}	$+4 \times 10^{-3}$	-70×10^{-3}

[a] All values are for room temperature.

Now, with measurements of ρ, α, and n in hand, we have an experimental basis for refining our central question about the conduction of electricity in solids: *What features make diamond an insulator, copper a metal, and silicon a semiconductor?* Again, quantum mechanics provides the answers.

42-3 ENERGY LEVELS IN A CRYSTALLINE SOLID

The distance between adjacent copper atoms in solid copper is 260 pm. Figure 42-2a shows two isolated copper atoms separated by a distance r that is much greater than that. As Fig. 42-2b shows, each of these isolated neutral atoms stacks up its 29 electrons in an array of discrete subshells, as follows:

$$1s^2\ 2s^2\ 2p^6\ 3s^2\ 3p^6\ 3d^{10}\ 4s^1.$$

Here we use the shorthand notation of Section 41-7 to identify the subshells. Recall, for example, that the subshell with principal quantum number $n = 3$ and orbital quantum number $l = 1$ is called the $3p$ subshell; it can hold up to $2(2l + 1) = 6$ electrons; the number it actually contains is indicated by a numerical superscript. The first six subshells in copper are filled, but the (outermost) $4s$ subshell, which can hold 2 electrons, holds only one.

If we bring the atoms of Fig. 42-2a closer together, they will—speaking loosely—begin to sense each other's presence. In the language of quantum mechanics, their wave functions will start to overlap, beginning with those of the outermost electrons.

With wave functions that overlap, we speak not of two independent atoms but of a single two-atom system containing $2 \times 29 = 58$ electrons. The Pauli exclusion principle also applies to this larger system and requires that each of these 58 electrons occupy a different quantum state. In

fact, 58 quantum states are available because each energy level of the isolated atom splits into *two* levels for the two-atom system.

If we bring up more atoms, we gradually assemble a lattice of solid copper. If, say, our lattice contains N atoms, then each level of an isolated copper atom must split into N levels in the solid. Thus, the individual energy levels of the solid form energy **bands**, adjacent bands being separated by an energy **gap**, which represents a range of energies that no electron can possess. A typical band is only a few electron-volts wide. Since N may be of the order of 10^{24}, we see that the individual levels within a band are very close together indeed, and there are a vast number of levels.

Figure 42-3 suggests the band–gap structure of the energy levels in a generalized crystalline solid. Note that bands of lower energy are narrower than those of higher energy. This occurs because electrons that occupy the lower energy bands spend most of their time deep within the atom's electron cloud. The wave functions of these core electrons do not overlap as much as the wave functions of the outer electrons. Hence the splitting of these levels is not as great as it is for the higher energy levels normally occupied by the outer electrons.

42-4 INSULATORS

A solid is said to be an insulator if no current exists when we apply a potential difference across it. For a current to exist, the kinetic energy of the average electron must increase. In other words, some electrons in the solid must move to a higher energy level. But as Fig. 42-4a shows, in an insulator the highest band containing any electrons is fully occupied, and the Pauli exclusion principle keeps electrons from moving to occupied levels.

So the electrons in the filled band of an insulator have no place to go; they are in gridlock. It is as if a child tries to

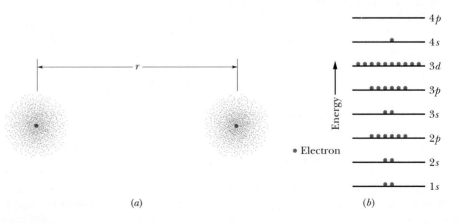

FIGURE 42-2 (a) Two copper atoms separated by a large distance; their electron distributions are represented by dot plots. (b) Each copper atom has 29 electrons distributed among a set of subshells. In the neutral atom in its ground state, all subshells up through the $3d$ level are filled, the $4s$ subshell contains one electron (it can hold two), and higher subshells are empty. For simplicity, the subshells are shown as being evenly spaced in energy.

(a)

(b)

FIGURE 42-3 The band-gap pattern of energy levels for an idealized crystalline solid. As the magnified view suggests, each band consists of a very large number of very closely spaced energy levels. (In many solids, adjacent bands may overlap; for clarity, we have not shown this condition.)

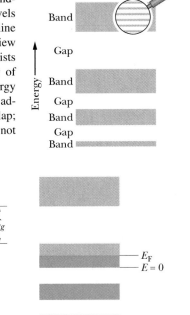

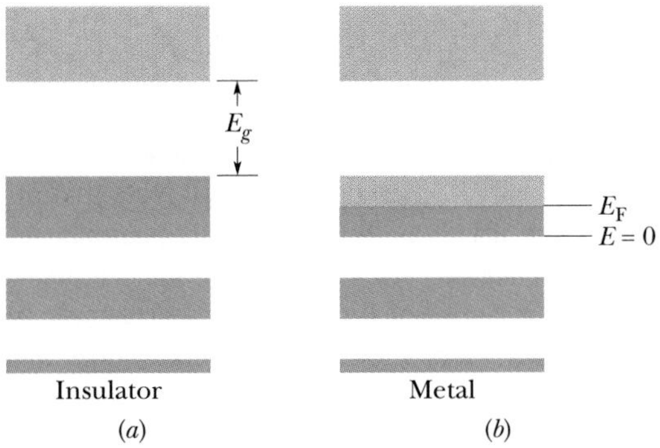

FIGURE 42-4 (a) The band-gap pattern for an insulator; filled levels are shown in red. Note that the highest filled level lies at the top of a band and the next highest vacant level is separated from it by a relatively large energy gap E_g. (b) The band-gap pattern for a metal. The highest filled level, called the Fermi level, lies near the middle of a band. Since vacant levels are available within that band, electrons in the band can easily change levels, and conduction can take place.

climb a ladder that already has a child standing on each rung; since there are no vacant rungs, no one can move.

There are plenty of vacant levels in the band above the filled band in Fig. 42-4a. However, if an electron is to occupy one of those levels, it must acquire enough energy to bridge the substantial gap that separates the two bands. In diamond, this gap is so wide (the energy needed to cross it is 5.5 eV, about 140 times the average thermal energy of a free particle at room temperature) that essentially no electron can jump it. Diamond is thus an insulator, and a very good one.

SAMPLE PROBLEM 42-1

In Chapter 41 we used Eq. 41-21,

$$\frac{N_x}{N_0} = e^{-(E_x - E_0)/kT}, \qquad (42\text{-}1)$$

to relate the population N_x of the atoms at energy level E_x to the population N_0 at energy level E_0, where the atoms are part

of a system at temperature T (in kelvins). The constant k is the Boltzmann constant (8.62×10^{-5} eV/K, from Eq. 20-21).

We can use the same equation to find the likelihood that an electron in an insulator will jump the energy gap E_g in Fig. 42-4a. To do so, we set $E_x - E_0 = E_g$; then N_x/N_0 is the ratio of the number of electrons just above the energy gap to the number of electrons just below the energy gap.

What is the probability that, at room temperature (300 K), an electron at the top of the valence band in diamond will jump the gap E_g which, for diamond, is 5.5 eV?

SOLUTION: For diamond, the exponent in Eq. 42-1 is

$$-\frac{E_g}{kT} = -\frac{5.5 \text{ eV}}{(8.62 \times 10^{-5} \text{ eV/K})(300 \text{ K})} = -213.$$

The required probability is then

$$\frac{N_x}{N_0} = e^{-(E_g/kT)} = e^{-213} \approx 3 \times 10^{-93}. \quad \text{(Answer)}$$

No wonder diamond is such a good insulator. Even in a diamond as large as Earth, the chance for a single electron to jump the gap at 300 K would be vanishingly small!

42-5 METALS

The feature that defines a metal is that, as Fig. 42-4b shows, the highest occupied energy level falls somewhere near the middle of an energy band. If we apply a potential difference across a sample of such a solid, a current can exist because there are plenty of vacant levels at higher energies into which electrons can be raised. So a metal can conduct electricity because electrons in its highest occupied band can easily move into higher energy levels within that band.

In Section 27-6 we introduced the **free-electron model** of a metal, in which the conduction electrons are free to move throughout the volume of the sample like the molecules of a gas in a closed container. We used this model to derive an expression for the resistivity of a metal, assuming that the electrons follow the laws of Newtonian mechanics. Here we use that same model to explain the behavior of the electrons—called the **conduction electrons**—in the partially filled band of Fig. 42-4b. However, we follow the laws of quantum mechanics by assuming the energies of these electrons to be quantized and the Pauli exclusion principle to hold.

We assume too that the electric potential energy of a conduction electron has the same constant value at all points within the lattice. If we choose this value of the potential energy to be zero, as we are free to do, then the energy E of the conduction electrons is entirely kinetic.

The level at the bottom of the partially filled band of Fig. 42-4b corresponds to $E = 0$. The highest occupied level in this band (at absolute zero, $T = 0$ K) is called the **Fermi level**, and the energy corresponding to it is called the **Fermi energy** E_F; for copper, $E_F = 7.0$ eV.

The electron speed corresponding to the Fermi energy is called the **Fermi speed** v_F. For copper the Fermi speed is 1.6×10^6 m/s. This fact should be enough to shatter the popular misconception that all motion ceases at absolute zero; at that temperature—and solely because of the Pauli exclusion principle—the conduction electrons are stacked up in the partially filled band of Fig. 42-4b with energies that range from zero to the Fermi energy.

Conductivity at $T > 0$

Our practical interest in the conduction of electricity in metals is at temperatures above absolute zero. What happens to the electron distribution of Fig. 42-4b at such higher temperatures? As we shall see, surprisingly little.

Of the electrons in the partially filled band of Fig. 42-4b, only those that are close to the Fermi energy find vacant levels above them, and only those electrons are free to be boosted to these higher levels by thermal agitation. Even at $T = 1000$ K, a temperature at which copper would glow brightly in a dark room, the distribution of electrons among the available levels does not differ much from the distribution at $T = 0$ K.

Let us see why. The quantity kT, where k is the Boltzmann constant, is a convenient measure of the energy that may be given to a conduction electron by the random thermal motions of the lattice. At $T = 1000$ K, we have $kT = 0.086$ eV. No electron can hope to have its energy changed by more than a few times this relatively small amount by thermal agitation alone. So at best, only those few conduction electrons whose energies are close to the Fermi energy are likely to be boosted to higher energy levels by thermal agitation. Poetically stated, thermal agitation normally causes only ripples on the surface of the Fermi sea of electrons; the vast depths of that sea lie undisturbed.

How Many Quantum States Are There?

The ability of a metal to conduct electricity depends on how many quantum states are available to its electrons and what the energies of these states are. Thus a question arises: What are the energies of the individual states in the partially filled band of Fig. 42-4b? This question is too difficult to answer because we cannot possibly list the energies of so many states individually. We ask instead: How many states have energies in the energy range E to $E + dE$? We write this number as $N(E)$ dE, where $N(E)$ is called the **density of states** at energy E. The conventional unit for $N(E)$ dE is states per cubic meter (states/m³, or

simply m⁻³); the corresponding unit for $N(E)$ is states per cubic meter per electron-volt (m⁻³ eV⁻¹).

We can find an expression for the density of states by counting the number of standing electron matter waves that can fit into a box the size of the metal sample we are considering. This is analogous to counting the number of standing waves of sound that can exist in a closed organ pipe. The differences are that our problem is three-dimensional (the organ pipe problem is one-dimensional) and the waves are quantum-mechanical matter waves (the organ-pipe waves are sound waves). The result of such counting can be shown to be

$$N(E) = \frac{8\sqrt{2}\pi m^{3/2}}{h^3} E^{1/2} \quad \text{(density of states),} \quad (42\text{-}2)$$

where m is the mass of the electron and E is the kinetic energy at which $N(E)$ is to be evaluated. Note that nothing in this equation involves the shape of the sample, its temperature, or the material of which it is made. Figure 42-5, a half-parabola, is a plot of Eq. 42-2. As an example, it tells us that there are about 2×10^{28} states per cubic meter of sample whose energies lie in the 1.0 eV energy range centered at 8 eV.

CHECKPOINT 1: (a) Is the spacing between adjacent energy levels at $E = 4$ eV in copper larger than, the same as, or smaller than the spacing at $E = 6$ eV? (b) Is the spacing between adjacent energy levels at $E = 4$ eV in copper larger than, the same as, or smaller than the spacing for an identical volume of aluminum at that same energy?

The Occupancy Probability $P(E)$

The ability of a metal to conduct electricity depends on the probability that available vacant levels will actually be occupied. Thus another question arises: If an energy level is

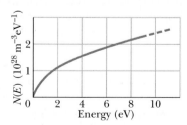

FIGURE 42-5 The density of states $N(E)$, that is, the number of electron energy levels per unit energy interval and per unit volume, plotted as a function of electron energy. The density of states function simply counts the available states; it says nothing about whether these states are or are not occupied by electrons.

available at energy E, what is the probability $P(E)$ that it is actually occupied by an electron? At $T = 0$ K, we know that for all levels with energies below the Fermi energy, $P(E) = 1$, corresponding to a certainty that the level is occupied. We also know that, at $T = 0$ K, for all levels with energies above the Fermi energy, $P(E) = 0$, corresponding to a certainty that the level is *not* occupied. Figure 42-6a illustrates this situation.

To find $P(E)$ at temperatures above absolute zero, we must use a set of quantum counting rules called **Fermi–Dirac statistics**, named for the physicists who introduced them. Using these rules, it is possible to show that the **occupancy probability** $P(E)$ is

$$P(E) = \frac{1}{e^{(E-E_F)/kT} + 1} \quad \begin{array}{l}\text{(occupancy} \\ \text{probability),}\end{array} \quad (42\text{-}3)$$

in which E_F is the Fermi energy. Note that $P(E)$ depends not on the energy E of the level but only on the difference $E - E_F$, which may be positive or negative.

To see whether Eq. 42-3 describes Fig. 42-6a, we substitute $T = 0$ K in it. Then,

For $E < E_F$, the exponential term in Eq. 42-3 is $e^{-\infty}$, or zero, so $P(E) = 1$, in agreement with Fig. 42-6a.

For $E > E_F$, the exponential term is $e^{+\infty}$, so $P(E) = 0$, again in agreement with Fig. 42-6a.

Figure 42-6b is a plot of $P(E)$ for $T = 1000$ K. It shows that, as stated above, changes in the distribution of electrons among the available states involve only states whose energies are near the Fermi energy E_F. Note that if $E = E_F$ (no matter what the temperature T), the exponential term in Eq. 42-3 is $e^0 = 1$ and $P(E) = 0.5$. This leads us to a more useful definition of the Fermi energy:

> The Fermi energy of a given material is the energy of a quantum state that has the probability 0.5 of being occupied by an electron.

In a given sample, however, there may not be a quantum state available at that energy.

How Many *Occupied* States Are There?

Equation 42-2 and Fig. 42-5 tell us how the available states are distributed in energy. The occupancy probability of Eq. 42-3 gives us the probability that any given state will actually be occupied by an electron. To find $N_o(E)$, the density of *occupied* states, we must weight each available state by the appropriate value of the occupancy probability; that is,

$$N_o(E) = N(E)\, P(E) \quad \begin{array}{l}\text{(density of} \\ \text{occupied states).}\end{array} \quad (42\text{-}4)$$

Figure 42-7a is a plot of Eq. 42-4 for copper at $T = 0$ K. It is found by multiplying at each energy, the value of the density of states function (Fig. 42-5) by the value of the occupancy probability for absolute zero (Fig. 42-6a). Fig-

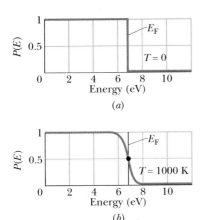

(a)

(b)

FIGURE 42-6 The occupancy probability $P(E)$ gives the probability that an energy level will be occupied by an electron. (a) At $T = 0$ K, $P(E)$ is unity for levels with energies E up to the Fermi energy and zero for levels with higher energies. (b) At $T = 1000$ K, a few electrons whose energies were slightly less than the Fermi energy at $T = 0$ K move up to states with energies slightly greater than the Fermi energy. The dot on the curve shows that, for $E = E_F$, $P(E) = 0.5$.

FIGURE 42-7 (a) The density of occupied states $N_o(E)$ for copper at absolute zero. The area under the curve is the number density of electrons n. Note that all states with energies up to the Fermi energy are occupied, and all those with energies above the Fermi energy are vacant. (b) The same for copper at $T = 1000$ K. Note that only electrons whose energies are near the Fermi energy have been affected by thermal agitation and redistributed.

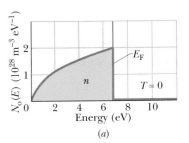

(a)

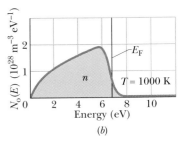

(b)

ure 42-7b, calculated similarly, shows the density of occupied states for copper at $T = 1000$ K.

Calculating the Fermi Energy

Suppose we add up (via integration) the number of occupied states in Fig. 42-7a at all energies between $E = 0$ and
$E = E_F$. The result must equal n, the number of conduction electrons per unit volume for the metal. In equation
form, we have

$$n = \int_0^{E_F} N_o(E) \, dE. \qquad (42\text{-}5)$$

(Graphically, the integral here represents the area under the
distribution curve of Fig. 42-7a.) Because $P(E) = 1$ for all
energies below the Fermi energy, we can replace $N_o(E)$ in
Eq. 42-5 by $N(E)$ and then use Eq. 42-5 to find the Fermi
energy E_F. If we substitute Eq. 42-2 into Eq. 42-5, we find
that

$$n = \frac{8\sqrt{2}\pi m^{3/2}}{h^3} \int_0^{E_F} E^{1/2} \, dE = \frac{8\sqrt{2}\pi m^{3/2}}{h^3} \frac{2E_F^{3/2}}{3}.$$

Solving for E_F now leads to

$$E_F = \left(\frac{3}{16\sqrt{2}\pi}\right)^{2/3} \frac{h^2}{m} n^{2/3} = \frac{0.121h^2}{m} n^{2/3}. \quad (42\text{-}6)$$

Thus when we know n, the number of conduction electrons
per unit volume, we can find the Fermi energy for a metal.

SAMPLE PROBLEM 42-2

A cube of copper is 1.00 cm on edge. In the partially filled
band of Fig. 42-4b, what is the number N of quantum states in
the energy range from $E = 5.000$ eV to $E = 5.010$ eV?
(These energy values are so close that we can assume the
density of states $N(E)$ is constant over the interval.)

SOLUTION: We can find the number of states N from

$$\left(\begin{array}{c}\text{number of states}\\\text{in sample}\end{array}\right)$$

$$= \left(\begin{array}{c}\text{density of}\\\text{states, m}^{-3}\text{eV}^{-1}\end{array}\right)\left(\begin{array}{c}\text{energy}\\\text{range, eV}\end{array}\right)\left(\begin{array}{c}\text{volume of}\\\text{sample, m}^3\end{array}\right),$$

or $\qquad N = N(E) \, \Delta E \, V, \qquad (42\text{-}7)$

where $\Delta E = 0.010$ eV and V is the volume of the cubical
sample. From Eq. 42-2 with $E = 5.000$ eV, we get

$$N(E) = \frac{8\sqrt{2}\pi m^{3/2}}{h^3} E^{1/2}$$

$$= (8\sqrt{2}\pi)(9.11 \times 10^{-31} \text{ kg})^{3/2}$$

$$\times \frac{(5.000 \text{ eV})^{1/2}(1.60 \times 10^{-19} \text{ J/eV})^{1/2}}{(6.63 \times 10^{-34} \text{ J}\cdot\text{s})^3}$$

$$= 9.48 \times 10^{46} \text{ m}^{-3} \text{ J}^{-1} = 1.52 \times 10^{28} \text{ m}^{-3}\text{eV}^{-1}.$$

Since $V = a^3$, where a is the length of the cube edge, Eq. 42-7
gives us

$$N = N(E) \, \Delta E \, a^3$$

$$= (1.52 \times 10^{28} \text{ m}^{-3}\text{eV}^{-1})(0.010 \text{ eV})(1 \times 10^{-2} \text{ m})^3$$

$$= 1.52 \times 10^{20}. \qquad (\text{Answer})$$

This is an enormous number of states, but expectedly so. Even
though all these states fall into an energy range that is only
0.01 eV wide, they originate from the enormous number of
atoms that forms our sample.

SAMPLE PROBLEM 42-3

(a) What is the probability that a quantum state whose energy
is 0.10 eV above the Fermi energy will be occupied? Assume
a sample temperature of 800 K.

SOLUTION: We can find $P(E)$ from Eq. 42-3. But let us first
calculate the (dimensionless) exponent in that equation:

$$\frac{E - E_F}{kT} = \frac{0.10 \text{ eV}}{(8.62 \times 10^{-5} \text{ eV/K})(800 \text{ K})} = 1.45.$$

Inserting this exponent into Eq. 42-3 yields

$$P(E) = \frac{1}{e^{1.45} + 1} = 0.19 \text{ or } 19\%. \qquad (\text{Answer})$$

(b) What is the probability of occupancy for a state that is
0.10 eV *below* the Fermi energy?

SOLUTION: The exponent in Eq. 42-3 has the same absolute
value as in (a) but is now negative. Thus from this equation

$$P(E) = \frac{1}{e^{-1.45} + 1} = 0.81 \text{ or } 81\%. \qquad (\text{Answer})$$

For states below the Fermi energy, we are often more interested in the probability that the state is *not* occupied. This is
just $1 - P(E)$, or 19%. Note that it is the same as the probability of occupancy in (a).

42-6 SEMICONDUCTORS

If you compare Fig. 42-8a with Fig. 42-4a, you can see
that the band structure of a semiconductor is like that of an
insulator. The main difference is that the semiconductor
has a much smaller energy gap E_g between the top of the
highest filled band (called the **valence band**) and the bottom of the vacant band just above it (called the **conduction
band**). Thus there is no doubt that silicon ($E_g = 1.1$ eV) is
a semiconductor and diamond ($E_g = 5.5$ eV) is an insulator. In silicon—but not in diamond—there is a real possi-

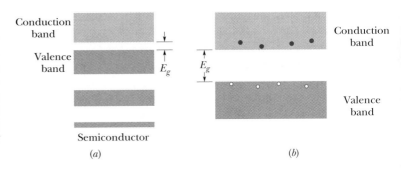

FIGURE 42-8 (*a*) The band–gap pattern for a semiconductor. It resembles that of an insulator (see Fig. 42-4*a*) except that here the energy gap E_g is much smaller; thus electrons, because of their thermal agitation, have some reasonable probability of being able to jump the gap. (*b*) Thermal agitation has caused a few electrons to jump the gap from the valence band to the conduction band, leaving an equal number of holes in the valence band.

bility that thermal agitation at room temperature will cause electrons to jump the gap from the valence band to the conduction band.

In Table 42-1 we compared three basic electrical properties of copper, our prototype metallic conductor, and silicon, our prototype semiconductor. Let us look again at that table, one row at a time, to see how a semiconductor differs from a metal.

Number Density of Charge Carriers *n*

The second row of Table 42-1 shows that copper has far more charge carriers per unit volume than silicon, by a factor of about 10^{13}. For copper, each atom contributes one electron, its single valence electron, to the conduction process. Charge carriers in silicon arise only because, at thermal equilibrium, thermal agitation causes a certain (very small) number of valence band electrons to jump the energy gap into the conduction band, leaving an equal number of vacant energy states, called **holes**, in the valence band. Figure 42-8*b* shows the situation.

Both the electrons in the conduction band and the holes in the valence band serve as charge carriers. The holes do so by permitting a certain freedom of movement to electrons in the valence band that, in the absence of holes, would be gridlocked. If an electric field **E** is set up in a semiconductor, the electrons in the valence band, being negatively charged, tend to drift in the direction opposite **E**. This causes the positions of the holes to drift in the direction of **E**. In effect, the holes behave like moving particles of charge $+e$.

It may help to think of a row of cars parked bumper to bumper, the leading car being one car's length from a barrier. If the leading car moves forward to the barrier, it opens up a car's length space behind it. The second car can then move up to fill that space, allowing the third car to move up, and so on. The motions of the many cars toward the barrier are most simply analyzed by focusing attention

on the drift of the single "hole" (parking space) away from the barrier.

In semiconductors, conduction by holes is just as important as conduction by electrons. In thinking about hole conduction, it is well to imagine that all unoccupied states in the valence band are occupied by particles of charge $+e$, and that all electrons in the valence band have been removed, so that these positive charge carriers can move freely throughout the band.

The Resistivity ρ

From Chapter 27 recall that the resistivity ρ of a material is $m/e^2 n\tau$, where m is the electron mass, e is the fundamental charge, n is the number of charge carriers per unit volume, and τ is the mean time between collisions of the charge carriers. Table 42-1 shows that, at room temperature, the resistivity of silicon is higher than that of copper, by a factor of about 10^{11}. This vast difference can be accounted for by the vast difference in n. Other factors enter, but their effect on the resistivity is swamped by the enormous difference in n.

The Temperature Coefficient of Resistivity α

Recall that α (see Eq. 27-17) is the fractional change in resistivity per unit change in temperature:

$$\alpha = \frac{1}{\rho}\frac{d\rho}{dT}. \tag{42-8}$$

The resistivity of copper *increases* with temperature (that is, $d\rho/dT > 0$) because collisions of copper's charge carriers occur more frequently at higher temperatures. Thus α is *positive* for copper.

The collision frequency also increases with temperature for silicon. However, the resistivity of silicon actually *decreases* with temperature ($d\rho/dT < 0$) because the number of charge carriers (electrons in the conduction band and holes in the valence band) increases so rapidly with temperature. (More electrons jump the gap from the valence band to the conduction band.) Thus the fractional change α is *negative* for silicon.

CHECKPOINT 2: The research laboratory of a large corporation developed three new solid materials whose electrical properties are shown below. Anticipating patent applications, the laboratory identified these materials with code names. Classify each material as a metal, an insulator, a semiconductor, or none of the above:

MATERIAL (CODE NAME)	n (m^{-3})	ρ $(\Omega \cdot m)$	α (K^{-1})
Cleveland	10^{29}	10^{-8}	$+10^{-3}$
Troy	10^{28}	10^{-9}	-10^{-3}
Seattle	10^{15}	10^{3}	-10^{-2}

42-7 DOPED SEMICONDUCTORS

The usefulness of semiconductors in technology can be greatly improved by introducing a small number of suitable replacement atoms (it seems pejorative to call them impurities) into the semiconductor lattice—a process called **doping**. Typically, only about 1 silicon atom in 10^7 is replaced by a dopant atom. Essentially all modern semiconducting devices are based on doped material. Such materials are of two types, called **n-type** and **p-type**; we discuss each in turn.

n-Type Semiconductors

The electrons in an isolated silicon atom are arranged in subshells according to the scheme

$$1s^2\, 2s^2\, 2p^6\, 3s^2\, 3p^2,$$

in which, as usual, the superscripts (which add to 14, the atomic number of silicon) represent the numbers of electrons in the specified subshell.

Figure 42-9a is a flattened out representation of a portion of the lattice of pure silicon in which the portion has been projected onto a plane; compare the figure with Fig. 42-1b, which represents the unit cell of the lattice in three dimensions. Each silicon atom contributes its pair of $3s$ electrons and its pair of $3p$ electrons to form a rigid two-electron covalent bond with each of its four nearest neighbors. (A covalent bond is a link between two atoms in which the atoms share a pair of electrons.) The four atoms that lie within the unit cell in Fig. 42-1b show these bonds.

The electrons that form the silicon–silicon bonds constitute the valence band of the silicon sample. If an electron is torn from one of these bonds so that it becomes free to wander throughout the lattice, we say that the electron has been raised from the valence band to the conduction band. The minimum energy required to do this is the gap energy E_g.

Because four of its electrons are involved in bonds, each silicon "atom" is actually an ion consisting of an inert neonlike electron cloud (containing 10 electrons) surrounding a nucleus whose charge is $+14e$, where 14 is the atomic number of silicon. The net charge of these ions is thus $+4e$, and the ions are said to have a *valence number* of 4.

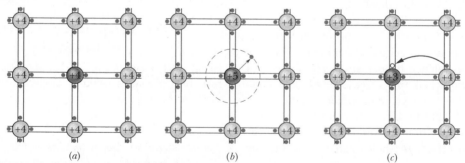

(a)   (b)   (c)

FIGURE 42-9 (a) A flattened-out representation of the lattice structure of pure silicon. Each silicon ion is coupled to its four nearest neighbors by a two-electron covalent bond (represented by a pair of red dots between two parallel black lines). The electrons belong to the bond—not to the individual atoms—and form the valence band of the sample. (b) One silicon atom is replaced by a phosphorus atom (valence = 5). The "extra" electron is only loosely bound to its ion core and may easily be elevated to the conduction band, where it is free to wander through the volume of the lattice. (c) One silicon atom is replaced by an aluminum atom (valence = 3). There is now a hole in one of the covalent bonds and thus in the valence band of the sample. The hole can easily migrate through the lattice as electrons from neighboring bonds move in to fill it. In the move shown, the hole migrates rightward.

In Fig. 42-9b the central silicon ion has been replaced by an atom of phosphorus (valence = 5). Four of the valence electrons of the phosphorus form bonds with the four surrounding silicon ions. The fifth ("extra") electron is only loosely bound to the phosphorus ion core. On an energy band diagram, we usually say that such an electron occupies a localized energy state that lies within the energy gap, at an average energy interval E_d below the bottom of the conduction band; this is indicated in Fig. 42-10a. Because $E_d \ll E_g$, the energy required to excite electrons from *these* levels into the conduction band is much less than that required to excite silicon valence electrons into the conduction band.

The phosphorus atom is called a **donor** atom because it readily *donates* an electron to the conduction band. In fact, at room temperature virtually *all* the electrons contributed by the donor atoms are in the conduction band. By adding donor atoms, it is possible to increase greatly the number of electrons in the conduction band, by a factor very much larger than Fig. 42-10a suggests.

Semiconductors doped with donor atoms are called **n-type semiconductors**; the "n" stands for "negative," to imply that the negative charge carriers introduced into the conduction band greatly outnumber the positive charge carriers, which are the holes in the valence band. In n-type semiconductors, the electrons are called the **majority carriers**, and the holes the **minority carriers**.

p-Type Semiconductors

Now consider Fig. 42-9c, in which one of the silicon atoms (valence = 4) has been replaced by an atom of aluminum (valence = 3). The aluminum atom can bond covalently with only three silicon atoms, so there is now a "missing" electron (a hole) in one aluminum–silicon bond. With a small expenditure of energy, an electron can be torn from a neighboring silicon–silicon bond to fill this hole, thereby

creating a hole in *that* bond. And, similarly, an electron from some other bond can be moved to fill the second hole. In this way, the hole can migrate through the lattice.

The aluminum atom is called an **acceptor** atom because it readily *accepts* an electron from a neighboring bond, that is, from the valence band of silicon. As Fig. 42-10b suggests, this electron occupies a localized acceptor state that lies within the energy gap, at an average energy interval E_a above the top of the valence band. By adding acceptor atoms, it is possible to increase very greatly the number of holes in the valence band, by a factor much larger than Fig. 42-10b suggests. In silicon at room temperature, virtually *all* the acceptor levels are occupied by electrons.

Semiconductors doped with acceptor atoms are called **p-type semiconductors**; the "p" stands for "positive" to imply that the holes introduced into the valence band, which behave like positive charge carriers, greatly outnumber the electrons in the conduction band. In p-type semiconductors, holes are the majority carriers and electrons are the minority carriers.

Table 42-2 summarizes the properties of a typical n-type and a typical p-type semiconductor. Note particularly that the donor and acceptor ion cores, although they are charged, are not charge *carriers* because at normal temperatures they remain fixed in their lattice sites.

SAMPLE PROBLEM 42-4
The number density n_0 of conduction electrons in pure silicon at room temperature is about 10^{16} m^{-3}. Assume that, by doping the silicon lattice with phosphorus, we want to increase this number by a factor of a million (10^6). What fraction of silicon atoms must we replace with phosphorus atoms? (Recall that at room temperature, thermal agitation is so effective that essentially every phosphorus atom donates its "extra" electron to the conduction band.)

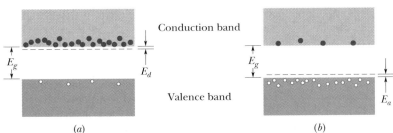

FIGURE 42-10 (a) In a doped n-type semiconductor, the energy levels of donor electrons lie a small interval E_d below the bottom of the conduction band. Because donor electrons can be easily excited to the conduction band, there are now many more electrons in that band. The valence band contains the same small number of holes as before. (b) In a doped p-type semiconductor, the acceptor levels lie a small interval E_a above the top of the valence band. There are now relatively many more holes in the valence band. The conduction band contains the same small number of electrons as before. The ratio of majority carriers to minority carriers in both (a) and (b) is very much greater than is suggested by these diagrams.

TABLE 42-2 PROPERTIES OF TWO DOPED SEMICONDUCTORS

PROPERTY	TYPE OF SEMICONDUCTOR	
	n	p
Matrix material	Silicon	Silicon
Matrix nuclear charge	$+14e$	$+14e$
Matrix energy gap	1.2 eV	1.2 eV
Dopant	Phosphorus	Aluminum
Type of dopant	Donor	Acceptor
Majority carriers	Electrons	Holes
Minority carriers	Holes	Electrons
Dopant energy gap	0.045 eV	0.067 eV
Dopant valence	5	3
Dopant nuclear charge	$+15e$	$+13e$
Dopant net ion charge	$+e$	$-e$

SOLUTION: The number density of conduction electrons added by doping will be equal to n_P, the number density of phosphorus atoms added. We want the total number density of electrons in the conduction band after doping, original plus added electrons, to be $10^6 n_0$, so

$$10^6 n_0 = n_0 + n_P.$$

Then

$$n_P = 10^6 n_0 - n_0 \approx 10^6 n_0$$
$$= (10^6)(10^{16} \text{ m}^{-3}) = 10^{22} \text{ m}^{-3}.$$

This tells us that we must add 10^{22} atoms of phosphorus to each cubic meter of silicon.

The number density of silicon atoms in a pure silicon lattice may be found from

$$n_{Si} = \frac{N_A d}{A},$$

in which N_A is the Avogadro constant (6.02×10^{23} mol^{-1}), d is the density of silicon (2330 kg/m³), and A is the molar mass of silicon (28.1 g/mol, or 0.0281 kg/mol). Substitution yields

$$n_{Si} = \frac{(6.02 \times 10^{23} \text{ mol}^{-1})(2330 \text{ kg/m}^3)}{0.0281 \text{ kg/mol}}$$
$$= 5 \times 10^{28} \text{ m}^{-3}.$$

The fraction we seek is approximately

$$\frac{n_P}{n_{Si}} = \frac{10^{22} \text{ m}^{-3}}{5 \times 10^{28} \text{ m}^{-3}} = \frac{1}{5 \times 10^6}. \quad \text{(Answer)}$$

If we replace only *one silicon atom in five million* with a phosphorus atom, the number of electrons in the conduction band will be increased by a factor of a million.

How can such a tiny admixture of phosphorus have what seems to be such a big effect? The answer is that, although the effect is very significant, it is not "big." The number density of conduction electrons was 10^{16} m^{-3} before doping and

10^{22} m^{-3} after doping. For copper, however, the conduction-electron number density (given in Table 42-1) is about 10^{29} m^{-3}. Thus, even after doping, the number density of conduction electrons in silicon remains much less than that of a typical metal, such as copper, by a factor of about 10^7.

42-8 THE *p-n* JUNCTION

A **p-n junction**, as Fig. 42-11a shows, is a single semiconductor crystal that has been selectively doped so that one region is *n*-type material and the adjacent region is *p*-type

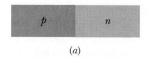

(a)

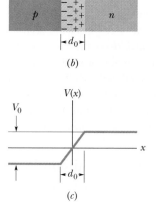

(b)

(c)

(d)

FIGURE 42-11 (a) A sample of *n*-type material and a sample of *p*-type material are intimately joined to form a *p-n* junction. (b) Motions of the majority charge carriers across the junction plane uncover a space charge associated with uncompensated donor ions (to the right of the plane) and acceptor ions (to the left). This depletion zone contains no free charge carriers; the donor and acceptor ions are fixed in their lattice sites. (c) Associated with the space charge is a contact potential difference V_0, which acts to limit the flow of majority carriers. (d) The diffusion of majority carriers (both electrons and holes) across the junction plane produces a diffusion current I_{diff}; in an isolated *p-n* junction, that current is just balanced by the drift current I_{drift} produced by minority carriers, with the result that the net current through the junction plane is zero. (In a real *p-n* junction, the boundaries of the depletion zone would not be sharp, as shown here, and the contact potential curve (c) would be smooth, with no sharp corners.)

material. Such junctions are at the heart of essentially all semiconductor devices.

We assume, for simplicity, that the junction has been formed mechanically, by butting together a bar of *n*-type semiconductor with a bar of *p*-type semiconductor. Thus the transition from one region to the other is perfectly sharp, occurring at a single **junction plane**.

Let us discuss the motions of electrons and holes just after the *n*-type bar and the *p*-type bar, both electrically neutral, have been jammed together to form the junction. We first examine the majority carriers, which are electrons in the *n*-type material and holes in the *p*-type material.

Motions of the Majority Carriers

If you burst a helium-filled balloon, helium atoms will diffuse (spread) outward into the surrounding air. This happens because there are very few helium atoms in normal air. In more formal language, there is a helium *density gradient* at the balloon–air interface (the number density of helium atoms varies across the interface); the helium atoms move so as to reduce the gradient.

In the same way, electrons on the *n* side of Fig. 42-11*a* that are close to the junction plane tend to diffuse across it (from right to left in the figure) and into the *p* side, where there are very few free electrons. Similarly, holes on the *p* side that are close to the junction plane tend to diffuse across that plane (from left to right) and into the *n* side, where there are very few holes. The motions of both the electrons and the holes contribute to a **diffusion current** I_{diff}, conventionally directed from left to right as indicated in Fig. 42-11*d*.

Recall that the *n*-side is studded throughout with positively charged donor ions, fixed firmly in their lattice sites. Normally, the excess positive charge of each of these ions is compensated electrically by one of the conduction-band electrons. When an *n*-side electron diffuses across the junction plane, however, the diffusion "uncovers" one of these donor ions, thus introducing a fixed positive charge near the junction plane on the *n* side.

When the diffusing electron arrives on the *p* side, it quickly combines with an acceptor ion (which lacks one electron), thus introducing a fixed negative charge near the junction plane on the *p* side.

In this way electrons diffusing through the junction plane from right to left in Fig. 42-11*a* result in a buildup of **space charge** on each side of the junction plane, as indicated in Fig. 42-11*b*. Holes diffusing through the junction plane from left to right have exactly the same effect. (Take the time now to convince yourself of that.) The motions of both majority carriers—electrons and holes—contribute to the buildup of these two space charge regions, one posi-

tive and one negative. These two regions form a **depletion zone**, so named because it is relatively free of *mobile* charge carriers; its width is shown as d_0 in Fig. 42-11*b*.

The buildup of space charge generates an associated **contact potential difference** V_0 across the depletion zone, as Fig. 42-11*c* shows. This potential difference serves to limit further diffusion of electrons and holes across the junction plane. Negative charges tend to avoid regions of low potential. Thus, an electron approaching the junction plane from the right in Fig. 42-11*b* is moving toward a region of low potential and would tend to turn back into the *n* side. Similarly, a positive charge (a hole) approaching the junction plane from the left is moving toward a region of high potential and would tend to turn back into the *p* side.

Motions of the Minority Carriers

As Fig. 42-10*a* shows, although the majority carriers in *n*-type material are electrons, there are nevertheless a few holes. Likewise in *p*-type material (Fig. 42-10*b*), although the majority carriers are holes, there are also a few electrons. These few holes and electrons are the minority carriers in the corresponding materials.

Although the potential difference V_0 in Fig. 42-11*c* acts as a barrier for the majority carriers, it is a downhill trip for the minority carriers, be they electrons on the *p*-side or holes on the *n*-side. Positive charges (holes) tend to seek regions of low potential; negative charges (electrons) tend to seek regions of high potential. Thus both types of carriers are *swept across* the junction plane by the contact potential difference and, together, constitute a **drift current** I_{drift} across the junction plane from right to left, as Fig. 42-11*d* indicates.

Thus an isolated *p-n* junction is in an equilibrium state in which a contact potential difference V_0 exists between its ends. At equilibrium, the average diffusion current I_{diff} that moves through the junction plane from the *p* side to the *n* side is just balanced by an average drift current I_{drift} that moves in the opposite direction. These two currents cancel because the net current through the junction plane must be zero; otherwise charge would be transferred without limit from one end of the junction to the other.

C<small>HECKPOINT</small> **3:** Which of the following five currents across the junction plane of Fig. 42-11*a* must be zero?
  (a) the net current due to holes, both majority and minority carriers included
  (b) the net current due to electrons, both majority and minority carriers included
  (c) the net current due to both holes and electrons, both majority and minority carriers included

(d) the net current due to majority carriers, both holes and electrons included

(e) the net current due to minority carriers, both holes and electrons included

42-9 THE JUNCTION RECTIFIER

Look now at Fig. 42-12. It shows that, if we place a potential difference across a *p-n* junction in one direction (here labeled + and "Forward bias"), there will be a current through the junction. However, if we reverse the direction of the potential difference, there will be approximately zero current through the junction.

One application of this property is the **junction rectifier**, whose symbol is shown in Fig. 42-13*b*: the arrowhead corresponds to the *p*-type terminal of the device and points in the allowed direction of conventional current. A sine wave input potential to the device (Fig. 42-13*a*) is transformed to a half-wave output potential (Fig. 42-13*c*) by the junction rectifier; that is, the rectifier acts as essentially a closed switch (zero resistance) for one polarity of the input potential and as essentially an open switch (infinite resistance) for the other.

The average value of the input voltage in Fig. 42-13*a* is zero, but that of the output voltage in Fig. 42-13*c* is not. Thus a junction rectifier can be used, with appropriate electronic filtering that is not shown in the figure, to convert an alternating potential difference into a constant potential difference, as for an electronic power supply.

Figure 42-14 shows why a *p-n* junction operates as a junction rectifier. In Fig. 42-14*a*, a battery is connected across the junction with its positive terminal connected at the *p* side. In this **forward-bias connection**, the *p* side becomes more positive than it was before the connection and the *n* side becomes more negative, thus *decreasing* the height of the potential barrier V_0 of Fig. 42-11*c*. More of the majority carriers can now surmount this smaller barrier;

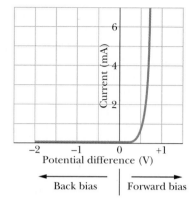

FIGURE 42-12 A current–voltage plot for a *p-n* junction, showing that the junction is highly conducting when forward-biased and essentially nonconducting when back-biased.

hence the diffusion current I_{diff} increases markedly.

The minority carriers that form the drift current, however, sense no barrier, so the drift current I_{drift} is not affected by the external battery. The nice current balance that existed at zero bias (see Fig. 42-11*d*) is thus upset and, as shown in Fig. 42-14*a*, a large net forward current I_F appears in the circuit.

Another effect of forward bias is to narrow the depletion zone, as a comparison of Figs. 42-11*b* and Fig. 42-14*a* shows. The depletion zone narrows because the reduced potential barrier associated with forward bias must be associated with a smaller space charge. Because the ions producing the space charge are fixed in their lattice sites, a reduction in their number can come about only through a reduction in the width of the depletion zone.

Because the depletion zone normally contains very few charge carriers, it is normally a region of high resistivity. But when its width is substantially reduced by a forward bias, its resistance is also reduced substantially, as is consistent with the large forward current.

Figure 42-14*b* shows the **back-bias** connection, in which the negative terminal of the battery is connected at the *p*-type end of the *p-n* junction. Now the applied emf *increases* the contact potential difference, the diffusion

FIGURE 42-13 A *p-n* junction connected as a junction rectifier. The action of the circuit in (*b*) is to pass the positive half of the input wave form (*a*) but to suppress the negative half. The average potential of the input wave form is zero; that of the output wave form (*c*) has a positive value V_{av}.

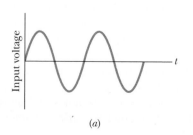

(*a*)

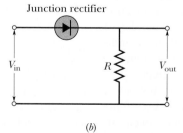

(*b*)

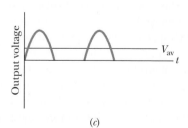

(*c*)

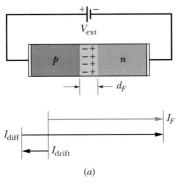

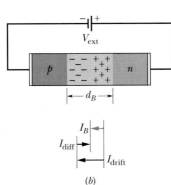

FIGURE 42-14 (a) The forward-bias connection of a p-n junction, showing the narrowed depletion zone and the large forward current I_F. (b) The back-bias connection, showing the widened depletion zone and the small back current I_B.

current *decreases* substantially while the drift current remains unchanged, and a relatively *small* back current I_B results. The depletion zone *widens*, its *high* resistance being consistent with the *small* back current I_B.

42-10 THE LIGHT-EMITTING DIODE (LED)

Nowadays, we can hardly avoid the brightly colored "electronic" numbers that glow at us from cash registers and gasoline pumps, microwave ovens and alarm clocks. And we cannot seem to do without the invisible infrared beams that control elevator doors and operate television sets via remote control. In nearly all cases this light is emitted from a p-n junction operating as a **light-emitting diode (LED)**. How can a p-n junction generate light?

Consider first a simple semiconductor. When an electron from the bottom of the conduction band falls into a hole at the top of the valence band, an energy E_g equal to the gap width is released. In silicon, germanium, and many other semiconductors, this energy is largely transformed into thermal energy of the vibrating lattice, and as a result, no light is emitted.

In some semiconductors, however, including gallium arsenide, the energy can be emitted as a photon of energy

hf and at wavelength

$$\lambda = \frac{c}{f} = \frac{c}{E_g/h} = \frac{hc}{E_g}. \qquad (42\text{-}9)$$

To emit enough light to be useful as an LED, the material must have a suitably large number of electron–hole transitions. This condition is *not* satisfied by a pure semiconductor because, at room temperature, there are simply not enough electron–hole pairs. As Fig. 42-10 suggests, doping will not help. In doped n-type material the number of conduction electrons is greatly increased, but there are not enough holes for them to combine with; in doped p-type material there are plenty of holes but not enough electrons to combine with them. Thus neither a pure semiconductor nor a doped semiconductor can provide enough electron–hole transitions to serve as a practical LED.

What we need is a semiconductor material with a very large number of electrons in the conduction band *and* a correspondingly large number of holes in the valence band. A device with this property can be fabricated by placing a strong forward bias on a heavily doped p-n junction, as in Fig. 42-15. In such an arrangement the current I through the device serves to inject electrons into the n-type material and to inject holes into the p-type material. If the doping is heavy enough and the current is great enough, the depletion zone can become very narrow, perhaps only a few micrometers wide. The result is a great number density of electrons in the n-type material facing a correspondingly great number density of holes in the p-type material, across the narrow depletion zone. Many electron–hole combinations occur, causing light to be emitted from that zone. Figure 42-16 shows the construction of an actual LED.

Commercial LEDs designed for the visible region are commonly based on gallium, suitably doped with arsenic

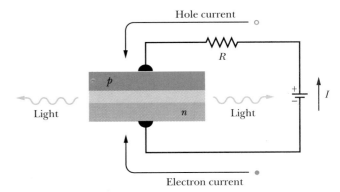

FIGURE 42-15 A forward-biased p-n junction, showing electrons being injected into the n-type material and holes into the p-type material. (Holes move in the conventional direction of the current I, equivalent to electrons moving in the opposite direction.) Light is emitted from the narrow depletion zone each time an electron and a hole combine across that zone.

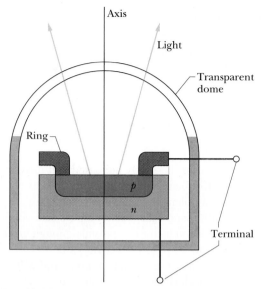

FIGURE 42-16 Cross section of an LED (the device has rotational symmetry about the central axis). The *p*-type material, which is thin enough to transmit light, is in the form of a circular disk. A connection is made to the *p*-type material through a circular metal ring that touches the disk at its periphery. The depletion zone between the *n*-type material and the *p*-type material is not shown.

and phosphorus atoms. An arrangement in which 60% of the nongallium sites are occupied by arsenic ions and 40% by phosphorus ions results in a gap width E_g of about 1.8 eV, corresponding to red light. Other doping and transition level arrangements make it possible to construct LEDs that emit light in essentially any desired region of the visible and near-visible spectra.

The Photo-Diode

Passing a current through a suitably arranged *p-n* junction can generate light. The reverse is also true. That is, shining light on a suitably arranged *p-n* junction can produce a current in a circuit that includes the junction. This is the basis for the **photo-diode**.

When you click your remote control, an LED in the device sends out a coded sequence of pulses of infrared light. The receiving device in your television set is an elaboration of the simple (two-terminal) photo-diode that not only detects the infrared signals but also amplifies them and transforms them into electrical signals that change the channel or adjust the volume, among other tasks.

The Junction Laser

In the arrangement of Fig. 42-15 there are many electrons in the conduction band of the *n*-type material and many holes in the valence band of the *p*-type material. Thus there is a **population inversion** for the electrons; that is, there are more electrons in higher energy levels than in lower energy levels. As we discussed in Section 41-10, this is normally a necessary—but not a sufficient—condition for laser action.

When a single electron moves from the conduction band to the valence band, it can release its energy as a photon. This photon can stimulate a second electron to fall into the valence band, producing a second photon by stimulated emission. In this way, if the current through the junction is great enough, a chain reaction of stimulated emission events can occur and laser light can be generated. To bring this about, opposite faces of the *p-n* junction crystal must be flat and parallel, so that light can be reflected back and forth within the crystal. (Recall that in the helium–neon laser of Fig. 41-21, a pair of mirrors served this purpose.) Thus a *p-n* junction can act as a **junction laser**, its light output being highly coherent and much more sharply defined in wavelength than light from an LED.

Junction lasers are built into compact disk (CD) players, where, by detecting reflections from the rotating disk, they are used to translate microscopic pits in the disk into sound. They are also much used in optical communication systems based on optical fibers. Figure 42-17 suggests their tiny scale. They are usually designed to operate in the infrared region of the electromagnetic spectrum because optical fibers have two ''windows'' in that region (at $\lambda = 1.31$ and 1.55 μm) for which the absorption per unit length of the fiber is a minimum.

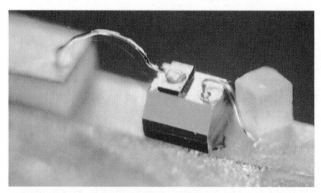

FIGURE 42-17 A semiconducting laser developed at the AT&T Bell Laboratories. The cube at the right is a grain of salt.

SAMPLE PROBLEM 42-5

An LED is constructed from a *p-n* junction based on a certain Ga-As-P semiconducting material, whose energy gap is 1.9 eV. What is the wavelength of the emitted light?

SOLUTION: If we assume that the transitions are from the bottom of the conduction band to the top of the valence band, Eq. 42-9 holds. From this equation

$$\lambda = \frac{hc}{E_g} = \frac{(6.63 \times 10^{-34} \text{ J} \cdot \text{s})(3.00 \times 10^8 \text{ m/s})}{(1.9 \text{ eV})(1.60 \times 10^{-19} \text{ J/eV})}$$

$$= 6.5 \times 10^{-7} \text{ m} = 650 \text{ nm}. \qquad \text{(Answer)}$$

Light of this wavelength is red.

$\mathbb{C}$HECKPOINT **4:** In Sample Problem 42-5 we calculated the wavelength of the light emitted from a certain LED to be 650 nm. Is this (a) the only possible wavelength to be emitted, (b) the maximum emitted wavelength, (c) the minimum emitted wavelength, or (d) the average emitted wavelength?

42-11 THE TRANSISTOR

A **transistor** is a three-terminal semiconducting device that can be used to amplify input signals. Figure 42-18 shows a generalized **f**ield-**e**ffect **t**ransistor (FET); in it, the flow of electrons from terminal S (the **source**) to terminal D (the **drain**) can be controlled by an electric field (hence **field effect**) set up within the device by a suitable electric potential applied to terminal G (the **gate**). Transistors are available in many types; we shall discuss only a particular FET called a **MOSFET**, or **m**etal-**o**xide-**s**emiconductor-**f**ield-**e**ffect **t**ransistor. The MOSFET has been described as the workhorse of the modern electronics industry.

For many applications the MOSFET is operated in only two states: with the drain-to-source current I_{DS} ON ("gate open") or with it OFF ("gate closed"). The first of these can represent a "1" and the other a "0" in the binary arithmetic on which digital logic is based, and therefore MOSFETs can be used in digital logic circuits. Switching between the ON and OFF states can occur at high speed, so that binary logic data can be moved through MOSFET-based circuits very rapidly. As of 1996, MOSFETs about 500 nm in length—about the same as the wavelength of yellow light—were routinely being fabricated for use in electronic devices of all kinds.

Figure 42-19 shows the basic structure of a MOSFET. A single crystal of silicon or other semiconductor is lightly doped to form p-type material. Embedded in this substrate, by heavily "overdoping" with n-type dopants, are two "islands" of n-type material, forming the drain D and the source S. The drain and source are connected by a thin channel of n-type material, called the **n channel**. A thin insulating layer of silicon dioxide (hence the "O" in MOSFET) is deposited on the crystal and penetrated by two metallic terminals (hence the "M") at D and S, so that electrical contact can be made with the drain and the source. A thin metallic layer—the gate G—is deposited facing the n channel. Note that the gate makes no electrical contact with the transistor proper, being separated from it by the insulating oxide layer.

Consider first that the source and p-type substrate are grounded (at zero potential) and the gate is "floating"; that is, the gate is not connected to an external source of emf. Let a potential V_{DS} be applied between the drain and the source, such that the drain is positive. Electrons will then flow through the n channel from source to drain, and the conventional current I_{DS}, as shown in Fig. 42-19, will be from drain to source.

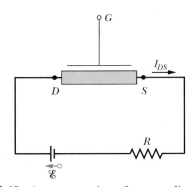

FIGURE 42-18 A representation of a generalized field effect transistor, in which electrons flow through the device from the source terminal S to the drain terminal D. (The conventional current I_{DS} is in the opposite direction.) The magnitude of I_{DS} is controlled by the electric field set up within the body of the device by a potential applied to G, the gate terminal.

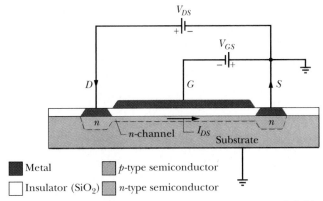

FIGURE 42-19 Representation of a particular type of field-effect transistor known as a MOSFET. The magnitude of the drain–source current through the n channel is controlled by the potential difference V_{GS} applied between the source S and the gate G. A depletion zone that exists between the n-type material and the p-type material is not shown.

Now let a potential V_{GS} be applied to the gate, making it negative with respect to the source. The negative gate sets up within the device an electric field (hence the "field effect") that tends to repel electrons from the n channel into the substrate. This electron movement widens the (naturally occurring) depletion zone between the n channel and the substrate, at the expense of the n channel. The reduced width of the n channel, coupled with a reduction in the number of charge carriers in that channel, increases the resistance of that channel and thus decreases the current I_{DS}. With the proper value of V_{GS}, this current can be shut off completely; hence, by controlling V_{GS}, the MOSFET can be switched between its ON and OFF modes.

Charge carriers do not flow through the *substrate* because the substrate (1) is lightly doped, (2) is not a good conductor, and (3) is separated from the n-channel and the two n-type islands by an insulating depletion zone, not specifically shown in Fig. 42-19. Such a depletion zone always exists at a boundary between n-type material and p-type material, as Fig. 42-11b shows.

Integrated Circuits

Computers and other electronic devices employ thousands (if not millions) of transistors and other electronic components such as capacitors and resistors. These are not assembled as separate units but are crafted into a single semiconducting **chip**, forming an **integrated circuit**.

Figure 42-20 shows a Power PC 620 microprocessor chip, manufactured by Motorola. It incorporates almost 7

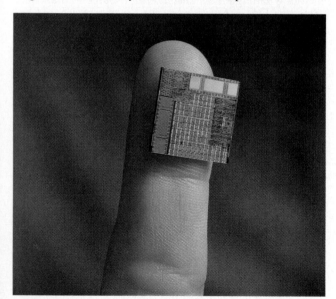

FIGURE 42-20 An integrated circuit for the Motorola Power PC 620 chip, for use mainly in computer workstations and file servers. It will be encapsulated in a ceramic coating for installation and use.

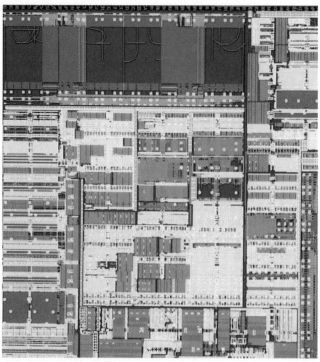

FIGURE 42-21 Enlarged photograph of the layout of the chip shown in Fig. 42-20.

million transistors, along with many other electronic components. Figure 42-21 shows a greatly enlarged view of part of the layout of that chip, the different colors identifying different layers of the chip.

At Intel's Rio Rancho plant, chips are fabricated in a 140 step process on 8 inch silicon wafers, each wafer holding about 300 chips. The individual electronic chip components are so small that the tiniest speck of dust can ruin a chip. Precautions are taken to maintain a dust-free atmosphere in the plant's clean rooms, which are thousands of times more pristine than a hospital operating room. That is the reason for the workers' protective clothing, shown in the photograph that opens this chapter. As part of the cleaning process, highly filtered air circulates through the perforated floor at about 100 ft/min. There are also air showers and wipedown stations for removing cosmetics from employees.

CHECKPOINT 5: In the MOSFET of Fig. 42-19 the gate potential V_{GS} is increased in magnitude until the n channel is blocked off so that I_{DS} falls to zero. Does the blocking (a) start near the source end of the n channel and progress along its length, (b) start near the drain end and progress along the channel, or (c) occur simultaneously at all points along the channel?

REVIEW & SUMMARY

Conductors, Semiconductors, and Insulators

Three electrical properties that can be used to distinguish among crystalline solids are the **resistivity** ρ, the **temperature coefficient of resistivity** α, and the **number density of charge carriers** n. Solids can be broadly divided into **conductors** (with small ρ) and **insulators** (with large ρ). Conductors can be further divided into **metals** (with small ρ, positive α, large n) and **semiconductors** (with larger ρ, negative α, and smaller n).

Energy Levels and Gaps in a Crystalline Solid

An isolated atom can exist in only a discrete set of energy levels. As atoms come together to form a solid, the levels of the individual atoms merge to form the discrete energy **bands** of the solid. These energy bands are separated by energy **gaps**, each of which corresponds to a range of energies that no electron may possess.

Any energy band is made up of an enormous number of very closely spaced levels. The Pauli exclusion principle asserts that only one electron may occupy each of these levels.

Insulators

In an insulator, the highest band containing electrons is completely filled and is separated from the vacant band above it by an energy gap so large that electrons can essentially never become thermally agitated enough to jump across the gap.

Metals

In a **metal**, the highest band that contains any electrons is only partially filled. The energy of the highest filled level at a temperature of 0 K is called the **Fermi energy** E_F for the metal; for copper, $E_F = 7.0$ eV.

The **density of states** function $N(E)$ is the number of available energy levels per unit volume of the sample and per unit energy interval and is given by

$$N(E) = \frac{8\sqrt{2}\,\pi m^{3/2}}{h^3}\,E^{1/2} \quad \text{(density of states).} \quad (42\text{-}2)$$

The **occupancy probability** $P(E)$ (the probability that a given available state will be occupied by an electron) is given by

$$P(E) = \frac{1}{e^{(E-E_F)/kT} + 1} \quad \begin{array}{l}\text{(occupancy} \\ \text{probability).}\end{array} \quad (42\text{-}3)$$

The **density of occupied states** $N_o(E)$ is given by the product of the two quantities above:

$$N_o(E) = N(E)\,P(E) \quad \begin{array}{l}\text{(density of} \\ \text{occupied states).}\end{array} \quad (42\text{-}4)$$

The Fermi energy for a metal can be found by integrating $N_o(E)$ for $T = 0$ from $E = 0$ to $E = E_F$. The result is

$$E_F = \left(\frac{3}{16\sqrt{2}\,\pi}\right)^{2/3}\frac{h^2}{m}\,n^{2/3} = \frac{0.121h^2}{m}\,n^{2/3}. \quad (42\text{-}6)$$

Semiconductors

The band structure of a **semiconductor** is like that of an insulator except that the gap width E_g is much smaller in the semiconductor. For silicon (a semiconductor) at room temperature, thermal agitation raises a few electrons to the **conduction band**, leaving an equal number of **holes** in the **valence band**. Both electrons and holes serve as charge carriers.

The number of electrons in the conduction band of silicon can be increased greatly by doping with small amounts of phosphorus, thus forming **n-type material**. The number of holes in the valence band can be greatly increased by doping with aluminum, thus forming **p-type material**.

The p-n Junction

A **p-n junction** is a single semiconducting crystal with one end doped to form p-type material and the other end doped to form n-type material, the two types meeting at a **junction plane**. At thermal equilibrium, the following occurs at that plane:

The **majority carriers** (electrons on the n side and holes on the p side) diffuse across the junction plane, producing a **diffusion current** I_{diff}.

The **minority carriers** (holes on the n side and electrons on the p side) are swept across the junction plane, forming a **drift current** I_{drift}. These two currents are equal in magnitude, so the net current is zero.

A **depletion zone**, consisting largely of space-charged donor and acceptor ions, forms across the junction plane.

A **contact potential difference** of height V_0 develops across the depletion zone.

Applications of the p-n Junction

When a potential difference is applied across a p-n junction, the device conducts electricity more readily for one polarity of the applied potential difference than for the other. Thus a p-n junction can serve as a **junction rectifier**.

When a p-n junction is forward biased, it can emit light, hence can serve as a **light-emitting diode** (LED). The wavelength of the emitted light is given by

$$\lambda = \frac{c}{f} = \frac{hc}{E_g}. \quad (42\text{-}9)$$

A strongly forward-biased p-n junction with parallel end faces can operate as a **junction laser**, emitting light of a sharply defined wavelength.

MOSFETS

In a MOSFET, a type of three-terminal transistor, a potential applied to the **gate** terminal G controls the internal flow of electrons from the **source** terminal S to the **drain** terminal D. Commonly, a MOSFET is operated only in its ON (conducting) or its OFF (not conducting) conditions. Installed by the thousands and millions on silicon wafers (**chips**) to form **integrated circuits**, MOSFETs form the basis for computer hardware.

QUESTIONS

1. Figure 42-1*a* shows 14 atoms that represent the unit cell of copper. Since, however, each of these atoms is shared with one or more adjoining unit cells, only a fraction of each atom belongs to the unit cell shown. What is the number of atoms per unit cell for copper? (To answer, count up the fractional atoms belonging to a single unit cell.)

2. Figure 42-1*b* shows 18 atoms that represent the unit cell of silicon. Fourteen of these atoms, however, are shared with one or more adjoining unit cells. What is the number of atoms per unit cell for silicon? (See Question 1.)

3. Does the interval between adjacent energy levels in the highest occupied band of a metal depend on (a) the material of which the sample is made, (b) the size of the sample, (c) the position of the level in the band, (d) the temperature of the sample, or (e) the Fermi energy of the metal?

4. Compare the drift speed v_d of the conduction electrons in a current-carrying copper wire with the Fermi speed v_F for copper? Is v_d (a) about equal to v_F, (b) much greater than v_F, or (c) much less than v_F?

5. In a silicon lattice, where should you look if you want to find (a) a conduction electron, (b) a valence electron, and (c) an electron associated with the $2p$ subshell of the isolated silicon atom?

6. Which of the following statements, if any, are true? (a) At low enough temperatures, silicon behaves like an insulator. (b) At high enough temperatures, silicon becomes a good conductor. (c) At high enough temperatures, silicon behaves like a metal.

7. The energy gaps E_g for the semiconductors silicon and germanium are, respectively, 1.12 and 0.67 eV. Which of the following statements, if any, are true? (a) Both substances have the same number density of charge carriers at room temperature. (b) At room temperature, germanium has a greater number density of charge carriers than silicon. (c) Both substances have a greater number density of conduction electrons than holes. (d) For each substance, the number density of electrons equals that of holes.

8. An isolated atom of germanium has 32 electrons, arranged in subshells according to this scheme:

$$1s^2\ 2s^2\ 2p^6\ 3s^2\ 3p^6\ 3d^{10}\ 4s^2\ 4p^2.$$

This element has the same crystal structure as silicon and, like silicon, is a semiconductor. Which of these electrons form the valence band of crystalline germanium?

9. Germanium ($Z = 32$) has the same crystal structure and the same bonding pattern as silicon. Is the net charge on a germanium ion within its lattice $+e$, $+2e$, $+4e$, $+28e$, or $+32e$?

10. (a) Of the elements arsenic, indium, tin, gallium, antimony, and boron, which would produce *n*-type material if used as a dopant in silicon? (b) Which would produce *p*-type material? (c) Which would be unsuitable as a dopant? (*Hint*: Consult the periodic table in Appendix G.)

11. A sample of silicon is doped with phosphorus. Which of the following statements, if any, are true? (a) The number of holes in the sample is slightly increased. (b) The resistivity is increased. (c) The sample becomes positively charged. (d) The sample becomes negatively charged. (e) The gap between the valence band and the conduction band decreases slightly.

12. To fabricate an *n*-type semiconductor, would you use (a) silicon doped with arsenic or (b) germanium doped with indium? (*Hint*: Consult the periodic table.)

13. In the biased *p-n* junctions shown in Fig. 42-14, there is an electric field **E** in the two depletion zones, associated with the potential difference that exists across the zone in each case. (a) Does **E** point from left to right or from right to left? (b) Is its magnitude greater for forward bias or for back bias?

14. A certain isolated *p-n* junction develops a contact potential difference V_0 across its depletion zone of 0.78 V. A voltmeter is connected across the terminals of the junction, the positive terminal of the meter being connected to the *p* side of the junction. Will the meter read (a) +0.78 V, (b) −0.78 V, (c) zero, or (d) something else? (*Hint*: Contact potentials appear at the connections between the *p-n* junction and the voltmeter leads.)

15. Which of the following obey Ohm's law: (a) a bar of pure silicon, (b) a bar of *n*-type silicon, (c) a bar of *p*-type silicon, (d) a *p-n* junction?

16. An LED based on a gallium–arsenic–phosphorus semiconducting crystal emits red light. If you look at a white surface through such a crystal, will you see (a) red, (b) blue, (c) nothing, because the crystal is opaque, or (d) white?

EXERCISES & PROBLEMS

SECTION 42-5 Metals

1E. Copper is a monovalent metal with a molar mass of 63.5 g/mol and a density of 8.96 g/cm³. Show that the number density of conduction electrons in copper is 8.43×10^{28} m⁻³.

2E. At what pressure, in atmospheres, would an ideal gas have a number density of molecules equal to the number density of the conduction electrons in copper, with both gas and copper at temperature $T = 300$ K?

3E. Verify the numerical factor 0.121 in Eq. 42-6.

4E. What is the number density of conduction electrons in gold, which is a monovalent metal? Use the molar mass and density provided in Appendix F.

5E. Calculate $d\rho/dT$ at room temperature for (a) copper and (b) silicon, using data from Table 42-1.

6E. Use Eq. 42-6 to verify that the Fermi energy of copper is 7.0 eV.

7E. The Fermi energy of copper is 7.0 eV. Verify that the corresponding Fermi speed is 1600 km/s.

8E. (a) Show that Eq. 42-2 can be written as $N(E) = CE^{1/2}$, where $C = 6.78 \times 10^{27}$ m^{-3}eV$^{-3/2}$. (b) Calculate $N(E)$ for $E = 5.00$ eV.

9E. What is the probability that a state 0.062 eV above the Fermi energy will be occupied at (a) $T = 0$ K and (b) $T = 320$ K?

10E. Calculate the density of states $N(E)$ for a metal at energy $E = 8.0$ eV and show that your result is consistent with the curve of Fig. 42-5.

11E. Show that Eq. 42-6 can be written as $E_F = An^{2/3}$, where the constant A has the value 3.65×10^{-19} m$^2 \cdot$ eV.

12E. The density of gold is 19.3 g/cm^3, and each gold atom contributes one electron to the conduction band. Use the result of Exercise 4 to calculate the Fermi energy of gold.

13E. A state 63 meV above the Fermi level has a probability of occupancy of 0.090. What is the probability of occupancy for a state 63 meV *below* the Fermi level?

14P. The Fermi energy for copper is 7.0 eV. For copper at 1000 K, (a) find the energy of the energy level whose probability of being occupied by an electron is 0.90. For this energy, evaluate (b) the density of states and (c) the density of occupied states.

15P. The density and molar mass of sodium (a metal) are 971 kg/m^3 and 23.0 g/mol, respectively; the radius of the Na$^+$ ion is 98 pm. (a) What percent of metallic sodium is available to its conduction electrons? (b) Carry out the same calculation for copper, which has density, molar mass, and ionic radius of 8960 kg/m^3, 63.5 g/mol, and 135 pm, respectively. (c) For which of these metals do you think the conduction electrons behave more like a free-electron gas?

16P. Show that $P(E)$, the occupancy probability in Eq. 42-3, is symmetrical about the value of the Fermi energy. That is, show that

$$P(E_F + \Delta E) + P(E_F - \Delta E) = 1.$$

17P. In Eq. 42-3 let $E - E_F = \Delta E = 1.00$ eV. (a) At what temperature does the result of using this quantum equation differ by 1.0% from the result of using the classical Boltzmann equation $P(E) = e^{-\Delta E/kT}$? (b) At what temperature do these results differ by 10%?

18P. What is the probability that an electron will jump from the valence band to the conduction band in a diamond whose mass is equal to the mass of Earth? Use the result of Sample Problem 42-1 and the molar mass of carbon in Appendix F; assume that in diamond there is one valence electron per carbon atom.

19P. Calculate the number density for (a) molecules of oxygen gas at 0°C and 1.0 atm pressure and (b) conduction electrons in copper. (c) What is the ratio of the latter to the former? (d) What is the average distance between particles in each case? Assume this distance is the edge length of a cube whose volume is equal to the available volume per particle.

20P. Calculate $N_o(E)$, the density of occupied states, for copper at $T = 1000$ K for the energies $E = 4.00$, 6.75, 7.00, 7.25, and 9.00 eV. Compare your results with the graph of Fig. 42-7b. The Fermi energy for copper is 7.00 eV.

21P. The Fermi energy for silver is 5.5 eV. (a) At $T = 0$°C, what are the probabilities that states with the following energies are occupied: 4.4, 5.4, 5.5, 5.6, and 6.4 eV? (b) At what temperature is the probability 0.16 that a state with energy $E = 5.6$ eV is occupied?

22P. The Fermi energy of aluminum is 11.6 eV; its density and molar mass are 2.70 g/cm^3 and 27.0 g/mol, respectively. From these data, determine the number of free electrons per atom.

23P. Show that the probability $P_h(E)$ that a hole exists at energy E (that is, that an energy level at energy E is not occupied) is

$$P_h(E) = \frac{1}{e^{-\Delta E/kT} + 1},$$

where $\Delta E = E - E_F$.

24P. Zinc is a bivalent metal. Calculate (a) the number density of conduction electrons, (b) the Fermi energy, (c) the Fermi speed, and (d) the de Broglie wavelength corresponding to this electron speed. See Appendix F for the needed data on zinc.

25P. Silver is a monovalent metal. Calculate (a) the number density of conduction electrons, (b) the Fermi energy, (c) the Fermi speed, and (d) the de Broglie wavelength corresponding to this electron speed. See Appendix F for the needed data on silver.

26P. At $T = 300$ K, how close to the Fermi energy will we find a state whose probability of occupation by a conduction electron is 0.10?

27P. (a) Show that the density of states at the Fermi energy is given by

$$N(E_F) = \frac{(4)(3^{1/3})(\pi^{2/3})mn^{1/3}}{h^2}$$

$$= (4.11 \times 10^{18} \text{ m}^{-2}\text{eV}^{-1})n^{1/3},$$

in which n is the number density of conduction electrons. (b) Calculate $N(E_F)$ for copper using the result of Exercise 1, and verify your calculation with the curve of Fig. 42-5, recalling that $E_F = 7.0$ eV for copper.

28P. (a) Show that the slope dP/dE of Eq. 42-3 at $E = E_F$ is $-1/4kT$. (b) Show that the tangent line to the curve of Fig. 42-6b at $E = E_F$ intercepts the horizontal axis at $E = E_F + 2kT$.

29P. Show that, at $T = 0$ K, the average energy E_{av} of the conduction electrons in a metal is equal to $\frac{3}{5}E_F$. (*Hint*: By definition of average, $E_{av} = (1/n)\int E\,N_o(E)\,dE$, where n is the number density of charge carriers.)

30P. Use the result of Problem 29 to calculate the total translational kinetic energy of the conduction electrons in 1.0 cm^3 of copper at $T = 0$ K.

31P. (a) Using the result of Problem 29, estimate how much energy would be released by the conduction electrons in a penny (assumed all copper and of mass 3.1 g) if we could suddenly turn off the Pauli exclusion principle. (b) For how long would this amount of energy light a 100 W lamp? (*Note*: There is no way to turn off the Pauli principle!)

32P. At 1000 K, the fraction of the conduction electrons in a metal that have energies greater than the Fermi energy is equal to the area under the curve of Fig. 42-7b beyond E_F divided by the area under the entire curve. It is difficult to find these areas by direct integration. However, an approximation to this fraction at any temperature T is

$$frac = \frac{3kT}{2E_F}.$$

Note that *frac* = 0 for T = 0 K, just as we would expect. What is this fraction for copper at (a) 300 K and at (b) 1000 K? For copper, E_F = 7.0 eV. (c) If you can, check your answers by numerical integration using Eq. 42-4.

33P. At what temperature do 1.3% of the conduction electrons in lithium (a metal) have energies greater than the Fermi energy E_F, which is 4.7 eV? (See Problem 32.)

34P. Silver melts at 961°C. At the melting point, what fraction of the conduction electrons are in states with energies greater than the Fermi energy of 5.5 eV? (See Problem 32.)

SECTION 42-6 Semiconductors

35P. (a) Find the angle θ between adjacent nearest-neighbor bonds in the silicon lattice. Recall that each silicon atom is bonded to four of its nearest neighbors. The four neighbors form a regular tetrahedron: a three-sided pyramid whose sides and base are equilateral triangles. (b) Find the bond length, given that the atoms at the corners of the tetrahedron are 388 pm apart.

36P. The compound gallium arsenide is a commonly used semiconductor, having an energy gap E_g of 1.43 eV. Its crystal structure is like that of silicon, except that half the silicon atoms are replaced by gallium atoms and half by arsenic atoms. Draw a flattened-out sketch of the gallium arsenide lattice, following the pattern of Fig. 42-9a. (a) What are the net charges of the gallium and the arsenic ion cores? (b) How many electrons per bond are there? (*Hint*: Consult the periodic table in Appendix G.)

37P. (a) What is the maximum wavelength of the light that will excite an electron in the valence band of diamond to the conduction band? The energy gap is 5.5 eV. (b) In what part of the electromagnetic spectrum does this wavelength lie?

38P. The occupancy probability function (Eq. 42-3) can be applied to semiconductors as well as to metals. In semiconductors the Fermi energy is close to the midpoint of the gap between the valence band and the conduction band; see Problem 39. For germanium, the gap width is 0.67 eV. What is the probability that (a) a state at the bottom of the conduction band is occupied and (b) a state at the top of the valence band is not occupied. Assume that T = 290 K. (*Note*: Figure 42-4b shows that, in a metal, the Fermi

energy lies symmetrically between the population of conduction electrons and the population of holes. To match this scheme in a semiconductor, the Fermi energy must lie near the center of the gap. There need not be an available state at the location of the Fermi energy.)

39P. In a simplified model of an undoped semiconductor, the actual distribution of energy states may be replaced by one in which there are N_v states in the valence band, all these states having the same energy E_v, and N_c states in the conduction band, all these states having the same energy E_c. The number of electrons in the conduction band equals the number of holes in the valence band. (a) Show that this last condition implies that

$$\frac{N_c}{\exp(\Delta E_c/kT) + 1} = \frac{N_v}{\exp(\Delta E_v/kT) + 1},$$

in which

$$\Delta E_c = E_c - E_F \quad \text{and} \quad \Delta E_v = -(E_v - E_F).$$

(*Hint*: See Problem 23.) (b) If the Fermi level is in the gap between the two bands and is far from both bands compared with kT, then the exponentials dominate in the denominators. Under these conditions show that

$$E_F = \frac{(E_c + E_v)}{2} + \frac{kT \ln(N_v/N_c)}{2}$$

and that, if $N_v \approx N_c$, the Fermi level for the undoped semiconductor is close to the gap's center, as stated in Problem 38.

SECTION 42-7 Doped Semiconductors

40P. Pure silicon at room temperature has an electron number density in the conduction band of about 5×10^{15} m^{-3} and an equal density of holes in the valence band. Suppose that one of every 10^7 silicon atoms is replaced by a phosphorus atom. (a) Which type will the doped semiconductor be, n or p? (b) What charge carrier number density will the phosphorus add? (c) What is the ratio of the charge carrier number density (electrons in the conduction band and holes in the valence band) in the doped silicon to that in pure silicon?

41P. What mass of phosphorus is needed to dope 1.0 g of silicon to the extent described in Sample Problem 42-4?

42P. Doping changes the Fermi energy of a semiconductor. Consider silicon, with a gap of 1.11 eV between the top of the valence band and the bottom of the conduction band. At 300 K the Fermi level of the pure material is nearly at the midpoint of the gap. Suppose that silicon is doped with donor atoms, each of which has a state 0.15 eV below the bottom of the conduction band, and suppose further that doping raises the Fermi level to 0.11 eV below the bottom of that band (Fig. 42-22). (a) For both pure and doped silicon, calculate the probability that a state at the bottom of the conduction band is occupied. (b) Calculate the probability that a donor state in the doped material is occupied.

43P. A silicon sample is doped with atoms having a donor state 0.110 eV below the bottom of the conduction band. (The energy

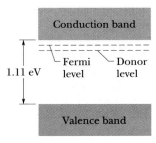

FIGURE 42-22 Problem 42.

gap in silicon is 1.11 eV.) (a) If each of these donor states is occupied with a probability of 5.00×10^{-5} at $T = 300$ K, where is the Fermi level with respect to the top of the valence band? (b) What then is the probability that a state at the bottom of the conduction band is occupied?

SECTION 42-9 The Junction Rectifier

44P. When a photon enters the depletion zone of a *p-n* junction, electron–hole pairs can be created as electrons absorb part of the photon's energy and are excited from the valence band to the conduction band. These junctions are thus often used as detectors for photons, especially in the x-ray and the gamma-ray regions of the electromagnetic spectrum. When a single 662 keV gamma-ray photon is totally absorbed by a semiconductor with an energy gap of 1.1 eV, what is the average number of electron–hole pairs created?

45P. For an ideal *p-n* junction rectifier, with a sharp boundary between its two semiconducting sides, the current I is related to the potential difference V across the rectifier by

$$I = I_0(e^{eV/kT} - 1),$$

where I_0, which depends on the materials but not on the current or the potential difference, is called the *reverse saturation current*.

V is positive if the rectifier is forward-biased and negative if it is back-biased. (a) Verify that this expression predicts the behavior of a junction rectifier by graphing I versus V over the range -0.12 V to $+0.12$ V. Take $T = 300$ K and $I_0 = 5.0$ nA. (b) For the same temperature, calculate the ratio of the current for a 0.50 V forward-bias to the current for a 0.50 V back-bias.

SECTION 42-10 The Light-Emitting Diode (LED)

46P. (a) In a particular crystal, the highest occupied band is full. The crystal is transparent to light of wavelengths longer than 295 nm but opaque at shorter wavelengths. Calculate, in electron-volts, the gap between the highest occupied band and the next higher (empty) band for this material.

47P. A potassium chloride crystal has an energy band gap of 7.6 eV above the topmost occupied band, which is full. Is this crystal opaque or transparent to light of wavelength 140 nm?

SECTION 42-11 The Transistor

48P. A Pentium computer chip, which is about the size of a postage stamp (1.0 in. $\times$ 0.875 in.), contains about 3.5 million transistors. If the transistors are square, what must be their *maximum* dimension? (*Note*: Devices other than transistors are also on the chip, and there must be room for the interconnections among the circuit elements. Transistors as small as 0.7 μm are commonly fabricated.)

49P. A silicon-based MOSFET has a square gate 0.50 μm on edge. The insulating silicon oxide layer that separates it from the *p*-type substrate is 0.20 μm thick and has a dielectric constant of 4.5. (a) What is the equivalent gate–substrate capacitance? (b) How many elementary charges e appear in the gate when there is a gate–source potential difference of 1.0 V?

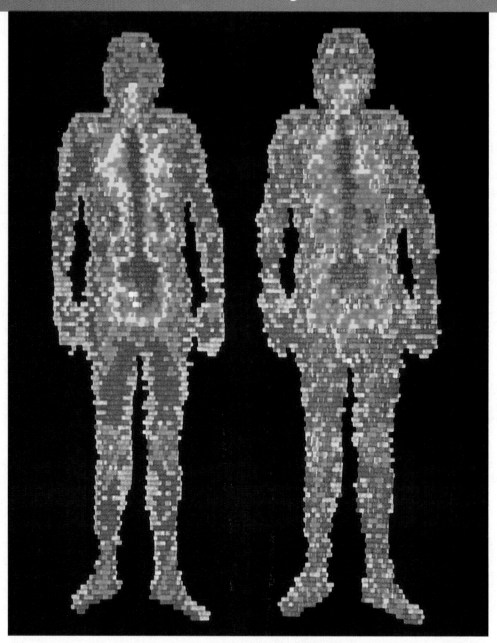

Radioactive nuclei that are injected into a patient collect at certain sites within the patient's body, undergo radioactive decay, and emit gamma rays. These gamma rays are recorded by a detector, and a color-coded image of the patient's body is produced on a video monitor. In the images reproduced here (the left one is a front view of a patient and the right one is a back view), you can tell just where the radioactive nuclei have collected (spine, pelvis, and ribs) by the color-coding of brown and orange. What happens to radioactive nuclei when they undergo decay, and what exactly does "decay" mean?

Appendix A
The International System of Units (SI)*

1. THE SI BASE UNITS

QUANTITY	NAME	SYMBOL	DEFINITION
length	meter	m	". . . the length of the path traveled by light in vacuum in 1/299,792,458 of a second." (1983)
mass	kilogram	kg	". . . this prototype [a certain platinum–iridium cylinder] shall henceforth be considered to be the unit of mass." (1889)
time	second	s	". . . the duration of 9,192,631,770 periods of the radiation corresponding to the transition between the two hyperfine levels of the ground state of the cesium-133 atom." (1967)
electric current	ampere	A	". . . that constant current which, if maintained in two straight parallel conductors of infinite length, of negligible circular cross section, and placed 1 meter apart in vacuum, would produce between these conductors a force equal to 2×10^{-7} newton per meter of length." (1946)
thermodynamic temperature	kelvin	K	". . . the fraction 1/273.16 of the thermodynamic temperature of the triple point of water." (1967)
amount of substance	mole	mol	". . . the amount of substance of a system which contains as many elementary entities as there are atoms in 0.012 kilogram of carbon-12." (1971)
luminous intensity	candela	cd	". . . the luminous intensity, in the perpendicular direction, of a surface of 1/600,000 square meter of a blackbody at the temperature of freezing platinum under a pressure of 101.325 newtons per square meter." (1967)

*Adapted from "The International System of Units (SI)," National Bureau of Standards Special Publication 330, 1972 edition. The definitions above were adopted by the General Conference of Weights and Measures, an international body, on the dates shown. In this book we do not use the candela.

2. SOME SI DERIVED UNITS

QUANTITY	NAME OF UNIT	SYMBOL	
area	square meter	m^2	
volume	cubic meter	m^3	
frequency	hertz	Hz	s^{-1}
mass density (density)	kilogram per cubic meter	kg/m^3	
speed, velocity	meter per second	m/s	
angular velocity	radian per second	rad/s	
acceleration	meter per second per second	m/s^2	
angular acceleration	radian per second per second	rad/s^2	
force	newton	N	$kg \cdot m/s^2$
pressure	pascal	Pa	N/m^2
work, energy, quantity of heat	joule	J	$N \cdot m$
power	watt	W	J/s
quantity of electric charge	coulomb	C	$A \cdot s$
potential difference, electromotive force	volt	V	W/A
electric field strength	volt per meter (or newton per coulomb)	V/m	N/C
electric resistance	ohm	Ω	V/A
capacitance	farad	F	$A \cdot s/V$
magnetic flux	weber	Wb	$V \cdot s$
inductance	henry	H	$V \cdot s/A$
magnetic flux density	tesla	T	Wb/m^2
magnetic field strength	ampere per meter	A/m	
entropy	joule per kelvin	J/K	
specific heat	joule per kilogram kelvin	$J/(kg \cdot K)$	
thermal conductivity	watt per meter kelvin	$W/(m \cdot K)$	
radiant intensity	watt per steradian	W/sr	

3. THE SI SUPPLEMENTARY UNITS

QUANTITY	NAME OF UNIT	SYMBOL
plane angle	radian	rad
solid angle	steradian	sr

Appendix B
Some Fundamental Constants of Physics*

CONSTANT	SYMBOL	COMPUTATIONAL VALUE	BEST (1986) VALUE VALUE[a]	BEST (1986) VALUE UNCERTAINTY[b]
Speed of light in a vacuum	c	3.00×10^8 m/s	2.99792458	exact
Elementary charge	e	1.60×10^{-19} C	1.60217733	0.30
Gravitational constant	G	6.67×10^{-11} m³/s²·kg	6.67259	128
Universal gas constant	R	8.31 J/mol·K	8.314510	8.4
Avogadro constant	N_A	6.02×10^{23} mol^{-1}	6.0221367	0.59
Boltzmann constant	k	1.38×10^{-23} J/K	1.380658	8.5
Stefan-Boltzmann constant	σ	5.67×10^{-8} W/m²·K⁴	5.67051	34
Molar volume of ideal gas at STP[d]	V_m	2.24×10^{-2} m³/mol	2.241409	8.4
Permittivity constant	ϵ_0	8.85×10^{-12} F/m	8.85418781762	exact
Permeability constant	μ_0	1.26×10^{-6} H/m	1.25663706143	exact
Planck constant	h	6.63×10^{-34} J·s	6.6260755	0.60
Electron mass[c]	m_e	9.11×10^{-31} kg	9.1093897	0.59
		5.49×10^{-4} u	5.48579903	0.023
Proton mass[c]	m_p	1.67×10^{-27} kg	1.6726231	0.59
		1.0073 u	1.0072764660	0.005
Ratio of proton mass to electron mass	m_p/m_e	1840	1836.152701	0.020
Electron charge-to-mass ratio	e/m_e	1.76×10^{11} C/kg	1.75881961	0.30
Neutron mass[c]	m_n	1.68×10^{-27} kg	1.6749286	0.59
		1.0087 u	1.0086649235	0.0023
Hydrogen atom mass[c]	m_{1_H}	1.0078 u	1.0078250316	0.0005
Deuterium atom mass[c]	m_{2_H}	2.0141 u	2.0141017779	0.0005
Helium atom mass[c]	$m_{4_{He}}$	4.0026 u	4.0026032	0.067
Muon mass	m_μ	1.88×10^{-28} kg	1.8835326	0.61
Electron magnetic moment	μ_e	9.28×10^{-24} J/T	9.2847701	0.34
Proton magnetic moment	μ_p	1.41×10^{-26} J/T	1.41060761	0.34
Bohr magneton	μ_B	9.27×10^{-24} J/T	9.2740154	0.34
Nuclear magneton	μ_N	5.05×10^{-27} J/T	5.0507866	0.34
Bohr radius	r_B	5.29×10^{-11} m	5.29177249	0.045
Rydberg constant	R	1.10×10^7 m^{-1}	1.0973731534	0.0012
Electron Compton wavelength	λ_C	2.43×10^{-12} m	2.42631058	0.089

[a]Values given in this column should be given the same unit and power of 10 as the computational value.   [b]Parts per million.   [c]Masses given in u are in unified atomic mass units, where 1 u = $1.6605402 \times 10^{-27}$ kg.   [d]STP means standard temperature and pressure: 0°C and 1.0 atm (0.1 MPa).

*The values in this table were largely selected from a longer list in *Symbols, Units and Nomenclature in Physics* (IUPAP), prepared by E. Richard Cohen and Pierre Giacomo, 1986.

Appendix C
Some Astronomical Data

SOME DISTANCES FROM THE EARTH

To the moon*	3.82×10^8 m
To the sun*	1.50×10^{11} m
To the nearest star (Proxima Centauri)	4.04×10^{16} m
To the center of our galaxy	2.2×10^{20} m
To the Andromeda Galaxy	2.1×10^{22} m
To the edge of the observable universe	$\sim 10^{26}$ m

*Mean distance.

THE SUN, THE EARTH, AND THE MOON

PROPERTY	UNIT	SUN	EARTH	MOON
Mass	kg	1.99×10^{30}	5.98×10^{24}	7.36×10^{22}
Mean radius	m	6.96×10^8	6.37×10^6	1.74×10^6
Mean density	kg/m³	1410	5520	3340
Free-fall acceleration at the surface	m/s²	274	9.81	1.67
Escape velocity	km/s	618	11.2	2.38
Period of rotation[a]	—	37 d at poles[b] 26 d at equator[b]	23 h 56 min	27.3 d
Radiation power[c]	W	3.90×10^{26}		

[a]Measured with respect to the distant stars.

[b]The sun, a ball of gas, does not rotate as a rigid body.

[c]Just outside the Earth's atmosphere solar energy is received, assuming normal incidence, at the rate of 1340 W/m².

SOME PROPERTIES OF THE PLANETS

	MERCURY	VENUS	EARTH	MARS	JUPITER	SATURN	URANUS	NEPTUNE	PLUTO
Mean distance from sun, 10^6 km	57.9	108	150	228	778	1430	2870	4500	5900
Period of revolution, y	0.241	0.615	1.00	1.88	11.9	29.5	84.0	165	248
Period of rotation,[a] d	58.7	-243^b	0.997	1.03	0.409	0.426	-0.451^b	0.658	6.39
Orbital speed, km/s	47.9	35.0	29.8	24.1	13.1	9.64	6.81	5.43	4.74
Inclination of axis to orbit	$<28°$	$\approx3°$	23.4°	25.0°	3.08°	26.7°	97.9°	29.6°	57.5°
Inclination of orbit to Earth's orbit	7.00°	3.39°		1.85°	1.30°	2.49°	0.77°	1.77°	17.2°
Eccentricity of orbit	0.206	0.0068	0.0167	0.0934	0.0485	0.0556	0.0472	0.0086	0.250
Equatorial diameter, km	4880	12,100	12,800	6790	143,000	120,000	51,800	49,500	2300
Mass (Earth = 1)	0.0558	0.815	1.000	0.107	318	95.1	14.5	17.2	0.002
Density (water = 1)	5.60	5.20	5.52	3.95	1.31	0.704	1.21	1.67	2.03
Surface value of g,[c] m/s^2	3.78	8.60	9.78	3.72	22.9	9.05	7.77	11.0	0.5
Escape velocity,[c] km/s	4.3	10.3	11.2	5.0	59.5	35.6	21.2	23.6	1.1
Known satellites	0	0	1	2	16 + ring	18 + rings	15 + rings	8 + rings	1

[a]Measured with respect to the distant stars.

[b]Venus and Uranus rotate opposite their orbital motion.

[c]Gravitational acceleration measured at the planet's equator.

Appendix **D**
Conversion Factors

Conversion factors may be read directly from these tables. For example, 1 degree = 2.778×10^{-3} revolutions, so $16.7° = 16.7 \times 2.778 \times 10^{-3}$ rev. The SI quantities are fully capitalized.

Adapted in part from G. Shortley and D. Williams, *Elements of Physics,* Prentice-Hall, Englewood Cliffs, NJ, 1971.

PLANE ANGLE

	°	′	″	RADIAN	rev
1 degree =	1	60	3600	1.745×10^{-2}	2.778×10^{-3}
1 minute =	1.667×10^{-2}	1	60	2.909×10^{-4}	4.630×10^{-5}
1 second =	2.778×10^{-4}	1.667×10^{-2}	1	4.848×10^{-6}	7.716×10^{-7}
1 RADIAN =	57.30	3438	2.063×10^{5}	1	0.1592
1 revolution =	360	2.16×10^{4}	1.296×10^{6}	6.283	1

SOLID ANGLE

1 sphere = 4π steradians = 12.57 steradians

LENGTH

	cm	METER	km	in.	ft	mi
1 centimeter =	1	10^{-2}	10^{-5}	0.3937	3.281×10^{-2}	6.214×10^{-6}
1 METER =	100	1	10^{-3}	39.37	3.281	6.214×10^{-4}
1 kilometer =	10^{5}	1000	1	3.937×10^{4}	3281	0.6214
1 inch =	2.540	2.540×10^{-2}	2.540×10^{-5}	1	8.333×10^{-2}	1.578×10^{-5}
1 foot =	30.48	0.3048	3.048×10^{-4}	12	1	1.894×10^{-4}
1 mile =	1.609×10^{5}	1609	1.609	6.336×10^{4}	5280	1

1 angström = 10^{-10} m
1 nautical mile = 1852 m
  = 1.151 miles = 6076 ft

1 fermi = 10^{-15} m
1 light-year = 9.460×10^{12} km
1 parsec = 3.084×10^{13} km

1 fathom = 6 ft
1 Bohr radius = 5.292×10^{-11} m
1 yard = 3 ft

1 rod = 16.5 ft
1 mil = 10^{-3} in.
1 nm = 10^{-9} m

AREA

	METER^2	cm^2	ft^2	in.^{2}
1 SQUARE METER =	1	10^{4}	10.76	1550
1 square centimeter =	10^{-4}	1	1.076×10^{-3}	0.1550
1 square foot =	9.290×10^{-2}	929.0	1	144
1 square inch =	6.452×10^{-4}	6.452	6.944×10^{-3}	1

1 square mile = 2.788×10^{7} ft^2
  = 640 acres
1 barn = 10^{-28} m^2

1 acre = 43,560 ft^2
1 hectare = 10^{4} m^2 = 2.471 acres

VOLUME

	METER^3	cm^3	L	ft^3	in.^{3}
1 CUBIC METER = 1		10^6	1000	35.31	6.102×10^4
1 cubic centimeter = 10^{-6}		1	1.000×10^{-3}	3.531×10^{-5}	6.102×10^{-2}
1 liter = 1.000×10^{-3}		1000	1	3.531×10^{-2}	61.02
1 cubic foot = 2.832×10^{-2}		2.832×10^4	28.32	1	1728
1 cubic inch = 1.639×10^{-5}		16.39	1.639×10^{-2}	5.787×10^{-4}	1

1 U.S. fluid gallon = 4 U.S. fluid quarts = 8 U.S. pints = 128 U.S. fluid ounces = 231 in.^{3}

1 British imperial gallon = 277.4 in.^{3} = 1.201 U.S. fluid gallons

MASS

Quantities in the colored areas are not mass units but are often used as such. When we write, for example, 1 kg "=" 2.205 lb, this means that a kilogram is a *mass* that *weighs* 2.205 pounds at a location where g has the standard value of 9.80665 m/s^2.

	g	KILOGRAM	slug	u	oz	lb	ton
1 gram = 1	0.001	6.852×10^{-5}	6.022×10^{23}	3.527×10^{-2}	2.205×10^{-3}	1.102×10^{-6}	
1 KILOGRAM = 1000	1	6.852×10^{-2}	6.022×10^{26}	35.27	2.205	1.102×10^{-3}	
1 slug = 1.459×10^4	14.59	1	8.786×10^{27}	514.8	32.17	1.609×10^{-2}	
1 atomic mass unit = 1.661×10^{-24}	1.661×10^{-27}	1.138×10^{-28}	1	5.857×10^{-26}	3.662×10^{-27}	1.830×10^{-30}	
1 ounce = 28.35	2.835×10^{-2}	1.943×10^{-3}	1.718×10^{25}	1	6.250×10^{-2}	3.125×10^{-5}	
1 pound = 453.6	0.4536	3.108×10^{-2}	2.732×10^{26}	16	1	0.0005	
1 ton = 9.072×10^5	907.2	62.16	5.463×10^{29}	3.2×10^4	2000	1	

1 metric ton = 1000 kg

DENSITY

Quantities in the colored areas are weight densities and, as such, are dimensionally different from mass densities. See note for mass table.

	slug/ft^3	KILOGRAM/ METER^3	g/cm^3	lb/ft^3	lb/in.^{3}
1 slug per foot^3 = 1		515.4	0.5154	32.17	1.862×10^{-2}
1 KILOGRAM per METER^3 = 1.940×10^{-3}		1	0.001	6.243×10^{-2}	3.613×10^{-5}
1 gram per centimeter^3 = 1.940		1000	1	62.43	3.613×10^{-2}
1 pound per foot^3 = 3.108×10^{-2}		16.02	1.602×10^{-2}	1	5.787×10^{-4}
1 pound per inch^3 = 53.71		2.768×10^4	27.68	1728	1

TIME

	y	d	h	min	SECOND
1 year = 1		365.25	8.766×10^3	5.259×10^5	3.156×10^7
1 day = 2.738×10^{-3}		1	24	1440	8.640×10^4
1 hour = 1.141×10^{-4}		4.167×10^{-2}	1	60	3600
1 minute = 1.901×10^{-6}		6.944×10^{-4}	1.667×10^{-2}	1	60
1 SECOND = 3.169×10^{-8}		1.157×10^{-5}	2.778×10^{-4}	1.667×10^{-2}	1

SPEED

	ft/s	km/h	METER/ SECOND	mi/h	cm/s
1 foot per second = 1	1.097	0.3048	0.6818	30.48
1 kilometer per hour = 0.9113	1	0.2778	0.6214	27.78
1 METER per SECOND = 3.281	3.6	1	2.237	100
1 mile per hour = 1.467	1.609	0.4470	1	44.70
1 centimeter per second = 3.281×10^{-2}	3.6×10^{-2}	0.01	2.237×10^{-2}	1

1 knot = 1 nautical mi/h = 1.688 ft/s   1 mi/min = 88.00 ft/s = 60.00 mi/h

FORCE

Force units in the colored areas are now little used. To clarify: 1 gram-force (= 1 gf) is the force of gravity that would act on an object whose mass is 1 gram at a location where g has the standard value of 9.80665 m/s^2.

	dyne	NEWTON	lb	pdl	gf	kgf
1 dyne = 1	10^{-5}	2.248×10^{-6}	7.233×10^{-5}	1.020×10^{-3}	1.020×10^{-6}
1 NEWTON = 10^5	1	0.2248	7.233	102.0	0.1020
1 pound = 4.448×10^5	4.448	1	32.17	453.6	0.4536
1 poundal = 1.383×10^4	0.1383	3.108×10^{-2}	1	14.10	1.410×10^{-2}
1 gram-force = 980.7	9.807×10^{-3}	2.205×10^{-3}	7.093×10^{-2}	1	0.001
1 kilogram-force = 9.807×10^5	9.807	2.205	70.93	1000	1

PRESSURE

	atm	dyne/cm²	inch of water	cm Hg	PASCAL	lb/in.²	lb/ft²
1 atmosphere = 1	1.013×10^6	406.8	76	1.013×10^5	14.70	2116
1 dyne per centimeter² = 9.869×10^{-7}	1	4.015×10^{-4}	7.501×10^{-5}	0.1	1.405×10^{-5}	2.089×10^{-3}
1 inch of water[a] at 4°C = 2.458×10^{-3}	2491	1	0.1868	249.1	3.613×10^{-2}	5.202
1 centimeter of mercury[a] at 0°C = 1.316×10^{-2}	1.333×10^4	5.353	1	1333	0.1934	27.85
1 PASCAL = 9.869×10^{-6}	10	4.015×10^{-3}	7.501×10^{-4}	1	1.450×10^{-4}	2.089×10^{-2}
1 pound per inch² = 6.805×10^{-2}	6.895×10^4	27.68	5.171	6.895×10^3	1	144
1 pound per foot² = 4.725×10^{-4}	478.8	0.1922	3.591×10^{-2}	47.88	6.944×10^{-3}	1

[a] Where the acceleration of gravity has the standard value of 9.80665 m/s^2.

1 bar = 10^6 dyne/cm² = 0.1 MPa   1 millibar = 10^3 dyne/cm² = 10^2 Pa   1 torr = 1 mm Hg

ENERGY, WORK, HEAT

Quantities in the colored areas are not properly energy units but are included for convenience. They arise from the relativistic mass–energy equivalence formula $E = mc^2$ and represent the energy released if a kilogram or unified atomic mass unit (u) is completely converted to energy (bottom two rows) or the mass that would be completely converted to one unit of energy (rightmost two columns).

	Btu	erg	ft·lb	hp·h	JOULE	cal	kW·h	eV	MeV	kg	u
1 British thermal unit =	1	1.055×10^{10}	777.9	3.929×10^{-4}	1055	252.0	2.930×10^{-4}	6.585×10^{21}	6.585×10^{15}	1.174×10^{-14}	7.070×10^{12}
1 erg =	9.481×10^{-11}	1	7.376×10^{-8}	3.725×10^{-14}	10^{-7}	2.389×10^{-8}	2.778×10^{-14}	6.242×10^{11}	6.242×10^{5}	1.113×10^{-24}	670.2
1 foot-pound =	1.285×10^{-3}	1.356×10^{7}	1	5.051×10^{-7}	1.356	0.3238	3.766×10^{-7}	8.464×10^{18}	8.464×10^{12}	1.509×10^{-17}	9.037×10^{9}
1 horsepower-hour =	2545	2.685×10^{13}	1.980×10^{6}	1	2.685×10^{6}	6.413×10^{5}	0.7457	1.676×10^{25}	1.676×10^{19}	2.988×10^{-11}	1.799×10^{16}
1 JOULE =	9.481×10^{-4}	10^{7}	0.7376	3.725×10^{-7}	1	0.2389	2.778×10^{-7}	6.242×10^{18}	6.242×10^{12}	1.113×10^{-17}	6.702×10^{9}
1 calorie =	3.969×10^{-3}	4.186×10^{7}	3.088	1.560×10^{-6}	4.186	1	1.163×10^{-6}	2.613×10^{19}	2.613×10^{13}	4.660×10^{-17}	2.806×10^{10}
1 kilowatt-hour =	3413	3.600×10^{13}	2.655×10^{6}	1.341	3.600×10^{6}	8.600×10^{5}	1	2.247×10^{25}	2.247×10^{19}	4.007×10^{-11}	2.413×10^{16}
1 electron-volt =	1.519×10^{-22}	1.602×10^{-12}	1.182×10^{-19}	5.967×10^{-26}	1.602×10^{-19}	3.827×10^{-20}	4.450×10^{-26}	1	10^{-6}	1.783×10^{-36}	1.074×10^{-9}
1 million electron-volts =	1.519×10^{-16}	1.602×10^{-6}	1.182×10^{-13}	5.967×10^{-20}	1.602×10^{-13}	3.827×10^{-14}	4.450×10^{-20}	10^{-6}	1	1.783×10^{-30}	1.074×10^{-3}
1 kilogram =	8.521×10^{13}	8.987×10^{23}	6.629×10^{16}	3.348×10^{10}	8.987×10^{16}	2.146×10^{16}	2.497×10^{10}	5.610×10^{35}	5.610×10^{29}	1	6.022×10^{26}
1 unified atomic mass unit =	1.415×10^{-13}	1.492×10^{-3}	1.101×10^{-10}	5.559×10^{-17}	1.492×10^{-10}	3.564×10^{-11}	4.146×10^{-17}	9.320×10^{8}	932.0	1.661×10^{-27}	1

POWER

	Btu/h	ft·lb/s	hp	cal/s	kW	WATT
1 British thermal unit per hour =	1	0.2161	3.929×10^{-4}	6.998×10^{-2}	2.930×10^{-4}	0.2930
1 foot-pound per second =	4.628	1	1.818×10^{-3}	0.3239	1.356×10^{-3}	1.356
1 horsepower =	2545	550	1	178.1	0.7457	745.7
1 calorie per second =	14.29	3.088	5.615×10^{-3}	1	4.186×10^{-3}	4.186
1 kilowatt =	3413	737.6	1.341	238.9	1	1000
1 WATT =	3.413	0.7376	1.341×10^{-3}	0.2389	0.001	1

MAGNETIC FIELD

	gauss	TESLA	milligauss
1 gauss =	1	10^{-4}	1000
1 TESLA =	10^{4}	1	10^{7}
1 milligauss =	0.001	10^{-7}	1

1 tesla = 1 weber/meter^2

MAGNETIC FLUX

	maxwell	WEBER
1 maxwell =	1	10^{-8}
1 WEBER =	10^{8}	1

Appendix E
Mathematical Formulas

GEOMETRY

Circle of radius r: circumference $= 2\pi r$; area $= \pi r^2$.

Sphere of radius r: area $= 4\pi r^2$; volume $= \frac{4}{3}\pi r^3$.

Right circular cylinder of radius r and height h:
area $= 2\pi r^2 + 2\pi rh$; volume $= \pi r^2 h$.

Triangle of base a and altitude h: area $= \frac{1}{2}ah$.

QUADRATIC FORMULA

If $ax^2 + bx + c = 0$, then $x = \dfrac{-b \pm \sqrt{b^2 - 4ac}}{2a}$.

TRIGONOMETRIC FUNCTIONS OF ANGLE θ

$\sin\theta = \dfrac{y}{r}$ $\cos\theta = \dfrac{x}{r}$

$\tan\theta = \dfrac{y}{x}$ $\cot\theta = \dfrac{x}{y}$

$\sec\theta = \dfrac{r}{x}$ $\csc\theta = \dfrac{r}{y}$

PYTHAGOREAN THEOREM

In this right triangle,
$$a^2 + b^2 = c^2$$

TRIANGLES

Angles are A, B, C

Opposite sides are a, b, c

Angles $A + B + C = 180°$

$$\frac{\sin A}{a} = \frac{\sin B}{b} = \frac{\sin C}{c}$$

$c^2 = a^2 + b^2 - 2ab \cos C$

Exterior angle $D = A + C$

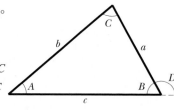

MATHEMATICAL SIGNS AND SYMBOLS

$=$ equals

$\approx$ equals approximately

$\sim$ is the order of magnitude of

$\neq$ is not equal to

$\equiv$ is identical to, is defined as

$>$ is greater than ($\gg$ is much greater than)

$<$ is less than ($\ll$ is much less than)

$\geq$ is greater than or equal to (or, is no less than)

$\leq$ is less than or equal to (or, is no more than)

$\pm$ plus or minus

$\propto$ is proportional to

Σ the sum of

$\bar{x}$ the average value of x

TRIGONOMETRIC IDENTITIES

$\sin(90° - \theta) = \cos\theta$

$\cos(90° - \theta) = \sin\theta$

$\sin\theta/\cos\theta = \tan\theta$

$\sin^2\theta + \cos^2\theta = 1$

$\sec^2\theta - \tan^2\theta = 1$

$\csc^2\theta - \cot^2\theta = 1$

$\sin 2\theta = 2\sin\theta\cos\theta$

$\cos 2\theta = \cos^2\theta - \sin^2\theta = 2\cos^2\theta - 1 = 1 - 2\sin^2\theta$

$\sin(\alpha \pm \beta) = \sin\alpha\cos\beta \pm \cos\alpha\sin\beta$

$\cos(\alpha \pm \beta) = \cos\alpha\cos\beta \mp \sin\alpha\sin\beta$

$\tan(\alpha \pm \beta) = \dfrac{\tan\alpha \pm \tan\beta}{1 \mp \tan\alpha\tan\beta}$

$\sin\alpha \pm \sin\beta = 2\sin\frac{1}{2}(\alpha \pm \beta)\cos\frac{1}{2}(\alpha \mp \beta)$

$\cos\alpha + \cos\beta = 2\cos\frac{1}{2}(\alpha + \beta)\cos\frac{1}{2}(\alpha - \beta)$

$\cos\alpha - \cos\beta = -2\sin\frac{1}{2}(\alpha + \beta)\sin\frac{1}{2}(\alpha - \beta)$

BINOMIAL THEOREM

$$(1 + x)^n = 1 + \frac{nx}{1!} + \frac{n(n-1)x^2}{2!} + \cdots \qquad (x^2 < 1)$$

EXPONENTIAL EXPANSION

$$e^x = 1 + x + \frac{x^2}{2!} + \frac{x^3}{3!} + \cdots$$

LOGARITHMIC EXPANSION

$$\ln(1 + x) = x - \tfrac{1}{2}x^2 + \tfrac{1}{3}x^3 - \cdots \qquad (|x| < 1)$$

TRIGONOMETRIC EXPANSIONS
(θ in radians)

$$\sin \theta = \theta - \frac{\theta^3}{3!} + \frac{\theta^5}{5!} - \cdots$$

$$\cos \theta = 1 - \frac{\theta^2}{2!} + \frac{\theta^4}{4!} - \cdots$$

$$\tan \theta = \theta + \frac{\theta^3}{3} + \frac{2\theta^5}{15} + \cdots$$

CRAMER'S RULE

Two simultaneous equations in unknowns x and y,

$$a_1 x + b_1 y = c_1 \qquad \text{and} \qquad a_2 x + b_2 y = c_2,$$

have the solutions

$$x = \frac{\begin{vmatrix} c_1 & b_1 \\ c_2 & b_2 \end{vmatrix}}{\begin{vmatrix} a_1 & b_1 \\ a_2 & b_2 \end{vmatrix}} = \frac{c_1 b_2 - c_2 b_1}{a_1 b_2 - a_2 b_1}$$

and

$$y = \frac{\begin{vmatrix} a_1 & c_1 \\ a_2 & c_2 \end{vmatrix}}{\begin{vmatrix} a_1 & b_1 \\ a_2 & b_2 \end{vmatrix}} = \frac{a_1 c_2 - a_2 c_1}{a_1 b_2 - a_2 b_1}.$$

PRODUCTS OF VECTORS

Let $\mathbf{i}$, $\mathbf{j}$, and $\mathbf{k}$ be unit vectors in the x, y, and z directions. Then

$$\mathbf{i} \cdot \mathbf{i} = \mathbf{j} \cdot \mathbf{j} = \mathbf{k} \cdot \mathbf{k} = 1, \qquad \mathbf{i} \cdot \mathbf{j} = \mathbf{j} \cdot \mathbf{k} = \mathbf{k} \cdot \mathbf{i} = 0,$$

$$\mathbf{i} \times \mathbf{i} = \mathbf{j} \times \mathbf{j} = \mathbf{k} \times \mathbf{k} = 0,$$

$$\mathbf{i} \times \mathbf{j} = \mathbf{k}, \qquad \mathbf{j} \times \mathbf{k} = \mathbf{i}, \qquad \mathbf{k} \times \mathbf{i} = \mathbf{j},$$

Any vector $\mathbf{a}$ with components a_x, a_y, and a_z along the x, y, and z axes can be written

$$\mathbf{a} = a_x \mathbf{i} + a_y \mathbf{j} + a_z \mathbf{k}.$$

Let $\mathbf{a}$, $\mathbf{b}$, and $\mathbf{c}$ be arbitrary vectors with magnitudes a, b, and c. Then

$$\mathbf{a} \times (\mathbf{b} + \mathbf{c}) = (\mathbf{a} \times \mathbf{b}) + (\mathbf{a} \times \mathbf{c})$$

$$(s\mathbf{a}) \times \mathbf{b} = \mathbf{a} \times (s\mathbf{b}) = s(\mathbf{a} \times \mathbf{b}) \qquad (s = \text{a scalar}).$$

Let θ be the smaller of the two angles between $\mathbf{a}$ and $\mathbf{b}$. Then

$$\mathbf{a} \cdot \mathbf{b} = \mathbf{b} \cdot \mathbf{a} = a_x b_x + a_y b_y + a_z b_z = ab \cos \theta$$

$$\mathbf{a} \times \mathbf{b} = -\mathbf{b} \times \mathbf{a} = \begin{vmatrix} \mathbf{i} & \mathbf{j} & \mathbf{k} \\ a_x & a_y & a_z \\ b_x & b_y & b_z \end{vmatrix}$$

$$= \mathbf{i} \begin{vmatrix} a_y & a_z \\ b_y & b_z \end{vmatrix} - \mathbf{j} \begin{vmatrix} a_x & a_z \\ b_x & b_z \end{vmatrix} + \mathbf{k} \begin{vmatrix} a_x & a_y \\ b_x & b_y \end{vmatrix}$$

$$= (a_y b_z - b_y a_z)\mathbf{i}$$
$$+ (a_z b_x - b_z a_x)\mathbf{j} + (a_x b_y - b_x a_y)\mathbf{k}$$

$$|\mathbf{a} \times \mathbf{b}| = ab \sin \theta$$

$$\mathbf{a} \cdot (\mathbf{b} \times \mathbf{c}) = \mathbf{b} \cdot (\mathbf{c} \times \mathbf{a}) = \mathbf{c} \cdot (\mathbf{a} \times \mathbf{b})$$

$$\mathbf{a} \times (\mathbf{b} \times \mathbf{c}) = (\mathbf{a} \cdot \mathbf{c})\mathbf{b} - (\mathbf{a} \cdot \mathbf{b})\mathbf{c}$$

DERIVATIVES AND INTEGRALS

In what follows, the letters u and v stand for any functions of x, and a and m are constants. To each of the indefinite integrals should be added an arbitrary constant of integration. The *Handbook of Chemistry and Physics* (CRC Press Inc.) gives a more extensive tabulation.

1. $\dfrac{dx}{dx} = 1$

2. $\dfrac{d}{dx}(au) = a\dfrac{du}{dx}$

3. $\dfrac{d}{dx}(u+v) = \dfrac{du}{dx} + \dfrac{dv}{dx}$

4. $\dfrac{d}{dx}x^m = mx^{m-1}$

5. $\dfrac{d}{dx}\ln x = \dfrac{1}{x}$

6. $\dfrac{d}{dx}(uv) = u\dfrac{dv}{dx} + v\dfrac{du}{dx}$

7. $\dfrac{d}{dx}e^x = e^x$

8. $\dfrac{d}{dx}\sin x = \cos x$

9. $\dfrac{d}{dx}\cos x = -\sin x$

10. $\dfrac{d}{dx}\tan x = \sec^2 x$

11. $\dfrac{d}{dx}\cot x = -\csc^2 x$

12. $\dfrac{d}{dx}\sec x = \tan x \sec x$

13. $\dfrac{d}{dx}\csc x = -\cot x \csc x$

14. $\dfrac{d}{dx}e^u = e^u\dfrac{du}{dx}$

15. $\dfrac{d}{dx}\sin u = \cos u\dfrac{du}{dx}$

16. $\dfrac{d}{dx}\cos u = -\sin u\dfrac{du}{dx}$

1. $\int dx = x$

2. $\int au\,dx = a\int u\,dx$

3. $\int (u+v)\,dx = \int u\,dx + \int v\,dx$

4. $\int x^m\,dx = \dfrac{x^{m+1}}{m+1}$ $(m \neq -1)$

5. $\int \dfrac{dx}{x} = \ln|x|$

6. $\int u\dfrac{dv}{dx}\,dx = uv - \int v\dfrac{du}{dx}\,dx$

7. $\int e^x\,dx = e^x$

8. $\int \sin x\,dx = -\cos x$

9. $\int \cos x\,dx = \sin x$

10. $\int \tan x\,dx = \ln|\sec x|$

11. $\int \sin^2 x\,dx = \tfrac{1}{2}x - \tfrac{1}{4}\sin 2x$

12. $\int e^{-ax}\,dx = -\dfrac{1}{a}e^{-ax}$

13. $\int xe^{-ax}\,dx = -\dfrac{1}{a^2}(ax+1)e^{-ax}$

14. $\int x^2e^{-ax}\,dx = -\dfrac{1}{a^3}(a^2x^2+2ax+2)e^{-ax}$

15. $\int_0^\infty x^ne^{-ax}\,dx = \dfrac{n!}{a^{n+1}}$

16. $\int_0^\infty x^{2n}e^{-ax^2}\,dx = \dfrac{1\cdot 3\cdot 5 \cdots (2n-1)}{2^{n+1}a^n}\sqrt{\dfrac{\pi}{a}}$

17. $\int \dfrac{dx}{\sqrt{x^2+a^2}} = \ln(x+\sqrt{x^2+a^2})$

18. $\int \dfrac{x\,dx}{(x^2+a^2)^{3/2}} = -\dfrac{1}{(x^2+a^2)^{1/2}}$

19. $\int \dfrac{dx}{(x^2+a^2)^{3/2}} = \dfrac{x}{a^2(x^2+a^2)^{1/2}}$

Appendix F
Properties of the Elements

All physical properties are for a pressure of 1 atm unless otherwise specified.

ELEMENT	SYMBOL	ATOMIC NUMBER, Z	MOLAR MASS, g/mol	DENSITY, g/cm³ AT 20°C	MELTING POINT, °C	BOILING POINT, °C	SPECIFIC HEAT, J/(g·°C) AT 25°C
Actinium	Ac	89	(227)	10.06	1323	(3473)	0.092
Aluminum	Al	13	26.9815	2.699	660	2450	0.900
Americium	Am	95	(243)	13.67	1541	—	—
Antimony	Sb	51	121.75	6.691	630.5	1380	0.205
Argon	Ar	18	39.948	1.6626×10^{-3}	−189.4	−185.8	0.523
Arsenic	As	33	74.9216	5.78	817 (28 atm)	613	0.331
Astatine	At	85	(210)	—	(302)	—	—
Barium	Ba	56	137.34	3.594	729	1640	0.205
Berkelium	Bk	97	(247)	14.79	—	—	—
Beryllium	Be	4	9.0122	1.848	1287	2770	1.83
Bismuth	Bi	83	208.980	9.747	271.37	1560	0.122
Boron	B	5	10.811	2.34	2030	—	1.11
Bromine	Br	35	79.909	3.12 (liquid)	−7.2	58	0.293
Cadmium	Cd	48	112.40	8.65	321.03	765	0.226
Calcium	Ca	20	40.08	1.55	838	1440	0.624
Californium	Cf	98	(251)	—	—	—	—
Carbon	C	6	12.01115	2.26	3727	4830	0.691
Cerium	Ce	58	140.12	6.768	804	3470	0.188
Cesium	Cs	55	132.905	1.873	28.40	690	0.243
Chlorine	Cl	17	35.453	3.214×10^{-3} (0°C)	−101	−34.7	0.486
Chromium	Cr	24	51.996	7.19	1857	2665	0.448
Cobalt	Co	27	58.9332	8.85	1495	2900	0.423
Copper	Cu	29	63.54	8.96	1083.40	2595	0.385
Curium	Cm	96	(247)	13.3	—	—	—
Dysprosium	Dy	66	162.50	8.55	1409	2330	0.172
Einsteinium	Es	99	(254)	—	—	—	—
Erbium	Er	68	167.26	9.15	1522	2630	0.167
Europium	Eu	63	151.96	5.243	817	1490	0.163
Fermium	Fm	100	(237)	—	—	—	—
Fluorine	F	9	18.9984	1.696×10^{-3} (0°C)	−219.6	−188.2	0.753
Francium	Fr	87	(223)	—	(27)	—	—
Gadolinium	Gd	64	157.25	7.90	1312	2730	0.234
Gallium	Ga	31	69.72	5.907	29.75	2237	0.377
Germanium	Ge	32	72.59	5.323	937.25	2830	0.322
Gold	Au	79	196.967	19.32	1064.43	2970	0.131
Hafnium	Hf	72	178.49	13.31	2227	5400	0.144
Hahnium	Ha	105	—	—	—	—	—
Hassium	Hs	108	—	—	—	—	—

continued on next page

ELEMENT	SYMBOL	ATOMIC NUMBER, Z	MOLAR MASS, g/mol	DENSITY, g/cm³ AT 20°C	MELTING POINT, °C	BOILING POINT, °C	SPECIFIC HEAT, J/(g·°C) AT 25°C
Helium	He	2	4.0026	0.1664×10^{-3}	−269.7	−268.9	5.23
Holmium	Ho	67	164.930	8.79	1470	2330	0.165
Hydrogen	H	1	1.00797	0.08375×10^{-3}	−259.19	−252.7	14.4
Indium	In	49	114.82	7.31	156.634	2000	0.233
Iodine	I	53	126.9044	4.93	113.7	183	0.218
Iridium	Ir	77	192.2	22.5	2447	(5300)	0.130
Iron	Fe	26	55.847	7.874	1536.5	3000	0.447
Krypton	Kr	36	83.80	3.488×10^{-3}	−157.37	−152	0.247
Lanthanum	La	57	138.91	6.189	920	3470	0.195
Lawrencium	Lr	103	(257)		—	—	
Lead	Pb	82	207.19	11.35	327.45	1725	0.129
Lithium	Li	3	6.939	0.534	180.55	1300	3.58
Lutetium	Lu	71	174.97	9.849	1663	1930	0.155
Magnesium	Mg	12	24.312	1.738	650	1107	1.03
Manganese	Mn	25	54.9380	7.44	1244	2150	0.481
Meitnerium	Mt	109	—	—	—	—	—
Mendelevium	Md	101	(256)	—	—	—	—
Mercury	Hg	80	200.59	13.55	−38.87	357	0.138
Molybdenum	Mo	42	95.94	10.22	2617	5560	0.251
Neodymium	Nd	60	144.24	7.007	1016	3180	0.188
Neon	Ne	10	20.183	0.8387×10^{-3}	−248.597	−246.0	1.03
Neptunium	Np	93	(237)	20.25	637	—	1.26
Nickel	Ni	28	58.71	8.902	1453	2730	0.444
Nielsbohrium	Ns	107	—	—	—	—	—
Niobium	Nb	41	92.906	8.57	2468	4927	0.264
Nitrogen	N	7	14.0067	1.1649×10^{-3}	−210	−195.8	1.03
Nobelium	No	102	(255)	—	—	—	—
Osmium	Os	76	190.2	22.59	3027	5500	0.130
Oxygen	O	8	15.9994	1.3318×10^{-3}	−218.80	−183.0	0.913
Palladium	Pd	46	106.4	12.02	1552	3980	0.243
Phosphorus	P	15	30.9738	1.83	44.25	280	0.741
Platinum	Pt	78	195.09	21.45	1769	4530	0.134
Plutonium	Pu	94	(244)	19.8	640	3235	0.130
Polonium	Po	84	(210)	9.32	254	—	—
Potassium	K	19	39.102	0.862	63.20	760	0.758
Praseodymium	Pr	59	140.907	6.773	931	3020	0.197
Promethium	Pm	61	(145)	7.22	(1027)	—	—
Protactinium	Pa	91	(231)	15.37 (estimated)	(1230)	—	—
Radium	Ra	88	(226)	5.0	700	—	—
Radon	Rn	86	(222)	9.96×10^{-3} (0°C)	(−71)	−61.8	0.092
Rhenium	Re	75	186.2	21.02	3180	5900	0.134
Rhodium	Rh	45	102.905	12.41	1963	4500	0.243
Rubidium	Rb	37	85.47	1.532	39.49	688	0.364
Ruthenium	Ru	44	101.107	12.37	2250	4900	0.239
Rutherfordium	Rf	104	—	—	—	—	—
Samarium	Sm	62	150.35	7.52	1072	1630	0.197

continued on next page

Element	Symbol	Atomic Number, Z	Molar Mass, g/mol	Density, g/cm³ at 20°C	Melting Point, °C	Boiling Point, °C	Specific Heat, J/(g·°C) at 25°C
Scandium	Sc	21	44.956	2.99	1539	2730	0.569
Seaborgium	Sg	106	—	—	—	—	—
Selenium	Se	34	78.96	4.79	221	685	0.318
Silicon	Si	14	28.086	2.33	1412	2680	0.712
Silver	Ag	47	107.870	10.49	960.8	2210	0.234
Sodium	Na	11	22.9898	0.9712	97.85	892	1.23
Strontium	Sr	38	87.62	2.54	768	1380	0.737
Sulfur	S	16	32.064	2.07	119.0	444.6	0.707
Tantalum	Ta	73	180.948	16.6	3014	5425	0.138
Technetium	Tc	43	(99)	11.46	2200	—	0.209
Tellurium	Te	52	127.60	6.24	449.5	990	0.201
Terbium	Tb	65	158.924	8.229	1357	2530	0.180
Thallium	Tl	81	204.37	11.85	304	1457	0.130
Thorium	Th	90	(232)	11.72	1755	(3850)	0.117
Thulium	Tm	69	168.934	9.32	1545	1720	0.159
Tin	Sn	50	118.69	7.2984	231.868	2270	0.226
Titanium	Ti	22	47.90	4.54	1670	3260	0.523
Tungsten	W	74	183.85	19.3	3380	5930	0.134
Uranium	U	92	(238)	18.95	1132	3818	0.117
Vanadium	V	23	50.942	6.11	1902	3400	0.490
Xenon	Xe	54	131.30	5.495×10^{-3}	−111.79	−108	0.159
Ytterbium	Yb	70	173.04	6.965	824	1530	0.155
Yttrium	Y	39	88.905	4.469	1526	3030	0.297
Zinc	Zn	30	65.37	7.133	419.58	906	0.389
Zirconium	Zr	40	91.22	6.506	1852	3580	0.276

The values in parentheses in the column of molar masses are the mass numbers of the longest-lived isotopes of those elements that are radioactive. Melting points and boiling points in parentheses are uncertain.

The data for gases are valid only when these are in their usual molecular state, such as H_2, He, O_2, Ne, etc. The specific heats of the gases are the values at constant pressure.

Source: Adapted from Wehr, Richards, Adair, *Physics of the Atom,* 4th ed., Addison-Wesley, Reading, MA, 1984, and from J. Emsley, *The Elements,* 2nd ed., Clarendon Press, Oxford, 1991.

Appendix G
Periodic Table of the Elements

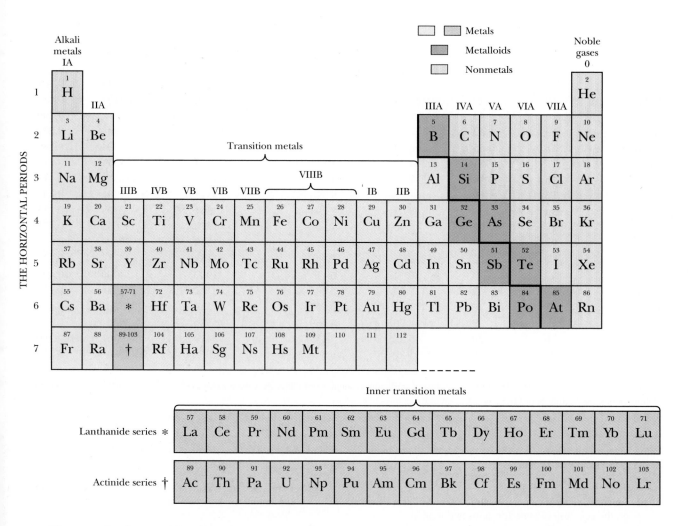

The names for elements 104–109 (Rutherfordium, Hahnium, Seaborgium, Nielsbohrium, Hassium, and Meitnerium, respectively) are those recommended by the American Chemical Society Nomenclature Committee. As of 1996, the names and symbols for elements 104–108 have not yet been approved by the appropriate international body. Elements 110, 111 and 112 have been discovered but, as of 1996, have not been provisionally named.

Chapter 1

EP **3.** (a) 186 mi; (b) 3.0×10^8 mm **5.** (a) 10^9; (b) 10^{-4}; (c) 9.1×10^5 **7.** 32.2 km **9.** 0.020 km^3 **11.** (a) 250 ft^2; (b) 23.3 m^2; (c) 3060 ft^3; (d) 86.6 m^3 **13.** 8×10^2 km **15.** (a) 11.3 m^2/L; (b) 1.13×10^4 m^{-1}; (c) 2.17×10^{-3} gal/ft^2 **17.** (a) $d_{Sun}/d_{Moon} = 400$; (b) $V_{Sun}/V_{Moon} = 6.4 \times 10^7$; (c) 3.5×10^3 km **19.** (a) 0.98 ft/ns; (b) 0.30 mm/ps **21.** 3.156×10^7 s **23.** 5.79×10^{12} days **25.** (a) 0.013; (b) 0.54; (c) 10.3; (d) 31 m/s **27.** 15° **29.** 3.3 ft **31.** 2 days 5 hours **33.** (a) 2.99×10^{-26} kg; (b) 4.68×10^{46} **35.** 1.3×10^9 kg **37.** (a) 10^3 kg/m^3; (b) 158 kg/s **39.** (a) 1.18×10^{-29} m^3; (b) 0.282 nm

Chapter 2

CP **1.** b and c **2.** zero **3.** (a) 1 and 4; (b) 2 and 3; (c) 3 **4.** (a) plus; (b) minus; (c) minus; (d) plus **5.** 1 and 4 **6.** (a) plus; (b) minus; (c) $a = -g = -9.8$ m/s^2 **Q** **1.** (a) yes; (b) no; (c) yes; (d) yes **3.** (a) 2, 3; (b) 1, 3; (c) 4 **5.** all tie (see Eq. 2-16) **7.** (a) $-g$; (b) 2 m/s upward **9.** same **11.** $x = t^2$ and $x = 8(t - 2) + (1.5)(t - 2)^2$ **13.** increase **EP** **1.** (a) Lewis: 10.0 m/s, Rodgers: 5.41 m/s; (b) 1 h 10 min **3.** 309 ft **5.** 2 cm/y **7.** 6.71×10^8 mi/h, 9.84×10^8 ft/s, 1.00 ly/y **9.** (a) 5.7 ft/s; (b) 7.0 ft/s **11.** (a) 45 mi/h (72 km/h); (b) 43 mi/h (69 km/h); (c) 44 mi/h (71 km/h); (d) 0 **13.** (a) 28.5 cm/s; (b) 18.0 cm/s; (c) 40.5 cm/s; (d) 28.1 cm/s; (e) 30.3 cm/s **15.** (a) mathematically, an infinite number; (b) 60 km **17.** (a) $4 \text{ s} > t > 2$ s; (b) $3 \text{ s} > t > 0$; (c) $7 \text{ s} > t > 3$ s; (d) $t = 3$ s **19.** 100 m **23.** (a) The signs of v and a are: AB: $+, -$; BC: 0, 0; CD: $+, +$; DE: $+, 0$; (b) no; (c) no **25.** (e) situations (a), (b), and (d) **27.** (a) 80 m/s; (b) 110 m/s; (c) 20 m/s^2 **29.** (a) 1.10 m/s, 6.11 mm/s^2; (b) 1.47 m/s, 6.11 mm/s^2 **31.** (a) 2.00 s; (b) 12 cm from left edge of screen; (c) 9.00 cm/s^2, to the left; (d) to the right; (e) to the left; (f) 3.46 s **33.** 0.556 s **35.** each, 0.28 m/s^2 **37.** 2.8 m/s^2 **39.** 1.62×10^{15} m/s^2 **41.** $21g$ **43.** (a) $25g$; (b) 400 m **45.** 90 m **47.** (a) 5.0 m/s^2; (b) 4.0 s; (c) 6.0 s; (d) 90 m **49.** (a) 5.00 m/s; (b) 1.67 m/s^2; (c) 7.50 m **51.** (a) 0.74 s; (b) -20 ft/s^2 **53.** (a) 0.75 s; (b) 50 m **55.** (a) 34.7 ft; (b) 41.6 s **57.** (a) 3.26 ft/s^2 **61.** (a) 31 m/s; (b) 6.4 s **63.** (a) 48.5 m/s; (b) 4.95 s; (c) 34.3 m/s; (d) 3.50 s **65.** (a) 5.44 s; (b) 53.3 m/s; (d) 5.80 m **67.** (a) 3.2 s; (b) 1.3 s **69.** 4.0 m/s **71.** (a) 350 ms; (b) 82 ms (each is for ascent and descent through the 15 cm) **73.** 857 m/s^2, upward **75.** (a) 1.23 cm; (b) 4 times, 9 times, 16 times, 25 times **77.** (a) 8.85 m/s; (b) 1.00 m **79.** 22 cm and 89 cm below the nozzle **81.** (a) 3.41 s; (b) 57 m **83.** (a) 40.0 ft/s **85.** 1.5 s **87.** (a) 5.4 s; (b) 41 m/s **89.** 20.4 m

91. (a) $d = v_i^2/2a' + T_R v_i$; (b) 9.0 m/s^2; (c) 0.66 s. **93.** (a) $v_f^2 = 2a'd_0(j - 1) + v_1^2$; (c) 7.0 m/s^2; (d) 14 m.

Chapter 3

CP **1.** (a) 7 m; (b) 1 m **2.** c, d, f **3.** (a) $+$, $+$; (b) $+$, $-$; (c) $+$, $+$ **4.** (a) 90°; (b) 0 (vectors are parallel); (c) 180° (vectors are antiparallel) **5.** (a) 0° or 180°; (b) 90° **Q** **1.** **A** and **B** **3.** No, but **a** and $-$**b** are commutative: **a** $+$ $(-$**b**$) = (-$**b**$) +$ **a**. **5.** (a) **a** and **b** are parallel; (b) **b** $= 0$; (c) **a** and **b** are perpendicular **7.** (a)–(c) yes (example: 5**i** and -2**i**) **9.** all but e **11.** (a) minus, minus; (b) minus, minus **13.** (a) **B** and **C**, **D** and **E**; (b) **D** and **E** **15.** no (their orientations can differ) **17.** (a) 0 (vectors are parallel); (b) 0 (vectors are antiparallel) **EP** **1.** The displacements should be (a) parallel, (b) antiparallel, (c) perpendicular **3.** (b) 3.2 km, 41° south of west **5.** **a** $+$ **b**: 4.2, 40° east of north; **b** $-$ **a**: 8.0, 24° north of west **7.** (a) 38 units at 320°; (b) 130 units at 1.2°; (c) 62 units at 130° **9.** $a_x = -2.5$, $a_y = -6.9$ **11.** $r_x = 13$ m, $r_y = 7.5$ m **13.** (a) 14 cm, 45° left of straight down; (b) 20 cm, vertically up; (c) zero **15.** 4.74 km **17.** 168 cm, 32.5° above the floor **19.** $r_x = 12$, $r_y = -5.8$, $r_z = -2.8$ **21.** (a) 8**i** $+$ 2**j**, 8.2, 14°; (b) 2**i** $-$ 6**j**, 6.3, $-72°$ relative to **i** **23.** (a) 5.0, $-37°$; (b) 10, 53°; (c) 11, 27°; (d) 11, 80°; (e) 11, 260°; the angles are relative to $+x$, the last two vectors are in opposite directions **25.** 4.1 **27.** (a) $r_x = 1.59$, $r_y = 12.1$; (b) 12.2; (c) 82.5° **29.** 3390 ft, horizontally **31.** (a) -2.83 m, -2.83 m, $+5.00$ m, 0 m, 3.00 m, 5.20 m; (b) 5.17 m, 2.37 m; (c) 5.69 m, 24.6° north of east; (d) 5.69 m, 24.6° south of west **35.** (a) $a_x = 9.51$ m, $a_y = 14.1$ m; (b) $a_x' = 13.4$ m, $a_y' = 10.5$ m **37.** (a) $+y$; (b) $-y$; (c) 0; (d) 0; (e) $+z$; (f) $-z$; (g) ab, both; (h) ab/d, $+z$ **39.** yes **41.** (a) up, unit magnitude; (b) zero; (c) south, unit magnitude; (d) 1.00; (e) 0 **43.** (a) -18.8; (b) 26.9, $+z$ direction **45.** (a) 12, out of page; (b) 12, into page; (c) 12, out of page **47.** (a) 11**i** $+$ 5**j** $-$ 7**k**; (b) 120° **51.** (a) 57°; (b) $c_x = \pm 2.2$, $c_y = \mp 4.5$ **53.** (a) -21; (b) -9; (c) 5**i** $-$ 11**j** $-$ 9**k**

Chapter 4

CP **1.** (a) $(8\mathbf{i} - 6\mathbf{j})$ m; (b) yes, the xy plane **2.** (a) first; (b) third **3.** (1) and (3) a_x and a_y are both constant and thus **a** is constant; (2) and (4) a_y is constant but a_x is not, thus **a** is not **4.** 4 m/s^3, -2 m/s, 3 m **5.** (a) v_x constant; (b) v_y initially positive, decreases to zero, and then becomes progressively more negative; (c) $a_x = 0$ throughout; (d) $a_y = -g$ throughout **6.** (a) $-(4$ m/s$)\mathbf{i}$; (b) $-(8$ m/s$^2)\mathbf{j}$ **7.** (1) 0, distance not changing; (2) $+70$ km/h, distance increasing; (3) $+80$ km/h, distance decreasing **Q** **1.** (1) and (3) a_y is constant but a_x is not and thus **a** is not; (2) a_x is constant but a_y

is not and thus **a** is not; (4) a_x and a_y are both constant and thus **a** is constant; -2 m/s², 3 m/s **3.** (a) highest point; (b) lowest point **5.** (a) all tie; (b) 1 and 2 tie (the rocket is shot upward), then 3 and 4 tie (it is shot into the ground!) **7.** $(2\mathbf{i} - 4\mathbf{j})$ m/s **9.** (a) all tie; (b) all tie; (c) c, b, a; (d) c, b, a **11.** (a) no; (b) same **13.** (a) in your hands; (b) behind you; (c) in front of you **15.** (a) straight down; (b) curved; (c) more curved **17.** (a) 3; (b) 4. **EP 1.** (a) $(-5.0\mathbf{i} + 8.0\mathbf{j})$ m; (b) 9.4 m, 122° from $+x$; (d) $(8\mathbf{i} - 8\mathbf{j})$ m; (e) 11 m, $-45°$ from $+x$ **3.** (a) $(-7.0\mathbf{i} + 12\mathbf{j})$ m; (b) xy plane **5.** (a) 671 mi, 63.4° south of east; (b) 298 mi/h, 63.4° south of east; (c) 400 mi/h **7.** (a) 6.79 km/h; (b) 6.96° **9.** (a) $(3\mathbf{i} - 8t\mathbf{j})$ m/s; (b) $(3\mathbf{i} - 16\mathbf{j})$ m/s; (c) 16 m/s, $-79°$ to $+x$ **11.** (a) $(8t\mathbf{j} + \mathbf{k})$ m/s; (b) $8\mathbf{j}$ m/s² **13.** $(-2.10\mathbf{i} + 2.81\mathbf{j})$ m/s² **15.** (a) $-1.5\mathbf{j}$ m/s; (b) $(4.5\mathbf{i} - 2.25\mathbf{j})$ m **17.** 60.0° **19.** (a) 63 ms; (b) 1.6×10^3 ft/s **21.** (a) 2.0 ns; (b) 2.0 mm; (c) $(1.0 \times 10^9\mathbf{i} - 2.0 \times 10^8\mathbf{j})$ cm/s **23.** (a) 3.03 s; (b) 758 m; (c) 29.7 m/s **25.** (a) 16 m/s, 23° above the horizontal; (b) 27 m/s, 57° below the horizontal **27.** (a) 32.4 m; (b) -37.7 m **29.** (b) 76° **31.** (a) 51.8 m; (b) 27.4 m/s; (c) 67.5 m **33.** (a) 194 m/s; (b) 38° **35.** 1.9 in. **37.** (a) 11 m; (b) 23 m; (c) 17 m/s, 63° below horizontal **41.** (a) 73 ft; (b) 7.6°; (c) 1.0 s **43.** 23 ft/s **45.** (a) 11 m; (b) 45 m/s **47.** 30 m above the release point **49.** 19 ft/s **51.** (a) 202 m/s; (b) 806 m; (c) 161 m/s, -171 m/s **53.** (a) 20 cm; (b) no, the ball hits the net only 4.4 cm above the ground **55.** yes; its center passes about 4.1 ft above the fence **57.** (a) 9.00×10^{22} m/s², toward the center; (b) 1.52×10^{-16} s **59.** (a) 6.7×10^6 m/s; (b) 1.4×10^{-7} s **61.** (a) 7.49 km/s; (b) 8.00 m/s² **63.** (a) 0.94 m; (b) 19 m/s; (c) 2400 m/s², toward center; (d) 0.05 s **65.** (a) 1.3×10^5 m/s; (b) 7.9×10^5 m/s² or $(8.0 \times 10^4)g$, toward the center; (c) both answers increase **67.** (a) 0.034 m/s²; (b) 84 min **69.** 2.58 cm/s² **71.** 160 m/s² **73.** 36 s, no **75.** 0.018 mi/s² from either frame **77.** 130° **79.** 60° **81.** (a) 5.8 m/s; (b) 16.7 m; (c) 67° **83.** 185 km/h, 22° south of west **85.** (a) from 75° east of south; (b) 30° east of north; substitute west for east to get second solution **87.** (a) 30° upstream; (b) 69 min; (c) 80 min; (d) 80 min; (e) perpendicular to the current, the shortest possible time is 60 min **89.** $0.83c$ **91.** (a) $0.35c$; (b) $0.62c$ **93.** For launch angles from 5° to 70°, it always moves away from the launch site. For a 75° launch angle, it moves toward the site from 11.5 s to 18.5 s after launch. For an 80° launch angle, it moves toward the site from 10.5 s to 20.5 s after launch. For an 85° launch angle, it moves toward the site from 10.5 s to 20.5 s after launch. For a 90° launch angle, it moves toward the site from 10 s to 20.5 s after launch. **95.** (a) 1.6 s; (b) no; (c) 14 m/s; (d) yes **97.** (a) $\Delta\mathbf{D} = (1.0 \text{ m})\mathbf{i} - (2.0 \text{ m})\mathbf{j} + (1.0 \text{ m})\mathbf{k}$; (b) 2.4 m; (c) $\bar{\mathbf{v}} = (0.025 \text{ m/s})\mathbf{i} - (0.050 \text{ m/s})\mathbf{j} + (0.025 \text{ m/s})\mathbf{k}$ (d) cannot be determined without additional information

Chapter 5

CP 1. $c, d,$ and e **2.** (a) and (b) 2 N, leftward (acceleration is zero in each situation) **3.** (a) and (b) 1, 4, 3, 2 **4.** (a) equal; (b) greater (acceleration is upward, thus net force on body must be upward) **5.** (a) equal; (b) greater; (c) less **6.** (a) increase; (b) yes; (c) same; (d) yes **7.** (a) $F \sin\theta$; (b) increase **8.** 0 **Q 1.** (a) yes; (b) yes; (c) yes; (d) yes **3.** (a) 2 and 4; (b) 2 and 4 **5.** (a) 50 N, upward; (b) 150 N, upward **7.** (a) less; (b) greater **9.** (a) no; (b) no; (c) no **11.** (a) increases; (b) increases; (c) decreases; (d) decreases **13.** (a) 20 kg; (b) 18 kg; (c) 10 kg; (d) all tie; (e) 3, 2, 1 **15.** d, c, a, b **EP 1.** (a) $F_x = 1.88$ N, $F_y = 0.684$ N; (b) $(1.88\mathbf{i} + 0.684\mathbf{j})$ N **3.** (a) $(-6.26\mathbf{i} - 3.23\mathbf{j})$ N; (b) 7.0 N, 207° relative to $+x$ **5.** $(-2\mathbf{i} + 6\mathbf{j})$ N **7.** (a) 0; (b) $+20$ N; (c) -20 N; (d) -40 N; (e) -60 N **9.** (a) $(1\mathbf{i} - 1.3\mathbf{j})$ m/s²; (b) 1.6 m/s² at $-50°$ from $+x$ **11.** (a) $\mathbf{F}_2$ and $\mathbf{F}_3$ are in the $-x$ direction, $\mathbf{a} = 0$; (b) $\mathbf{F}_2$ and $\mathbf{F}_3$ are in the $-x$ direction, $\mathbf{a}$ is on the x axis, $a = 0.83$ m/s²; (c) $\mathbf{F}_2$ and $\mathbf{F}_3$ are at 34° from $-x$ direction; $\mathbf{a} = 0$ **13.** (a) 22 N, 2.3 kg; (b) 1100 N, 110 kg; (c) 1.6×10^4 N, 1.6×10^3 kg **15.** (a) 11 N, 2.2 kg; (b) 0, 2.2 kg **17.** (a) 44 N; (b) 78 N; (c) 54 N; (d) 152 N **19.** 1.18×10^4 N **21.** 1.2×10^5 N **23.** 16 N **25.** (a) 13 ft/s²; (b) 190 lb **27.** (a) 42 N; (b) 72 N; (c) 4.9 m/s² **29.** (a) 0.02 m/s²; (b) 8×10^4 km; (c) 2×10^3 m/s **31.** (a) 1.1×10^{-15} N; (b) 8.9×10^{-30} N **33.** (a) 5500 N; (b) 2.7 s; (c) 4 times as far; (d) twice the time **35.** (a) 4.9×10^5 N; (b) 1.5×10^6 N **37.** (a) 110 lb, up; (b) 110 lb, down **39.** (a) 0.74 m/s²; (b) 7.3 m/s² **41.** (a) $\cos\theta$; (b) $\sqrt{\cos\theta}$ **43.** 1.8×10^4 N **45.** (a) 4.6×10^3 N; (b) 5.8×10^3 N **47.** (a) 250 m/s²; (b) 2.0×10^4 N **49.** 23 kg **51.** (a) 620 N; (b) 580 N **53.** 1.9×10^5 lb **55.** (a) rope breaks; (b) 1.6 m/s² **57.** 4.6 N **59.** (a) allow a downward acceleration with magnitude ≥ 4.2 ft/s²; (b) 13 ft/s or greater **61.** 195 N, up **63.** (a) 566 N; (b) 1130 N **65.** 18,000 N **67.** (a) 1.4×10^4 N; (b) 1.1×10^4 N; (c) 2700 N, toward the counterweight **69.** 6800 N, at 21° to the line of motion of the barge **71.** (a) 4.6 m/s²; (b) 2.6 m/s² **73.** (b) $Fl/(m + M)$; (c) $MFl/(m + M)$; (d) $F(m + 2M)/2(m + M)$ **75.** $T_1 = 13$ N, $T_2 = 20$ N, $a = 3.2$ m/s²

Chapter 6

CP 1. (a) zero (because there is no attempt at sliding); (b) 5 N; (c) no; (d) yes **2.** (a) same (10 N); (b) decreases; (c) decreases **3.** greater **4.** (a) **a** downward; **N** upward; (b) **a** and **N** upward **5.** (a) $4R_1$; (b) $4R_1$ **6.** (a) same; (b) increases; (c) increases **Q 1.** They slide at the same angle for all orders. **3.** (a) upward; (b) horizontal, toward you; (c) no change; (d) increases; (e) increases **5.** The frictional force $\mathbf{f}_s$ is initially directed up the ramp, decreases in magnitude to zero, and then is directed down the ramp, increasing in magnitude until the magnitude reaches $f_{s,max}$; thereafter, the magnitude of the frictional force is f_k, which is a constant smaller value. **7.** (a) decreases; (b) decreases; (c) increases; (d) increases **9.** (a) zero; (b) infinite **11.** 4, 3; then 1, 2, and 5 tie **13.** (a) less; (b) greater **EP 1.** (a) 200 N; (b) 120 N **3.** 2° **5.** 440 N

7. (a) 110 N; (b) 130 N; (c) no; (d) 46 N; (e) 17 N
9. (a) 90 N; (b) 70 N; (c) 0.89 m/s^2 **11.** (a) no; (b) ($-12\mathbf{i}$ + 5$\mathbf{j}$) N **13.** 20° **15.** (a) 0.13 N; (b) 0.12 **17.** μ_s = 0.58, μ_k = 0.54 **19.** (a) 0.11 m/s^2, 0.23 m/s^2; (b) 0.041, 0.029 **21.** 36 m **23.** (a) 300 N; (b) 1.3 m/s^2 **25.** (a) 66 N; (b) 2.3 m/s^2 **27.** (a) $\mu_k mg/(\sin\theta - \mu_k \cos\theta)$; (b) $\theta_0 = \tan^{-1}\mu_s$ **29.** (b) 3.0×10^7 N **31.** 100 N **33.** 3.3 kg **35.** (a) 11 ft/s^2; (b) 0.46 lb; (c) blocks move independently **37.** (a) 27 N; (b) 3.0 m/s^2 **39.** (a) 6.1 m/s^2, leftward; (b) 0.98 m/s^2, leftward **41.** (a) 3.0×10^5 N; (b) 1.2° **43.** 9.9 s **45.** 3.75 **47.** 12 cm **49.** 68 ft **51.** (a) 3210 N; (b) yes **53.** 0.078 **55.** (a) 0.72 m/s; (b) 2.1 m/s^2; (c) 0.50 N **57.** $\sqrt{Mgr/m}$ **59.** (a) 30 cm/s; (b) 180 cm/s^2, radially inward; (c) 3.6×10^{-3} N, radially inward; (d) 0.37 **61.** (a) 275 N; (b) 877 N **63.** 874 N **65.** (a) at the bottom of the circle; (b) 31 ft/s **67.** (a) 9.5 m/s; (b) 20 m **69.** 13° **71.** (a) 0.0338 N; (b) 9.77 N

Chapter 7
CP 1. (a) decrease; (b) same; (c) negative, zero **2.** d, c, b, a **3.** (a) same; (b) smaller **4.** (a) positive; (b) negative; (c) zero **5.** zero **Q 1.** all tie **3.** (a) increasing; (b) same; (c) same; (d) increasing **5.** (a) positive; (b) negative; (c) negative **7.** (a) positive; (b) zero; (c) negative; (d) negative; (e) zero; (f) positive **9.** all tie **11.** c, d, a and b tie; then f, e. **13.** (a) 3 m; (b) 3 m; (c) 0 and 6 m; (d) negative direction of x **15.** (a) A; (b) B **17.** twice **EP 1.** 1.8×10^{13} J **3.** (a) 3610 J; (b) 1900 J; (c) 1.1×10^{10} J **5.** (a) 1×10^5 megatons TNT; (b) 1×10^7 bombs **7.** father, 2.4 m/s; son, 4.8 m/s **9.** (a) 200 N; (b) 700 m; (c) -1.4×10^5 J; (d) 400 N, 350 m, -1.4×10^5 J **11.** 5000 J **13.** 47 keV **15.** 7.9 J **17.** 530 J **19.** -37 J **21.** (a) 314 J; (b) -155 J; (c) 0; (d) 158 J **23.** (a) 98 N; (b) 4.0 cm; (c) 3.9 J; (d) -3.9 J **25.** (a) $-3Mgd/4$; (b) Mgd; (c) $Mgd/4$ (d) $\sqrt{gd/2}$ **27.** 25 J **31.** -6 J **33.** (a) 12 J; (b) 4.0 m; (c) 18 J **35.** (a) -0.043 J; (b) -0.13 J **37.** (a) 6.6 m/s; (b) 4.7 m **39.** (a) up; (b) 5.0 cm; (c) 5.0 J **41.** 270 kW **43.** 235 kW **45.** 490 W **47.** (a) 100 J; (b) 67 W; (c) 33 W **49.** 0.99 hp **51.** (a) 0; (b) -350 W **53.** (a) 79.4 keV; (b) 3.12 MeV; (c) 10.9 MeV **55.** (a) 32 J; (b) 8 W; (c) 78°

Chapter 8
CP 1. no **2.** 3, 1, 2 **3.** (a) all tie; (b) all tie **4.** (a) CD, AB, BC (zero); (b) positive direction of x **5.** 2, 1, 3 **6.** decrease **7.** (a) seventh excited state, with energy E_7; (b) 1.3 eV **Q 1.** -40 J **3.** (c) and (d) tie; then (a) and (b) tie **5.** (a) all tie; (b) all tie **7.** (a) 3, 2, 1; (b) 1, 2, 3 **9.** less than (smaller decrease in potential energy) **11.** (a) $E < 3$ J, $K < 2$ J; (b) $E < 5$ J, $K < 4$ J **13.** (a) increasing; (b) decreasing; (c) decreasing; (d) constant in AB and BC, decreasing in CD **EP 1.** 15 J **3.** (a) 167 J; (b) -167 J; (c) 196 J; (d) 29 J **5.** (a) 0; (b) $mgh/2$; (c) mgh; (d) $mgh/2$; (e) mgh **7.** (a) -0.80 J; (b) -0.80 J; (c) $+1.1$ J **9.** (a) $mgL(1 - \cos\theta)$; (b) $-mgL(1 - \cos\theta)$; (c) $mgL(1 - \cos\theta)$ **11.** (a) 18 J;

(b) 0; (c) 30 J; (d) 0; (e) parts b and d **13.** (a) 2.08 m/s; (b) 2.08 m/s **15.** (a) $\sqrt{2gL}$; (b) $2\sqrt{gL}$; (c) $\sqrt{2gL}$ **17.** 830 ft **19.** (a) 6.75 J; (b) -6.75 J; (c) 6.75 J; (d) 6.75 J; (e) -6.75 J; (f) 0.459 m **21.** (a) 21.0 m/s; (b) 21.0 m/s **23.** (a) 0.98 J; (b) -0.98 J; (c) 3.1 N/cm **25.** (a) 39.2 J; (b) 39.2 J; (c) 4.00 m **27.** (a) 54 m/s; (b) 52 m/s; (c) 76 m, below **29.** (a) 39 ft/s; (b) 4.3 in. **31.** (a) 300 J; (b) 93.8 J; (c) 6.38 m **33.** (a) 4.8 m/s; (b) 2.4 m/s **35.** (a) $[v_0^2 + 2gL(1 - \cos\theta_0)]^{1/2}$; (b) $(2gL\cos\theta_0)^{1/2}$; (c) $[gL(3 + 2\cos\theta_0)]^{1/2}$ **37.** (a) $U(x) = -Gm_1m_2/x$; (b) $Gm_1m_2d/x_1(x_1 + d)$ **39.** (a) $8mg$ leftward and mg downward; (b) $2.5R$ **43.** $mgL/32$ **47.** (a) $1.12(A/B)^{1/6}$; (b) repulsive; (c) attractive **49.** (a) turning point on left, none on right; molecule breaks apart; (b) turning points on both left and right; molecule does not break apart; (c) -1.2×10^{-19} J; (d) 2.2×10^{-19} J; (e) $\approx 1 \times 10^{-9}$ on each, directed toward the other; (f) $r < 0.2$ nm; (g) $r > 0.2$ nm; (h) $r = 0.2$ nm **51.** -25 J **53.** (a) 2200 J; (b) -1500 J; (c) 700 J **55.** 17 kW **57.** (a) -0.74 J; (b) -0.53 J **59.** -12 J **61.** 54% **63.** 880 MW **65.** (a) 39 kW; (b) 39 kW **67.** (a) 1.5 MJ; (b) 0.51 MJ; (c) 1.0 MJ; (d) 63 m/s **69.** (a) 67 J; (b) 67 J; (c) 46 cm **71.** Your force on the cabbage does work. **73.** (a) -0.90 J; (b) 0.46 J; (c) 1.0 m/s **75.** (a) 18 ft/s; (b) 18 ft **77.** 4.3 m **79.** (a) 31.0 J; (b) 5.35 m/s; (c) conservative **81.** 1.2 m **85.** in the center of the flat part **87.** (a) 24 ft/s; (b) 3.0 ft; (c) 9.0 ft; (d) 49 ft **89.** (a) 216 J; (b) 1180 N; (c) 432 J; (d) motor also supplies thermal energy to crate and belt **91.** (a) 1.1×10^{17} J; (b) 1.2 kg **93.** 7.28 MeV **95.** (a) release; (b) 17.6 MeV **97.** (a) 5.3 eV; (b) 0.9 eV **99.** (a) 7.2 J; (b) -7.2 J; (c) 86 cm; (d) 26 cm

Chapter 9
CP 1. (a) origin; (b) fourth quadrant; (c) on y axis below origin; (d) origin; (e) third quadrant; (f) origin **2.** (a) to (c) at the center of mass, still at the origin (their forces are internal to the system and cannot move the center of mass) **3.** (a) 1, 3, and then 2 and 4 tie (zero force); (b) 3 **4.** (a) 0; (b) no; (c) negative x **5.** (a) 500 km/h; (b) 2600 km/h; (c) 1600 km/h **6.** (a) yes; (b) no **Q 1.** point 4 **3.** (a) at the center of the sled; (b) $L/4$, to the right; (c) not at all (no net external force); (d) $L/4$, to the left; (e) L; (f) $L/2$; (g) $L/2$ **5.** (a) ac, cd, and bc; (b) bc; (c) bd and ad **7.** (a) 2 N, rightward; (b) 2 N, rightward; (c) greater than 2 N, rightward **9.** b, c, a **11.** (a) yes; (b) 6 kg·m/s in $-x$ direction; (c) can't tell **EP 1.** (a) 4600 km; (b) $0.73R_e$ **3.** (a) x_{cm} = 1.1 m, y_{cm} = 1.3 m; (b) shifts toward topmost particle **5.** x_{cm} = -0.25 m, y_{cm} = 0 **7.** in the iron, at midheight and midwidth, 2.7 cm from midlength **9.** x_{cm} = y_{cm} = 20 cm, z_{cm} = 16 cm **11.** (a) $H/2$; (b) $H/2$; (c) descends to lowest point and then ascends to $H/2$; (d) $(HM/m)(\sqrt{1 + m/M} - 1)$ **13.** 72 km/h **15.** (a) center of mass does not move; (b) 0.75 m **17.** 4.8 m/s **19.** (a) 22 m; (b) 9.3 m/s **21.** 53 m **23.** 13.6 ft **25.** (a) 52.0 km/h; (b) 28.8 km/h **27.** a proton **29.** (a) 30°; (b) $-0.572\mathbf{j}$ kg·m/s **31.** (a) $(-4.0 \times 10^4\ \mathbf{i})$ kg·m/s; (b) west; (c) 0 **33.** $0.707c$ **35.** 0.57 m/s, toward center of mass **37.** it increases by

4.4 m/s **39.** (a) rocket case: 7290 m/s, payload: 8200 m/s; (b) before: 1.271×10^{10} J, after: 1.275×10^{10} J **41.** (a) -1; (b) 1830; (c) 1830; (d) same **43.** 14 m/s, 135° from the other pieces **45.** 190 m/s **47.** (a) $0.200v_{rel}$; (b) $0.210v_{rel}$; (c) $0.209v_{rel}$ **49.** (a) 1.57×10^6 N; (b) 1.35×10^5 kg; (c) 2.08 km/s **51.** 108 m/s **53.** 2.2×10^{-3} **57.** fast barge: 46 N more; slow barge: no change **59.** (a) 7.8 MJ; (b) 6.2 **61.** 690 W **63.** 5.5×10^6 N **65.** 24 W **67.** 100 m **69.** (a) 860 N; (b) 2.4 m/s **71.** (a) 3.0×10^5 J; (b) 10 kW; (c) 20 kW **73.** (a) 2.1×10^6 kg; (b) $\sqrt{100 + 1.5t}$ m/s; (c) $(1.5 \times 10^6)/\sqrt{100 + 1.5t}$ N; (d) 6.7 km **75.** $t = (3d/2)^{2/3}(m/2P)^{1/3}$

Chapter 10

CP **1.** (a) unchanged; (b) unchanged; (c) decreased **2.** (a) zero; (b) positive; (c) positive direction of y **3.** (a) 4 kg·m/s; (b) 8 kg·m/s; (c) 3 J **4.** (a) 0; (b) 4 kg·m/s **5.** (a) 10 kg·m/s; (b) 14 kg·m/s; (c) 6 kg·m/s **6.** (a) 2 kg·m/s; (b) 3 kg·m/s **7.** (a) increases; (b) increases **Q** **1.** all tie **3.** b and c **5.** (a) one stationary; (b) 2; (c) 5; (d) equal (pool player's result) **7.** (a) 1 and 4 tie; then 2 and 3 tie; (b) 1; 3 and 4 tie; then 2 **9.** (a) rightward; (b) rightward; (c) smaller **11.** positive direction of x axis **EP** **1.** (a) 750 N; (b) 6.0 m/s **3.** 6.2×10^4 N **5.** 3000 N ($= 660$ lb) **7.** 1.1 m **9.** (a) 42 N·s; (b) 2100 N **11.** (a) $(7.4 \times 10^3 \,\mathbf{i} - 7.4 \times 10^3 \,\mathbf{j})$ N·s; (b) $(-7.4 \times 10^3 \,\mathbf{i})$ N·s; (c) 2.3×10^3 N; (d) 2.1×10^4 N; (e) $-45°$ **13.** (a) 1.0 kg·m/s; (b) 250 J; (c) 10 N; (d) 1700 N **15.** 5 N **17.** $2\mu v$ **19.** 990 N **21.** (a) 1.8 N·s, to the left; (b) 180 N, to the right **25.** 8 m/s **27.** 38 km/s **29.** 4.2 m/s **31.** (a) 99 g; (b) 1.9 m/s; (c) 0.93 m/s **33.** (a) 1.2 kg; (b) 2.5 m/s **35.** 7.8 kg **37.** (a) 1/3; (b) $4h$ **39.** 35 cm **41.** 3.0 m/s **43.** (a) $(10\mathbf{i} + 15\mathbf{j})$ m/s; (b) 500 J lost **45.** (a) 2.7 m/s; (b) 1400 m/s **47.** (a) A: 4.6 m/s, B: 3.9 m/s; (b) 7.5 m/s **49.** 20 J for the heavy particle, 40 J for the light particle **51.** $mv^2/6$ **53.** 13 tons **55.** 25 cm **57.** 0.975 m/s, 0.841 m/s **59.** (a) 4.1 ft/s; (b) 1700 ft·lb; (c) $v_{24} = 5.3$ ft/s, $v_{32} = 3.3$ ft/s **61.** (a) 30° from the incoming proton's direction; (b) 250 m/s and 430 m/s **63.** (a) 41°; (b) 4.76 m/s; (c) no **65.** $v = V/4$ **67.** (a) 117° from the final direction of B; (b) no **69.** 120° **71.** (a) 1.9 m/s, 30° to initial direction; (b) no **73.** (a) 3.4 m/s, deflected by 17° to the right; (b) 0.95 MJ **75.** (a) 117 MeV; (b) equal and opposite momenta; (c) π^- **77.** (a) 4.94 MeV; (b) 0; (c) 4.85 MeV; (d) 0.09 MeV

Chapter 11

CP **1.** (b) and (c) **2.** (a) and (d) **3.** (a) yes; (b) no; (c) yes; (d) yes **4.** all tie **5.** 1, 2, 4, 3 **6.** (a) 1 and 3 tie, 4; then 2 and 5 tie (zero) **7.** (a) downward in the figure; (b) less **Q** **1.** (a) positive; (b) zero; (c) negative; (d) negative **3.** (a) 2 and 3; (b) 1 and 3; (c) 4 **5.** (a) and (c) **7.** (a) all tie; (b) 2, 3; then 1 and 4 tie **9.** b, c, a **11.** less **13.** 90°; then 70° and 110° tie **15.** Finite angular

displacements are not commutative. **EP** **1.** (a) 1.50 rad; (b) 85.9°; (c) 1.49 m **3.** (a) 0.105 rad/s; (b) 1.75×10^{-3} rad/s; (c) 1.45×10^{-4} rad/s **5.** (a) $\omega(2) = 4.0$ rad/s, $\omega(4) = 28$ rad/s; (b) 12 rad/s²; (c) $\alpha(2) = 6.0$ rad/s², $\alpha(4) = 18$ rad/s² **7.** (a) $\omega_0 + at^4 - bt^3$; (b) $\theta_0 + \omega_0 t + at^5/5 - bt^4/4$ **9.** 11 rad/s **11.** (a) 9000 rev/min²; (b) 420 rev **13.** (a) 30 s; (b) 1800 rad **15.** 200 rev/min **17.** (a) 2.0 rad/s²; (b) 5.0 rad/s; (c) 10 rad/s; (d) 75 rad **19.** (a) 13.5 s; (b) 27.0 rad/s **21.** (a) 340 s; (b) -4.5×10^{-3} rad/s²; (c) 98 s **23.** (a) 1.0 rev/s²; (b) 4.8 s; (c) 9.6 s; (d) 48 rev **25.** 6.1 ft/s² (1.8 m/s²), toward the center **27.** 0.13 rad/s **29.** 5.6 rad/s² **31.** (a) 5.1 h; (b) 8.1 h **33.** (a) 2.50×10^{-3} rad/s; (b) 20.2 m/s²; (c) 0 **35.** (a) -1.1 rev/min²; (b) 9900 rev; (c) -0.99 mm/s²; (d) 31 m/s² **37.** (a) 310 m/s; (b) 340 m/s **39.** (a) 1.94 m/s²; (b) 75.1°, toward the center of the track **41.** 16 s **43.** (a) 73 cm/s²; (b) 0.075; (c) 0.11 **45.** 12.3 kg·m² **47.** first cylinder: 1100 J; second cylinder: 9700 J **49.** (a) 221 kg·m²; (b) 1.10×10^4 J **51.** (a) 6490 kg·m²; (b) 4.36 MJ **53.** 0.097 kg·m² **57.** (a) 1300 g·cm²; (b) 550 g·cm²; (c) 1900 g·cm²; (d) $A + B$ **59.** (a) 49 MJ; (b) 100 min **61.** 4.6 N·m **63.** (a) $r_1 F_1 \sin\theta_1 - r_2 F_2 \sin\theta_2$; (b) -3.8 N·m **65.** 1.28 kg·m² **67.** 9.7 rad/s², counterclockwise **69.** (a) 155 kg·m²; (b) 64.4 kg **71.** (a) 420 rad/s²; (b) 500 rad/s **73.** small sphere: (a) 0.689 N·m and (b) 3.05 N; large sphere: (a) 9.84 N·m and (b) 11.5 N **75.** 1.73 m/s²; 6.92 m/s² **77.** (a) 1.4 m/s²; (b) 1.4 m/s **79.** (a) 19.8 kJ; (b) 1.32 kW **81.** (a) 8.2×10^{28} N·m; (b) 2.6×10^{29} J; (c) 3.0×10^{21} kW **83.** $\sqrt{9g/4\ell}$ **85.** (a) 4.8×10^5 N; (b) 1.1×10^4 N·m; (c) 1.3×10^6 J **87.** (a) $3g(1 - \cos\theta)$; (b) $\frac{3}{2}g \sin\theta$; (c) 41.8° **89.** (a) 5.6 rad/s²; (b) 3.1 rad/s **91.** (a) 42.1 km/h; (b) 3.09 rad/s²; (c) 7.57 kW **93.** (a) 3.4×10^5 g·cm²; (b) 2.9×10^5 g·cm²; (c) 6.3×10^5 g·cm²; (d) (1.2 cm) $\mathbf{i}$ + (5.9 cm) $\mathbf{j}$

Chapter 12

CP **1.** (a) same; (b) less **2.** less **3.** (a) $\pm z$; (b) $+y$; (c) $-x$ **4.** (a) 1 and 3 tie, then 2 and 4 tie, then 5 (zero); (b) 2 and 3 **5.** (a) 3, 1; then 2 and 4 tie (zero); (b) 3 **6.** (a) all tie (same τ, same t, thus same ΔL); (b) sphere, disk, hoop (reverse order of I) **7.** (a) decreases; (b) same; (c) increases **Q** **1.** (a) same; (b) block; (c) block **3.** (a) greater; (b) same **5.** (a) L; (b) 1.5L **7.** b, then c and d tie; then a and e tie (zero) **9.** a, then b and c tie; then e, d (zero) **11.** (a) same; (b) increases, because of decrease in rotational inertia **13.** (a) 30 units clockwise; (b) 2 then 4, then the others; or 4 then 2, then the others **15.** (a) spins in place; (b) rolls toward you; (c) rolls away from you **EP** **1.** 1.00 **3.** (a) 59.3 rad/s; (b) -9.31 rad/s²; (c) 70.7 m **5.** (a) -4.11 m/s²; (b) -16.4 rad/s²; (c) -2.54 N·m **7.** (a) 8.0°; (b) $0.14g$ **9.** (a) 4.0 N, to the left; (b) 0.60 kg·m² **11.** (a) $\frac{1}{2}mR^2$; (b) a solid circular cylinder **13.** (a) $mg(R - r)$; (b) 2/7; (c) $(17/7)mg$ **15.** (a) 2.7R; (b) $(50/7)mg$ **17.** (a) 13 cm/s²; (b) 4.4 s; (c) 55 cm/s; (d) 1.8×10^{-2} J; (e) 1.4 J; (f) 27 rev/s **21.** (a) 24 N·m, in $+y$ direction; (b) 24 N·m, $-y$; (c) 12 N·m, $+y$;

(d) 12 N·m, $-y$ **23.** (a) $(-1.5\mathbf{i} - 4.0\mathbf{j} - \mathbf{k})$ N·m;
(b) $(-1.5\mathbf{i} - 4.0\mathbf{j} - \mathbf{k})$ N·m   **25.** $-2.0\mathbf{i}$ N·m   **27.** 9.8
kg·m²/s   **29.** (a) 12 kg·m²/s, out of page; (b) 3.0 N·m,
out of page   **31.** (a) 0; (b) $(8.0\mathbf{i} + 8.0\mathbf{k})$ N·m   **33.** (a) mvd;
(b) no; (c) 0, yes   **35.** (a) 3.15×10^{43} kg·m²/s; (b) 0.616
37. 4.5 N·m, parallel to xy plane at $-63°$ from $+x$
39. (a) 0; (b) 0; (c) $30t^3$ kg·m²/s, $90t^2$ N·m, both in $-z$
direction; (d) $30t^3$ kg·m²/s, $90t^2$ N·m, both in $+z$ direction
41. (a) $\frac{1}{2}mgt^2v_0 \cos\theta_0$; (b) $mgtv_0 \cos\theta_0$; (c) $mgtv_0 \cos\theta_0$
43. (a) -1.47 N·m; (b) 20.4 rad; (c) -29.9 J; (d) 19.9 W
45. (a) 12.2 kg·m²; (b) 308 kg·m²/s, down   **47.** (a) 1/3;
(b) 1/9   **49.** $\omega_0 R_1 R_2 I_1/(I_1 R_2^2 + I_2 R_1^2)$ **51.** (a) 3.6 rev/s;
(b) 3.0; (c) work done by man in moving weights inward
53. (a) 267 rev/min; (b) 2/3   **55.** 3.0 min   **57.** 2.6 rad/s
59. (a) they revolve in a circle of 1.5 m radius at 0.93 rad/s;
(b) 8.4 rad/s; (c) $K_a = 98$ J, $K_b = 880$ J; (d) from the work
done in pulling inward   **61.** $m/(M + m)(v/R)$
63. (a) $mvR/(I + MR^2)$; (b) $mvR^2/(I + MR^2)$ **65.** 1300 m/s
67. (a) 18 rad/s; (b) 0.92
69. $\theta = \cos^{-1}\left[1 - \dfrac{6m^2h}{\ell(2m + M)(3m + M)}\right]$
71. 5.28×10^{-35} J·s   **73.** Any three are spin up; the other is
spin down.   **75.** (a) The magnitude of the angular momentum
increases in proportion to t^2 and the magnitude of the torque
increases in proportion to t, in agreement with the second law
for rotation. (b) The magnitudes of the angular momentum and
torque again increase with time. But the change in the
magnitude of the angular momentum in any interval is less than
is predicted by proportionality to t^2 law and the change in the
torque is less than is predicted by proportionality to t. At any
position of the projectile the torque is less when drag is present
than when it is not.

Chapter 13
CP **1.** c, e, f **2.** (a) no; (b) at site of $\mathbf{F}_1$, perpendicular to
plane of figure; (c) 45 N   **3.** (a) at C (to eliminate forces there
from a torque equation); (b) plus; (c) minus; (d) equal   **4.** d
5. (a) equal; (b) B; (c) B **Q** **1.** (a) yes; (b) yes; (c) yes;
(d) no   **3.** b **5.** (a) yes; (b) no; (c) no (it could balance the
torques but the forces would then be unbalanced)   **7.** (a) a,
then b and c tie, then d **9.** (a) 20 N (the key is the pulley
with the 20 N weight); (b) 25 N   **11.** (a) $\sin\theta$; (b) same;
(c) larger   **13.** tie of A and B, then C **EP** **1.** (a) two;
(b) seven   **3.** (a) 2.5 m; (b) 7.3°   **5.** 120°   **7.** 7920 N
9. (a) 840 N; (b) 530 N   **11.** 0.536 m   **13.** (a) 2770 N;
(b) 3890 N   **15.** (a) 1160 N, down; (b) 1740 N, up; (c) left,
stretched; (d) right, compressed   **17.** (a) 280 N; (b) 880 N,
71° above the horizontal   **19.** bars BC, CD, and DA are under
tension due to forces T, diagonals AC and BD are compressed
due to forces $\sqrt{2}T$ **21.** (a) 1800 lb; (b) 822 lb; (c) 1270 lb
23. (a) 49 N; (b) 28 N; (c) 57 N; (d) 29°   **25.** (a) 1900 N, up;
(b) 2100 N, down   **27.** (a) 340 N; (b) 0.88 m; (c) increases,
decreases   **29.** $W\sqrt{2rh - h^2}/(r - h)$ **31.** (a) $L/2$; (b) $L/4$;
(c) $L/6$; (d) $L/8$; (e) $25L/24$ **33.** (a) 6630 N; (b) $F_h = 5740$ N;
(c) $F_v = 5960$ N   **35.** 2.20 m   **37.** (a) 1.50 m; (b) 433 N;

(c) 250 N   **39.** (a) $a_1 = L/2$, $a_2 = 5L/8$, $h = 9L/8$;
(b) $b_1 = 2L/3$, $b_2 = L/2$, $h = 7L/6$ **41.** (a) 47 lb; (b) 120 lb;
(c) 72 lb   **43.** (a) 445 N; (b) 0.50; (c) 315 N
45. (a) 3.9 m/s²; (b) 2000 N on each rear wheel, 3500 N on
each front wheel; (c) 790 N on each rear wheel, 1410 N on
each front wheel   **47.** (a) 1.9×10^{-3}; (b) 1.3×10^7 N/m²;
(c) 6.9×10^9 N/m²   **49.** 3.1 cm   **51.** 2.4×10^9 N/m²
53. (a) 1.8×10^7 N; (b) 1.4×10^7 N; (c) 16   **55.** (a) 867 N;
(b) 143 N; (c) 0.165

Chapter 14
CP **1.** all tie   **2.** (a) 1, tie of 2 and 4, then 3; (b) line d
3. negative y direction   **4.** (a) increase; (b) negative
5. (a) 2; (b) 1   **6.** (a) path 1 (decreased E (more negative)
gives decreased a); (b) less than (decreased a gives decreased T)
Q **1.** (a) between, closer to less massive particle; (b) no;
(c) no (other than infinity)   **3.** $3GM^2/d^2$, leftward   **5.** b, tie
of a and c, then d **7.** b, a, c **9.** (a) negative; (b) negative;
(c) postive; (d) all tie   **11.** (a) all tie; (b) all tie
13. (a) same; (b) greater   **EP** **1.** 19 m   **3.** 2.16
5. 1/2   **7.** 3.4×10^5 km   **9.** (a) 3.7×10^{-5} N, increasing y **11.** $M = m$ **13.** 3.2×10^{-7} N   **15.** $(GmM/d^2) \times$
$\left[1 - \dfrac{1}{8(1 - R/2d)^2}\right]$ **17.** 2.6×10^6 m   **19.** (a) $1.3 \times$
10^{12} m/s²; (b) 1.6×10^6 m/s   **21.** (a) 17 N; (b) 2.5
23. (b) 1.9 h   **27.** (a) $a_g = (3.03 \times 10^{43}$ kg·m/s²$)/M_h$;
(b) decrease; (c) 9.82 m/s²; (d) 7.30×10^{-15} m/s²; (e) no
29. 7.91 km/s   **31.** (a) $(3.0 \times 10^{-7}m)$ N; (b) $(3.3 \times 10^{-7}m)$
N; (c) $(6.7 \times 10^{-7}mr)$ N   **33.** (a) 9.83 m/s²; (b) 9.84 m/s²;
(c) 9.79 m/s²   **35.** (a) -1.4×10^{-4} J; (b) less; (c) positive;
(d) negative   **37.** (a) 0.74; (b) 3.7 m/s²; (c) 5.0 km/s
39. (a) 0.0451; (b) 28.5   **41.** $-Gm(M_E/R + M_M/r)$
43. (a) 5.0×10^{-11} J; (b) -5.0×10^{-11} J   **45.** (a) 1700 m/s;
(b) 250 km; (c) 1400 m/s   **47.** (a) 2.2×10^{-7} rad/s;
(b) 90 km/s   **51.** (a) -1.67×10^{-8} J; (b) 0.56×10^{-8} J
55. 6.5×10^{23} kg   **57.** 5×10^{10} **59.** (a) 7.82 km/s;
(b) 87.5 min   **61.** (a) 6640 km; (b) 0.0136   **63.** (a) 39.5
AU³/M_S·y²; (b) $T^2 = r^3/M$ **65.** (a) 1.9×10^{13} m;
(b) $3.5R_P$ **67.** south, at 35.4° above the horizon
71. $2\pi r^{3/2}/\sqrt{G(M + m/4)}$ **73.** $\sqrt{GM/L}$ **75.** (a) 2.8 y;
(b) 1.0×10^{-4} **77.** (a) 1/2; (b) 1/2; (c) B, by 1.1×10^8 J
79. (a) 54 km/s; (b) 960 m/s; (c) $R_p/R_a = v_a/v_p$ **81.** (a) $4.6 \times$
10^5 J; (b) 260   **83.** (a) 7.5 km/s; (b) 97 min; (c) 410 km;
(d) 7.7 km/s; (e) 92 min; (f) 3.2×10^{-3} N; (g) if the satellite–
Earth system is considered isolated, its $\mathbf{L}$ is conserved
85. (a) 5540 s; (b) 7.68 km/s; (c) 7.60 km/s; (d) 5.78×10^{10} J;
(e) -11.8×10^{10} J; (f) -6.02×10^{10} J; (g) $6.63 \times$
10^6 m; (h) 170 s, new orbit   **87.** (a) $(-7.0$ mm)$\mathbf{i} +$
$(3.0$ cm)$\mathbf{j}$; (b) $(-0.19$ m/s)$\mathbf{i} + (0.40$ m/s)$\mathbf{j}$ **89.** (a) $1.98 \times$
10^{30} kg; (b) 1.96×10^{30} kg

Chapter 15
CP **1.** all tie   **2.** (a) all tie; (b) $0.95\rho_0$, ρ_0, $1.1\rho_0$
3. 13 cm³/s, outward   **4.** (a) all tie; (b) 1, then 2 and 3 tie, 4;

(c) 4, 3, 2, 1   **Q   1.** e, then b and d tie, then a and c tie
3. (a) 1, 3, 2; (b) all tie; (c) no (you must consider the weight exerted on the scale via the walls)   **5.** 3, 4, 1, 2
7. (a) downward; (b) downward; (c) same   **9.** (a) same; (b) same; (c) lower; (d) higher   **11.** (a) block 1, counterclockwise; block 2, clockwise; (b) block 1, tip more; block 2, right itself   **EP   1.** 1000 kg/m³   **3.** 1.1×10^5 Pa or 1.1 atm   **5.** 2.9×10^4 N   **7.** 6.0 lb/in.²   **9.** 1.90×10^4 Pa   **11.** 5.4×10^4 Pa   **13.** 0.52 m   **15.** (a) 6.06×10^9 N; (b) 20 atm   **17.** 0.412 cm   **19.** $\frac{1}{4}\rho g A(h_2 - h_1)^2$
21. 44 km   **23.** (a) $\rho g W D^2/2$; (b) $\rho g W D^3/6$; (c) $D/3$
25. (a) 2.2; (b) 2.4   **27.** -3.9×10^{-3} atm   **29.** (a) fA/a; (b) 20 lb   **31.** 1070 g   **33.** 1.5 g/cm³   **35.** 600 kg/m³
37. (a) 670 kg/m³; (b) 740 kg/m³   **39.** 390 kg
41. (a) 1.2 kg; (b) 1300 kg/m³   **43.** 0.126 m³   **45.** five
47. (a) 1.80 m³; (b) 4.75 m³   **49.** 2.79 g/cm³
51. (a) 9.4 N; (b) 1.6 N   **53.** 4.0 m   **55.** 28 ft/s   **57.** 43 cm/s   **59.** (a) 2.40 m/s; (b) 245 Pa   **61.** (a) 12 ft/s; (b) 13 lb/in.²   **63.** 0.72 ft·lb/ft³   **65.** (a) 2; (b) $R_1/R_2 = \frac{1}{2}$; (c) drain it until $h_2 = h_1/4$ **67.** 116 m/s   **69.** (a) 6.4 m³; (b) 5.4 m/s; (c) 9.8×10^4 Pa   **71.** (a) 560 Pa; (b) 5.0×10^4 N
73. 40 m/s   **75.** (b) $H - h$; (c) $H/2$ **77.** (b) 0.69 ft³/s
79. (b) 63.3 m/s

Chapter 16

CP   1. (a) $-x_m$; (b) $+x_m$; (c) 0   **2.** a   **3.** (a) 5 J; (b) 2 J; (c) 5 J   **4.** all tie (in Eq. 16-32, m is included in I)
5. 1, 2, 3 (the ratio m/b matters; k does not)   **Q   1.** c
3. (a) 0; (b) between 0 and $+x_m$; (c) between $-x_m$ and 0; (d) between $-x_m$ and 0   **5.** (a) toward $-x_m$; (b) toward $+x_m$; (c) between $-x_m$ and 0; (d) between $-x_m$ and 0; (e) decreasing; (f) increasing   **7.** (a) 3, 2, 1; (b) all tie   **9.** 3, 2, 1
11. system with spring A **13.** b (infinite period; does not oscillate), c, a **15.** (a) same; (b) same; (c) same; (d) smaller; (e) smaller; (f) and (g) larger ($T = \infty$)   **EP   1.** (a) 0.50 s; (b) 2.0 Hz; (c) 18 cm   **3.** (a) 245 N/m; (b) 0.284 s
5. 708 N/m   **7.** $f > 500$ Hz   **9.** (a) 100 N/m; (b) 0.45 s
11. (a) 6.28×10^5 rad/s; (b) 1.59 mm   **13.** (a) 1.0 mm; (b) 0.75 m/s; (c) 570 m/s²   **15.** (a) 1.29×10^5 N/m; (b) 2.68 Hz   **17.** (a) 4.0 s; (b) $\pi/2$ rad/s; (c) 0.37 cm; (d) (0.37 cm) cos $\frac{\pi}{2}t$; (e) $(-0.58$ cm/s) sin $\frac{\pi}{2}t$; (f) 0.58 cm/s; (g) 0.91 cm/s²; (h) 0; (i) 0.58 cm/s   **19.** (b) 12.47 kg; (c) 54.43 kg   **21.** 1.6 kg   **23.** (a) 1.6 Hz; (b) 1.0 m/s, 0; (c) 10 m/s², ± 10 cm; (d) $(-10$ N/m)x **25.** 22 cm
27. (a) 25 cm; (b) 2.2 Hz   **29.** (a) 0.500 m; (b) -0.251 m; (c) 3.06 m/s   **31.** (a) 0.183A; (b) same direction
37. (a) $k_1 = (n + 1)k/n$, $k_2 = (n + 1)k$; (b) $f_1 = \sqrt{(n + 1)/n}f$, $f_2 = \sqrt{n + 1}f$ **39.** (b) 42 min   **41.** (a) 200 N/m; (b) 1.39 kg; (c) 1.91 Hz   **43.** (a) 130 N/m; (b) 0.62 s; (c) 1.6 Hz; (d) 5.0 cm; (e) 0.51 m/s   **45.** (a) 3/4; (b) 1/4; (c) $x_m/\sqrt{2}$
47. (a) 3.5 m; (b) 0.75 s   **49.** (a) 0.21 m; (b) 1.6 Hz; (c) 0.10 m   **51.** (a) 0.0625 J; (b) 0.03125 J   **53.** 12 s
55. (a) 39.5 rad/s; (b) 34.2 rad/s; (c) 124 rad/s²   **57.** (a) 8.3 s; (b) no   **59.** 9.47 m/s²   **61.** 8.77 s   **63.** 5.6 cm
65. $2\pi\sqrt{(R^2 + 2d^2)/2gd}$ **67.** (a) 0.205 kg·m²; (b) 47.7 cm; (c) 1.50 s   **71.** (a) $2\pi\sqrt{(L^2 + 12x^2)/12gx}$; (b) 0.289 m

73. 9.78 m/s²   **75.** $2\pi\sqrt{m/3k}$ **77.** $(1/2\pi)(\sqrt{g^2 + v^4/R^2}/L)^{1/2}$
79. (b) smaller   **81.** (a) 2.0 s; (b) 18.5 N·m/rad
83. 0.29L **85.** 0.39   **87.** (a) 0.102 kg/s; (b) 0.137 J
89. $k = 490$ N/cm, $b = 1100$ kg/s   **91.** 1.9 in.
93. (a) $y_m = 8.8 \times 10^{-4}$ m, $T = 0.18$ s, $\omega = 35$ rad/s; (b) $y_m = 5.6 \times 10^{-2}$ m, $T = 0.48$ s, $\omega = 13$ rad/s; (c) $y_m = 3.3 \times 10^{-2}$ m, $T = 0.31$ s, $\omega = 20$ rad/s

Chapter 17

CP   1. a, 2; b, 3; c, 1   **2.** (a) 2, 3, 1; (b) 3, then 1 and 2 tie
3. a **4.** 0.20 and 0.80 tie, then 0.60, 0.45   **5.** (a) 1; (b) 3; (c) 2   **6.** (a) 75 Hz; (b) 525 Hz   **Q   1.** 7d **3.** tie of A and B, then C, D **5.** intermediate (closer to fully destructive interference)   **7.** a and d tie, then b and c tie   **9.** (a) 8; (b) antinode; (c) longer; (d) lower   **11.** (a) integer multiples of 3; (b) node; (c) node   **13.** string A **15.** decrease
EP   1. (a) 75 Hz; (b) 13 ms   **3.** (a) 7.5×10^{14} to 4.3×10^{14} Hz; (b) 1.0 to 200 m; (c) 6.0×10^{16} to 3.0×10^{19} Hz
5. $y = 0.010 \sin \pi(3.33x + 1100t)$, with x and y in m and t in s   **11.** (a) $z = 3.0 \sin(60y - 10\pi t)$, with z in mm, y in cm, and t in s; (b) 9.4 cm/s   **13.** (a) $y = 2.0 \sin 2\pi(0.10x - 400t)$, with x and y in cm and t in s; (b) 50 m/s; (c) 40 m/s
15. (b) 2.0 cm/s; (c) $y = (4.0$ cm) $\sin(\pi x/10 - \pi t/5 + \pi)$, where x is in cm and t is in s; (d) -2.5 cm/s   **17.** 129 m/s
19. 135 N   **23.** (a) 15 m/s; (b) 0.036 N   **25.** $y = 0.12 \sin(141x + 628t)$, with y in mm, x in m, and t in s
27. (a) 5.0 cm; (b) 40 cm; (c) 12 m/s; (d) 0.033 s; (e) 9.4 m/s; (f) $5.0 \sin(16x + 190t + 0.79)$, with x in m, y in cm, and t in s   **29.** (a) $v_1 = 28.6$ m/s, $v_2 = 22.1$ m/s; (b) $M_1 = 188$ g, $M_2 = 313$ g   **31.** (a) $\sqrt{k(\Delta l)(l + \Delta l)/m}$ **33.** (a) $P_2 = 2P_1$; (b) $P_2 = P_1/4$ **35.** (a) 3.77 m/s; (b) 12.3 N; (c) zero; (d) 46.3 W; (e) zero; (f) zero; (g) ± 0.50 cm   **37.** 82.8°, 1.45 rad, 0.23 wavelength   **39.** 5.0 cm   **41.** (a) 4.4 mm; (b) 112°
43. (a) $0.83y_1$; (b) 37°   **45.** (a) $2f_3$; (b) λ_3 **47.** 10 cm
49. (a) 82.0 m/s; (b) 16.8 m; (c) 4.88 Hz   **51.** 240 cm, 120 cm, 80 cm   **53.** 7.91 Hz, 15.8 Hz, 23.7 Hz   **55.** $f_{1A} = f_{4B}$, $f_{2A} = f_{8B}$ **57.** (a) 2.0 Hz, 200 cm, 400 cm/s; (b) $x = 50$ cm, 150 cm, 250 cm, etc.; (c) $x = 0$, 100 cm, 200 cm, etc.
63. (a) 1.3 m; (b) $y' = 0.002 \sin(9.4x) \cos(3800t)$, with x and y in m and t in s   **67.** (b) in the positive x direction; interchange the amplitudes of the original two traveling waves; (c) largest at $x = \lambda/4 = 6.26$ cm; smallest at $x = 0$ and $x = \lambda/2 = 12.5$ cm; (d) the largest amplitude is 4.0 mm, which is the sum of the amplitudes of the original traveling waves; the smallest amplitude is 1.0 mm, which is the difference of the amplitudes of the original traveling waves

Chapter 18

CP   1. beginning to decrease (example: mentally move the curves of Fig. 18-6 rightward past the point at $x = 42$ m)
2. (a) fully constructive, 0; (b) fully constructive, 4   **3.** (a) 1 and 2 tie, then 3; (b) 3, then 1 and 2 tie   **4.** second
5. loosen   **6.** a, greater; b, less; c, can't tell; d, can't tell; e, greater; f, less   **7.** (a) 222 m/s; (b) $+20$ m/s   **Q   1.** pulse

along path 2   **3.** (a) 2.0 wavelengths; (b) 1.5 wavelengths; (c) fully constructive, fully destructive   **5.** (a) exactly out of phase; (b) exactly out of phase   **7.** 70 dB   **9.** (a) two; (b) antinode   **11.** all odd harmonics   **13.** 501, 503, and 508 Hz; or 505, 507, and 508 Hz   **EP 1.** (a) $\approx 6\%$ **3.** the radio listener by about 0.85 s   **5.** 7.9×10^{10} Pa   **7.** If only the length is uncertain, it must be known to within 10^{-4} m. If only the time is imprecise, the uncertainty must be no more than one part in 10^{8}.   **9.** 43.5 m   **11.** 40.7 m   **13.** 100 kHz   **15.** (a) 2.29, 0.229, 22.9 kHz; (b) 1.14, 0.114, 11.4 kHz   **17.** (a) 6.0 m/s; (b) $y = 0.30 \sin(\pi x/12 + 50\pi t)$, with x and y in cm and t in s   **19.** 4.12 rad   **21.** (a) $343 \times (1 + 2m)$ Hz, with m being an integer from 0 to 28; (b) $686m$ Hz, with m being an integer from 1 to 29   **23.** (a) eight; (b) eight   **25.** 64.7 Hz, 129 Hz   **27.** (a) 0.080 W/m²; (b) 0.013 W/m²   **29.** 36.8 nm   **31.** (a) 1000; (b) 32   **33.** (a) 39.7 μW/m²; (b) 171 nm; (c) 0.893 Pa   **35.** (a) 59.7; (b) 2.81×10^{-4} **37.** $s_m \propto r^{-1/2}$ **39.** (a) 5000; (b) 71; (c) 71   **41.** 171 m   **43.** 3.16 km   **45.** (a) 5200 Hz; (b) amplitude$_{SAD}$/amplitude$_{SBD}$ = 2   **47.** 20 kHz   **49.** by a factor of 4   **51.** water filled to a height of $\frac{7}{8}, \frac{5}{8}, \frac{3}{8}, \frac{1}{8}$ m   **53.** (a) 5.0 cm from one end; (b) 1.2; (c) 1.2   **55.** (a) 1130, 1500, and 1880 Hz   **57.** (a) 230 Hz; (b) higher   **59.** (a) node; (c) 22 s   **61.** 387 Hz   **63.** 0.02   **65.** 3.8 Hz   **67.** (a) 380 mi/h, away from owner; (b) 77 mi/h, away from owner   **69.** 15.1 ft/s   **71.** 2.6×10^{8} m/s   **73.** (a) 77.6 Hz; (b) 77.0 Hz   **75.** 33.0 km   **79.** (a) 970 Hz; (b) 1030 Hz; (c) 60 Hz, no   **81.** (a) 1.02 kHz; (b) 1.04 kHz   **83.** 1540 m/s   **85.** 41 kHz   **87.** (a) 2.0 kHz; (b) 2.0 kHz   **89.** (a) 485.8 Hz; (b) 500.0 Hz; (c) 486.2 Hz; (d) 500.0 Hz   **91.** 1×10^{6} m/s, receding   **93.** $0.13c$

Chapter 19

CP 1. (a) all tie; (b) 50°X, 50°Y, 50°W   **2.** (a) 2 and 3 tie, then 1, then 4; (b) 3, 2, then 1 and 4 tie   **3.** A **4.** c and e **5.** (a) zero; (b) negative   **6.** b and d tie, then a, c **Q 1.** 25 S°, 25 U°, 25 R°   **3.** c, then the rest tie   **5.** B, then A and C tie   **7.** (a) both clockwise; (b) both clockwise   **9.** c, a, b **11.** upward (with liquid water on the exterior and at the bottom, $\Delta T = 0$ horizontally and downward)   **13.** at the temperature of your fingers   **15.** 3, 2, 1   **EP 1.** 2.71 K   **3.** 0.05 kPa, nitrogen   **5.** (a) 320°F; (b) −12.3°F   **7.** (a) −96°F; (b) 56.7°C   **9.** (a) −40°; (b) 575°; (c) Celsius and Kelvin cannot give the same reading   **11.** (a) Dimensions are inverse time   **13.** 4.4×10^{-3} cm   **15.** 0.038 in.   **17.** (a) 9.996 cm; (b) 68°C   **19.** 170 km   **21.** 0.32 cm²   **23.** 29 cm³   **25.** 0.432 cm³   **27.** −157°C   **29.** 360°C   **35.** +0.68 s/h   **37.** (b) use 39.3 cm of steel and 13.1 cm of brass   **39.** (a) 523 J/kg·K; (b) 0.600; (c) 26.2 J/mol·K   **41.** 94.6 L   **43.** 109 g   **45.** 1.30 MJ   **47.** 1.9 times as great   **49.** (a) 33.9 Btu; (b) 172 F°   **51.** (a) 52 MJ; (b) 0°C   **53.** (a) 411 g; (b) 3.1¢   **55.** 0.41 kJ/kg·K   **57.** 3.0 min   **59.** 73 kW   **61.** 2.17 g   **63.** 33 m²   **65.** 33 g   **67.** (a) 0°C; (b) 2.5°C   **69.** 2500 J/kg·K   **71.** A: 120 J, B: 75 J, C: 30 J   **73.** (a) −200 J; (b) −293 J;

(c) −93 J   **75.** −5.0 J   **77.** 33.3 kJ   **79.** 766°C   **81.** (a) 1.2 W/m·K, 0.70 Btu/ft·F°·h; (b) 0.030 ft²·F°·h/Btu   **83.** 1660 J/s   **87.** arrangement b **89.** (a) 2.0 MW; (b) 220 W   **91.** (a) 17 kW/m²; (b) 18 W/m²   **93.** −6.1 nW   **95.** 0.40 cm/h   **97.** Cu-Al, 84.3°C; Al-brass, 57.6°C

Chapter 20

CP 1. all but c **2.** (a) all tie; (b) 3, 2, 1   **3.** gas A **4.** 5 (greatest change in T), then tie of 1, 2, 3, and 4   **5.** 1, 2, 3 ($Q_3 = 0$, Q_2 goes into work W_2, but Q_1 goes into greater work W_1 and increases gas temperature)   **Q 1.** increased but less than doubled   **3.** a, c, b   **5.** 1180 J   **7.** d, tie of a and b, then c   **9.** constant-volume process   **11.** (a) same; (b) increases; (c) decreases; (d) increases   **13.** −4 J   **15.** (a) 1, polyatomic; 2, diatomic; 3, monatomic; (b) more   **EP 1.** (a) 0.0127; (b) 7.65×10^{21} **3.** 6560   **5.** number of molecules in the ink $\approx 3 \times 10^{16}$; number of people $\approx 5 \times 10^{20}$; statement is wrong, by a factor of about 20,000   **7.** (a) 5.47×10^{-8} mol; (b) 3.29×10^{16} **9.** (a) 106; (b) 0.892 m³   **11.** 27.0 lb/in.²   **13.** (a) 2.5×10^{25}; (b) 1.2 kg   **15.** 5600 J   **17.** 1/5   **19.** (a) −45 J; (b) 180 K   **21.** 100 cm³   **23.** 198°F   **25.** 2.0×10^{5} Pa   **27.** 180 m/s   **29.** 9.53×10^{6} m/s   **31.** 313°C   **33.** 1.9 kPa   **35.** (a) 0.0353 eV, 0.0483 eV; (b) 3400 J, 4650 J   **37.** 9.1×10^{-6} **39.** (a) 6.75×10^{-20} J; (b) 10.7   **41.** 0.32 nm   **43.** 15 cm   **45.** (a) 3.27×10^{10}; (b) 172 m   **47.** (a) 22.5 L; (b) 2.25; (c) 8.4×10^{-5} cm; (d) same as (c)   **51.** (a) 3.2 cm/s; (b) 3.4 cm/s; (c) 4.0 cm/s   **53.** (a) v_P, v_{rms}, $\bar{v}$ (b) reverse ranking   **55.** (a) 1.0×10^{4} K, 1.6×10^{5} K; (b) 440 K, 7000 K   **57.** 4.7   **59.** (a) $2N/3v_0$; (b) $N/3$; (c) $1.22v_0$; (d) $1.31v_0$ **61.** $RT \ln(V_f/V_i)$ **63.** (a) 15.9 J; (b) 34.4 J/mol·K; (c) 26.1 J/mol·K   **65.** $(n_1C_1 + n_2C_2 + n_3C_3)/(n_1 + n_2 + n_3)$ **67.** (a) −5.0 kJ; (b) 2.0 kJ; (c) 5.0 kJ   **69.** (a) 0.375 mol; (b) 1090 J; (c) 0.714   **71.** (a) 14 atm; (b) 620 K   **79.** 0.63   **81.** (a) monatomic; (b) 2.7×10^{4} K; (c) 4.5×10^{4} mol; (d) 3.4 kJ, 340 kJ; (e) 0.01   **83.** 5 m³   **85.** (a) in joules, in the order Q, ΔE_{int}, W: 1 → 2: 3740, 3740, 0; 2 → 3: 0, −1810, 1810; 3 → 1: −3220, −1930, −1290; cycle: 520, 0, 520; (b) $V_2 = 0.0246$ m³, $p_2 = 2.00$ atm, $V_3 = 0.0373$ m³, $p_3 = 1.00$ atm

Chapter 21

CP 1. a, b, c   **2.** smaller   **3.** c, b, a   **4.** a, d, c, b   **5.** b **Q 1.** increase   **3.** (a) increase; (b) same   **5.** equal   **7.** lower the temperature of the low temperature reservoir   **9.** (a) same; (b) increase; (c) decrease   **11.** (a) same; (b) increase; (c) decrease   **13.** more than the age of the universe   **EP 1.** 1.86×10^{4} J   **3.** 2.75 mol   **7.** (a) 5.79×10^{4} J; (b) 173 J/K   **9.** +3.59 J/K   **11.** (a) 14.6 J/K; (b) 30.2 J/K   **13.** (a) 4.45 J/K; (b) no   **15.** (a) 4500 J; (b) −5000 J; (c) 9500 J   **17.** (a) 57.0°C; (b) −22.1 J/K; (c) +24.9 J/K; (d) +2.8 J/K   **19.** (a) −710 mJ/K; (b) +710 mJ/K; (c) +723 mJ/K;

(d) -723 mJ/K; (e) $+13$ mJ/K; (f) 0   **23.** (a) (I) constant T, $Q = pV \ln 2$; constant V, $Q = 4.5pV$; (II) constant T, $Q = -pV \ln 2$; constant p, $Q = 7.5pV$; (b) (I) constant T, $W = pV \ln 2$; constant V, $W = 0$; (II) constant T, $W = -pV \ln 2$; constant p, $W = 3pV$; (c) $4.5pV$ for either case; (d) $4R \ln 2$ for either case   **25.** 0.75 J/K   **27.** (a) -943 J/K; (b) $+943$ J/K; (c) yes   **29.** (a) $3p_0V_0$; (b) $6RT_0$, $(3/2)R \ln 2$; (c) both are zero   **33.** (a) 31%; (b) 16 kJ   **35.** engine A, first; engine B, first and second; engine C, second; engine D, neither   **37.** 97 K   **39.** 99.99995%   **41.** 7.2 J/cycle   **43.** (a) 7200 J; (b) 960 J; (c) 13%   **45.** (a) 2270 J; (b) 14,800 J; (c) 15.4%; (d) 75.0%, greater   **49.** (a) 78%; (b) 81 kg/s   **55.** (a) 49 kJ; (b) 7.4 kJ   **57.** 21 J   **59.** (a) 0.071 J; (b) 0.50 J; (c) 2.0 J; (d) 5.0 J   **61.** 1.08 MJ   **63.** $[1 - (T_2/T_1)] \div [1 - (T_4/T_3)]$ **67.** (a) 1.27×10^{30}; (b) 7.9%; (c) 7.3%; (d) 7.3%; (e) 1.1%; (f) 0.0023%   **69.** (a) $W = N!/(n_1! \, n_2! \, n_3!)$; (b) $[(N/2)! \, (N/2)!]/[(N/3)! \, (N/3)! \, (N/3)!]$; (c) 4.2×10^{16}

Chapter 22

CP   1. C and D attract; B and D attract   **2.** (a) leftward; (b) leftward; (c) leftward   **3.** (a) a, c, b; (b) less than   **4.** $-15e$ (net charge of $-30e$ is equally shared)
Q   1. No, only for charged particles, charged particle-like objects, and spherical shells (including solid spheres) of uniform charge   **3.** a and b **5.** two points: one to the left of the particles and one between the protons   **7.** $6q^2/4\pi\epsilon_0 d^2$, leftward   **9.** (a) same; (b) less than; (c) cancel; (d) add; (e) the adding components; (f) positive direction of y; (g) negative direction of y; (h) positive direction of x; (i) negative direction of x **11.** (a) A, B, and D; (b) all four; (c) Connect A and D; disconnect them; then connect one of them to B. (There are two more solutions.)   **13.** (a) possibly; (b) definitely   **15.** same   **17.** D **EP   1.** 0.50 C   **3.** 2.81 N on each   **5.** (a) 4.9×10^{-7} kg; (b) 7.1×10^{-11} C   **7.** $3F/8$ **9.** (a) 1.60 N; (b) 2.77 N   **11.** (a) $q_1 = 9q_2$; (b) $q_1 = -25q_2$ **13.** either -1.00 μC and $+3.00$ μC or $+1.00$ μC and -3.00 μC   **15.** (a) 36 N, $-10°$ from the x axis; (b) $x = -8.3$ cm, $y = +2.7$ cm   **17.** (a) 5.7×10^{13} C, no; (b) 6.0×10^5 kg   **19.** (a) $Q = -2\sqrt{2}q$; (b) no   **21.** 3.1 cm   **23.** 2.89×10^{-9} N   **25.** -1.32×10^{13} C   **27.** (a) 3.2×10^{-19} C; (b) two   **29.** (a) 8.99×10^{-19} N; (b) 625   **31.** 5.1 m below the electron   **33.** 1.3 days   **35.** (a) 0; (b) 1.9×10^{-9} N   **37.** 10^{18} N   **39.** (a) ^{9}B; (b) ^{13}N; (c) ^{12}C   **41.** (a) $F = (Q^2/4\pi\epsilon_0 d^2)\alpha(1 - \alpha)$; (b) 0.5; (d) 0.15 and 0.85

Chapter 23

CP   1. (a) rightward; (b) leftward; (c) leftward; (d) rightward (p and e have same charge magnitude, and p is farther)   **2.** all tie   **3.** (a) toward positive y; (b) toward positive x; (c) toward negative y **4.** (a) leftward; (b) leftward; (c) decrease   **5.** (a) all tie; (b) 1 and 3 tie, then 2 and 4 tie
Q   1. (a) toward positive x; (b) downward and to the right;

(c) A **3.** two points: one to the left of the particles, the other between the protons   **5.** (a) yes; (b) toward; (c) no (the field vectors are not along the same line); (d) cancel; (e) add; (f) adding components; (g) toward negative y **7.** (a) 3, then 1 and 2 tie (zero); (b) all tie; (c) 1 and 2 tie, then 3   **9.** (a) rightward; (b) $+q_1$ and $-q_3$, increase; q_2, decrease; n, same   **11.** a, b, c **13.** (a) 4, 3, 1, 2; (b) 3, then 1 and 4 tie, then 2   **EP   1.** (a) 6.4×10^{-18} N; (b) 20 N/C   **3.** to the right in the figure   **7.** 56 pC   **9.** 3.07×10^{21} N/C, radially outward   **13.** (a) $q/8\pi\epsilon_0 d^2$, to the left; $3q/\pi\epsilon_0 d^2$, to the right; $7q/16\pi\epsilon_0 d^2$, to the left   **15.** 0   **17.** 9:30   **19.** $E = q/\pi\epsilon_0 a^2$, along bisector, away from triangle   **21.** $7.4q/4\pi\epsilon_0 d^2$, $28°$ counterclockwise to $+x$ **23.** 6.88×10^{-28} C$\cdot$m   **25.** $(1/4\pi\epsilon_0)(p/r^3)$, antiparallel to $\mathbf{p}$ **29.** $R/\sqrt{2}$ **31.** $(1/4\pi\epsilon_0)(4q/\pi R^2)$, toward decreasing y **37.** (a) 0.10 μC; (b) 1.3×10^{17}; (c) 5.0×10^{-6} **39.** 3.51×10^{15} m/s^2 **41.** 6.6×10^{-15} N   **43.** 2.03×10^{-7} N/C, up   **45.** (a) -0.029 C; (b) repulsive forces would explode the sphere   **47.** (a) 1.92×10^{12} m/s^2; (b) 1.96×10^5 m/s   **49.** (a) 8.87×10^{-15} N; (b) 120   **51.** 1.64×10^{-19} C ($\approx$3% high)   **53.** (a) 0.245 N, $11.3°$ clockwise from the $+x$ axis; (b) $x = 108$ m, $y = -21.6$ m   **55.** 27μm   **57.** (a) yes; (b) upper plate, 2.73 cm   **59.** (a) 0; (b) 8.5×10^{-22} N$\cdot$m; (c) 0   **61.** $(1/2\pi)\sqrt{pE/I}$ **63.** (a) $E = (2q/4\pi\epsilon_0 d^2)(\alpha/(1 + \alpha^2)^{3/2})$; (c) 0.707; (d) 0.21 and 1.9

Chapter 24

CP   1. (a) $+EA$; (b) $-EA$; (c) 0; (d) 0   **2.** (a) 2; (b) 3; (c) 1   **3.** (a) equal; (b) equal; (c) equal   **4.** (a) $+50e$; (b) $-150e$ **5.** 3 and 4 tie, then 2, 1   **Q   1.** (a) 8 N$\cdot$m^2/C; (b) 0   **3.** (a) all tie (zero); (b) all tie   **5.** $+13q/\epsilon_0$ **7.** all tie   **9.** all tie   **11.** 2σ, σ, 3σ; or 3σ, σ, 2σ **13.** (a) all tie ($E = 0$); (b) all tie   **15.** (a) same ($E = 0$); (b) decrease; (c) decrease (to zero); (d) same   **EP   1.** (a) 693 kg/s; (b) 693 kg/s; (c) 347 kg/s; (d) 347 kg/s; (e) 575 kg/s   **3.** (a) 0; (b) -3.92 N$\cdot$m^2/C; (c) 0; (d) 0 for each field   **5.** (a) enclose $2q$ and $-2q$, or enclose all four charges; (b) enclose $2q$ and q; (c) not possible   **7.** 2.0×10^5 N$\cdot$m^2/C   **9.** $q/6\epsilon_0$ **11.** (a) $-\pi R^2 E$; (b) $\pi R^2 E$ **13.** -4.2×10^{-10} C   **15.** 0 through each of the three faces meeting at q, $q/24\epsilon_0$ through each of the other faces   **17.** 2.0 μC/m^2 **19.** (a) 4.5×10^{-7} C/m^2; (b) 5.1×10^4 N/C   **21.** (a) -3.0×10^{-6} C; (b) $+1.3 \times 10^{-5}$ C   **23.** (a) 0.32 μC; (b) 0.14 μC   **27.** (a) $E = q/2\pi\epsilon_0 Lr$, radially inward; (b) $-q$ on both inner and outer surfaces; (c) $E = q/2\pi\epsilon_0 Lr$, radially outward   **29.** 3.6 nC   **31.** (b) $\rho R^2/2\epsilon_0 r$ **33.** (a) 5.3×10^7 N/C; (b) 60 N/C   **35.** 5.0 nC/m^2 **37.** 0.44 mm   **39.** (a) 4.9×10^{-22} C/m^2; (b) downward   **41.** (a) $\rho x/\epsilon_0$; (b) $\rho d/2\epsilon_0$ **43.** (a) -750 N$\cdot$m^2/C; (b) -6.64 nC   **45.** (a) 4.0×10^6 N/C; (b) 0   **47.** (a) 0; (b) $q_a/4\pi\epsilon_0 r^2$; (c) $(q_a + q_b)/4\pi\epsilon_0 r^2$ **51.** (a) $-q$; (b) $+q$; (c) $E = q/4\pi\epsilon_0 r^2$, radially outward; (d) $E = 0$; (e) $E = q/4\pi\epsilon_0 r^2$, radially outward; (f) 0; (g) $E = q/4\pi\epsilon_0 r^2$, radially outward; (h) yes, charge is induced; (i) no; (j) yes; (k) no; (l) no   **53.** (a) $E = (q/4\pi\epsilon_0 a^3)r$; (b) $E = q/4\pi\epsilon_0 r^2$; (c) 0; (d) 0; (e) inner, $-q$; outer, 0   **55.** $q/2\pi a^2$ **59.** $\alpha = 0.80$

Chapter 25

CP **1.** (a) negative; (b) increase **2.** (a) positive;
(b) higher **3.** (a) rightward; (b) 1, 2, 3, 5: positive; 4,
negative; (c) 3, then 1, 2, and 5 tie, then 4 **4.** all tie **5.** a,
c (zero), b **6.** (a) 2, then 1 and 3 tie; (b) 3; (c) accelerate
leftward **7.** closer (half of 9.23 fm) **Q** **1.** (a) higher;
(b) positive; (c) negative; (d) all tie **3.** (a) 1 and 2; (b) none;
(c) no; (d) 1 and 2 yes, 3 and 4 no **5.** b, then a, c, and d tie
7. (a) negative; (b) zero **9.** (a) 1, then 2 and 3 tie; (b) 3
11. left **13.** a, b, c **15.** (a) c, b, a; (b) zero
17. (a) positive; (b) positive; (c) negative; (d) all tie
19. (a) no; (b) yes **21.** no (a particle at the intersection
would have two different potential energies) **23.** (a)–(b) all
tie; (c) C, B, A; (d) all tie **EP** **1.** 1.2 GeV **3.** (a) 3.0×10^{10} J; (b) 7.7 km/s; (c) 9.0×10^4 kg **7.** 2.90 kV **9.** 8.8
mm **11.** (a) 136 MV/m; (b) 8.82 kV/m **13.** (b) because
$V = 0$ point is chosen differently; (c) $q/(8\pi\epsilon_0 R)$; (d) potential
differences are independent of the choice for the $V = 0$ point
15. (a) -4500 V; (b) -4500 V **17.** 843 V **19.** 2.8×10^5
21. $x = d/4$ and $x = -d/2$ **23.** none **25.** (a) 3.3 nC;
(b) 12 nC/m^2 **27.** 6.4×10^8 V **29.** 190 MV
31. (a) -4.8 nm; (b) 8.1 nm; (c) no **33.** 16.3 μV
35. (a) $\dfrac{2\lambda}{4\pi\epsilon_0} \ln\left[\dfrac{L/2 + (L^2/4 + d^2)^{1/2}}{d}\right]$; (b) 0
37. (a) $-5Q/4\pi\epsilon_0 R$; (b) $-5Q/4\pi\epsilon_0(z^2 + R^2)^{1/2}$
39. $0.113\sigma R/\epsilon_0$ **41.** $(Q/4\pi\epsilon_0 L) \ln(1 + L/d)$ **43.** 670 V/m
45. $p/2\pi\epsilon_0 r^3$ **47.** 39 V/m, $-x$ direction
51. (a) $\dfrac{c}{4\pi\epsilon_0}[\sqrt{L^2 + y^2} - y]$; (b) $\dfrac{c}{4\pi\epsilon_0}\left[1 - \dfrac{y}{\sqrt{L^2 + y^2}}\right]$
53. (a) 2.5 MV; (b) 5.1 J; (c) 6.9 J **55.** (a) 2.72×10^{-14} J;
(b) 3.02×10^{-31} kg, about $\frac{1}{3}$ of accepted value **57.** (a) 0.484
MeV; (b) 0 **59.** 2.1 d **61.** 0 **63.** (a) 27.2 V; (b) -27.2
eV; (c) 13.6 eV; (d) 13.6 eV **65.** 1.8×10^{-10} J
67. 1.48×10^7 m/s **69.** $qQ/4\pi\epsilon_0 K$ **71.** 0.32 km/s
73. 1.6×10^{-9} m **77.** (a) $V_1 = V_2$; (b) $q_1 = q/3$, $q_2 = 2q/3$; (c) 2 **79.** (a) -0.12 V; (b) 1.8×10^{-8} N/C, radially
inward **81.** (a) 12,000 N/C; (b) 1800 V; (c) 5.8 cm
83. (c) 4.24 V

Chapter 26

CP **1.** (a) same; (b) same **2.** (a) decreases; (b) increases;
(c) decreases **3.** (a) V, $q/2$; (b) $V/2$, q **4.** (a) $q_0 = q_1 +
q_{34}$; (b) equal ($C_3$ and C_4 are in series) **5.** (a) same;
(b)–(d) increase; (e) same (same potential difference across
same plate separation) **6.** (a) same; (b) decrease;
(c) increase **Q** **1.** a, 2; b, 1; c, 3 **3.** (a) increase;
(b) same **5.** (a) parallel; (b) series **7.** (a) $C/3$; (b) $3C$;
(c) parallel **9.** (a) equal; (b) less **11.** (a)–(d) less
13. (a) 2; (b) 3; (c) 1 **15.** Increase plate separation d, but
also plate area A, keeping A/d constant. **EP** **1.** 7.5 pC
3. 3.0 mC **5.** (a) 140 pF; (b) 17 nC **7.** (a) 84.5 pF;
(b) 191 cm^2 **9.** (a) 11 cm^2; (b) 11 pF; (c) 1.2 V
13. (b) 4.6×10^{-5}/K **15.** 7.33 μF **17.** 315 mC
19. (a) 10.0 μF; (b) $q_2 = 0.800$ mC, $q_1 = 1.20$ mC; (c) 200 V
for both **21.** (a) $d/3$; (b) $3d$ **25.** (a) five in series; (b) three

arrays as in (a) in parallel (and other possibilities) **27.** 43 pF
29. (a) 50 V; (b) 5.0×10^{-5} C; (c) 1.5×10^{-4} C
31. (a) $q_1 = 9.0$ μC, $q_2 = 16$ μC, $q_3 = 9.0$ μC, $q_4 = 16$ μC;
(b) $q_1 = 8.4$ μC, $q_2 = 17$ μC, $q_3 = 11$ μC, $q_4 = 14$ μC
33. 99.6 nJ **35.** 72 F **37.** 4.9% **39.** 0.27 J **41.** 0.11
J/m^3 **43.** (a) 2.0 J **45.** (a) $q_1 = 0.21$ mC, $q_2 = 0.11$ mC,
$q_3 = 0.32$ mC; (b) $V_1 = V_2 = 21$ V, $V_3 = 79$ V; (c) $U_1 = 2.2$
mJ, $U_2 = 1.1$ mJ, $U_3 = 13$ mJ **47.** (a) $q_1 = q_2 = 0.33$ mC,
$q_3 = 0.40$ mC; (b) $V_1 = 33$ V, $V_2 = 67$ V, $V_3 = 100$ V;
(c) $U_1 = 5.6$ mJ, $U_2 = 11$ mJ, $U_3 = 20$ mJ **53.** Pyrex
55. (a) 6.2 cm; (b) 280 pF **57.** 0.63 m^2 **59.** (a) 2.85 m^3;
(b) 1.01×10^4 **61.** (a) $\epsilon_0 A/(d-b)$; (b) $d/(d-b)$;
(c) $-q^2 b/2\epsilon_0 A$, sucked in **65.** $\dfrac{\epsilon_0 A}{4d}\left(\kappa_1 + \dfrac{2\kappa_2\kappa_3}{\kappa_2 + \kappa_3}\right)$
67. (a) 13.4 pF; (b) 1.15 nC; (c) 1.13×10^4 N/C; (d) 4.33×10^3 N/C **69.** (a) 7.1; (b) 0.77 μC **71.** (a) 0.606; (b) 0.394

Chapter 27

CP **1.** 8 A, rightward **2.** (a)–(c) rightward **3.** a and c
tie, then b **4.** Device 2 **5.** (a) and (b) tie, then (d), then
(c) **Q** **1.** a, b, and c tie, then d (zero) **3.** b, a, c **5.** tie
of A, B, and C, then a tie of $A + B$ and $B + C$, then $A +
B + C$ **7.** (a)–(c) 1 and 2 tie, then 3 **9.** C, A, B
11. b, a, c **13.** (a) conductors: 1 and 4; semiconductors: 2
and 3; (b) 2 and 3; (c) all four **EP** **1.** 1.25×10^{15} **3.** 6.7
μC/m^2 **5.** 14-gauge **7.** (a) 2.4×10^{-5} A/m^2; (b) 1.8×10^{-15} m/s **9.** 0.67 A, toward the negative terminal
11. (a) 0.654 μA/m^2; (b) 83.4 MA **13.** 13 min
15. (a) $J_0 A/3$; (b) $2J_0 A/3$ **17.** 2.0×10^{-8} $\Omega \cdot$m
19. 100 V **21.** (a) 1.53 kA; (b) 54.1 MA/m^2; (c) 10.6×10^{-8} $\Omega \cdot$m, platinum **23.** (a) 253°C; (b) yes **25.** (a) 0.38 mV;
(b) negative; (c) 3 min 58 s **27.** 54 Ω **29.** 3.0
31. (a) 1.3 mΩ; (b) 4.6 mm **33.** (a) 6.00 mA; (b) 1.59×10^{-8} V; (c) 21.2 nΩ **35.** 2000 K **37.** (a) copper: 5.32×10^5 A/m^2, aluminum: 3.27×10^5 A/m^2; (b) copper: 1.01 kg/m,
aluminum: 0.495 kg/m **39.** 0.40 Ω **41.** (a) $R = \rho L/\pi ab$
43. 14 kC **45.** 11.1 Ω **47.** (a) 1.0 kW; (b) 25¢
49. 0.135 W **51.** (a) 1.74 A; (b) 2.15 MA/m^2; (c) 36.3
mV/m; (d) 2.09 W **53.** (a) 1.3×10^5 A/m^2; (b) 94 mV
55. (a) \$4.46 for a 31-day month; (b) 144 Ω; (c) 0.833 A
57. 660 W **59.** (a) 3.1×10^{11}; (b) 25 μA; (c) 1300 W,
25 MW **61.** 27 cm/s **63.** (a) 120 Ω; (b) 107 Ω; (c) 5.3×10^{-3}/C°; (d) 5.9×10^{-3}/C°; (e) 276 Ω

Chapter 28

CP **1.** (a) rightward; (b) all tie; (c) b, then a and c tie; (d) b,
then a and c tie **2.** (a) all tie; (b) R_1, R_2, R_3 **3.** (a) less;
(b) greater; (c) equal **4.** (a) $V/2$, i; (b) V, $i/2$ **5.** (a) 1, 2, 4,
3; (b) 4, tie of 1 and 2; then 3 **Q** **1.** 3, 4, 1, 2 **3.** (a) no;
(b) yes; (c) all tie (the circuits are the same) **5.** parallel, R_2,
R_1, series **7.** (a) equal; (b) more **9.** (a) less; (b) less;
(c) more **11.** C_1, 15 V; C_2, 35 V; C_3, 20 V; C_4, 20 V; C_5,
30 V **13.** 60 μC **15.** c, b, a **17.** (a) all tie; (b) 1, 3, 2
19. 1, 3, and 4 tie (8 V on each resistor), then 2 and 5 tie (4 V
on each resistor) **EP** **1.** (a) \$320; (b) 4.8¢ **3.** 11 kJ

5. (a) counterclockwise; (b) battery 1; (c) B   **7.** (a) 80 J;
(b) 67 J; (c) 13 J converted to thermal energy within battery
9. (a) 14 V; (b) 100 W; (c) 600 W; (d) 10 V, 100 W
11. (a) 50 V; (b) 48 V; (c) B is connected to the negative
terminal   **13.** 2.5 V   **15.** (a) 6.9 km; (b) 20 Ω
17. 8.0 Ω **19.** 10^{-6} **21.** the cable   **23.** (a) 1000 Ω;
(b) 300 mV; (c) 2.3×10^{-3} **25.** (a) 3.41 A or 0.586 A;
(b) 0.293 V or 1.71 V   **27.** 5.56 A   **29.** 4.0 Ω and 12 Ω
31. 4.50 Ω **33.** 0.00, 2.00, 2.40, 2.86, 3.00, 3.60, 3.75,
3.94 A   **35.** $V_d - V_c = +0.25$ V, by all paths   **37.** three
39. (a) 2.50 Ω; (b) 3.13 Ω **41.** nine   **43.** (a) left branch:
0.67 A down; center branch: 0.33 A up; right branch: 0.33 A
up; (b) 3.3 V   **47.** (a) 120 Ω; (b) $i_1 = 51$ mA, $i_2 = i_3 =$
19 mA, $i_4 = 13$ mA   **49.** (a) 19.5 Ω; (b) 0; (c) ∞; (d) 82.3 W,
57.6 W   **51.** (a) Cu: 1.11 A, Al: 0.893 A; (b) 126 m
53. (a) 13.5 kΩ; (b) 1500 Ω; (c) 167 Ω; (d) 1480 Ω
55. 0.45 A   **57.** (a) 12.5 V; (b) 50 A   **59.** -0.9%
65. (a) 0.41τ; (b) 1.1τ **67.** 4.6   **69.** (a) 0.955 μC/s;
(b) 1.08 μW; (c) 2.74 μW; (d) 3.82 μW   **71.** 2.35 MΩ
73. 0.72 MΩ **75.** 24.8 Ω to 14.9 kΩ **77.** (a) at $t = 0$,
$i_1 = 1.1$ mA, $i_2 = i_3 = 0.55$ mA; at $t = \infty$, $i_1 = i_2 = 0.82$ mA,
$i_3 = 0$; (c) at $t = 0$, $V_2 = 400$ V; at $t = \infty$, $V_2 = 600$ V;
(d) after several time constants ($\tau = 7.1$ s) have elapsed
79. (a) $V_T = -ir + \mathscr{E}$; (b) 13.6 V; (c) 0.060 Ω
81. (a) 6.4 V; (b) 3.6 W; (c) 17 W; (d) -5.6 W; (e) a

Chapter   29

CP   1. $a, +z$; $b, -x$; $c, F_B = 0$ **2.** 2, then tie of 1 and 3
(zero); (b) 4   **3.** (a) $+z$ and $-z$ tie, then $+y$ and $-y$ tie, then
$+x$ and $-x$ tie (zero); (b) $+y$ **4.** (a) electron;
(b) clockwise   **5.** $-y$ **6.** (a) all tie; (b) 1 and 4 tie, then 2
and 3 tie   **Q   1.** (a) all tie; (b) 1 and 2 (charge is negative)
3. a, no, $\mathbf{v}$ and $\mathbf{F}_B$ must be perpendicular; b, yes; c, no, $\mathbf{B}$ and
$\mathbf{F}_B$ must be perpendicular   **5.** (a) $\mathbf{F}_E$; (b) $\mathbf{F}_B$ **7.** (a) right;
(b) right   **9.** (a) negative; (b) equal; (c) equal; (d) half a
circle   **11.** (a) $\mathbf{B}_1$; (b) $\mathbf{B}_1$ into page; $\mathbf{B}_2$ out of page; (c) less
13. all   **15.** all tie   **17.** (a) positive; (b) (1) and (2) tie, then
(3) which is zero   **EP   1.** M/QT **3.** (a) 9.56×10^{-14} N, 0;
(b) $0.267°$ **5.** (a) east; (b) 6.28×10^{14} m/s²; (c) 2.98 mm
7. $0.75\mathbf{k}$ T   **9.** (a) 3.4×10^{-4} T, horizontal and to the left
as viewed along $\mathbf{v}_0$; (b) yes, if velocity is the same as the
electron's velocity   **11.** $(-11.4\mathbf{i} - 6.00\mathbf{j} + 4.80\mathbf{k})$ V/m
13. 680 kV/m   **17.** (b) 2.84×10^{-3} **19.** (a) 1.11×10^7 m/s;
(b) 0.316 mm   **21.** (a) 0.34 mm; (b) 2.6 keV
23. (a) 2.05×10^7 m/s; (b) 467 μT; (c) 13.1 MHz; (d) 76.3 ns
25. (a) 2.60×10^6 m/s; (b) 0.109 μs; (c) 0.140 MeV;
(d) 70 kV   **29.** (a) 1.0 MeV; (b) 0.5 MeV   **31.** $R_d = \sqrt{2}R_p$;
$R_\alpha = R_p$.   **33.** (a) $B\sqrt{mq/2V}\,\Delta x$; (b) 8.2 mm   **37.** (a) $-q$;
(b) $\pi m/qB$ **39.** $B_{\min} = \sqrt{mV/2ed^2}$ **41.** (a) 22 cm;
(b) 21 MHz   **43.** neutron moves tangent to original path,
proton moves in a circular orbit of radius 25 cm   **45.** 28.2 N,
horizontally west   **47.** 20.1 N   **49.** $Bitd/m$, away from
generator   **51.** $-0.35\mathbf{k}$ N   **53.** 0.10 T, at 31° from the
vertical   **55.** 4.3×10^{-3} N·m, negative y **59.** $qvaB/2$
61. (a) 540 Ω, in series; (b) 2.52 Ω, in parallel
63. (a) 12.7 A; (b) 0.0805 N·m   **65.** (a) 0.184 A·m²;

(b) 1.45 N·m   **67.** (a) 20 min; (b) 5.9×10^{-2} N·m
69. (a) $(8.0 \times 10^{-4}$ N·m$)(-1.2\mathbf{i} - 0.90\mathbf{j} + 1.0\mathbf{k})$;
(b) -6.0×10^{-4} J

Chapter   30

CP   1. a, c, b **2.** b, c, a **3.** d, tie of a and c, then b
4. d, a, tie of b and c (zero)   **Q   1.** c, d, then a and b tie
3. 2 and 4   **5.** a, b, c **7.** b, d, c, a (zero)   **9.** (a) 1, $+x$;
2, $-y$; (b) 1, $+y$; 2, $+x$ **11.** outward   **13.** c and
d tie, then b, a **15.** d, then tie of a and e, then b, c
17. 0 (dot product is zero)   **EP   1.** 32.1 A
3. (a) 3.3 μT; (b) yes   **5.** (a) $(0.24\mathbf{i})$ nT; (b) 0; (c) $(-43\mathbf{k})$ pT;
(d) $(0.14\mathbf{k})$ nT   **7.** (a) 16 A; (b) west to east   **9.** 0
11. (a) 0; (b) $\mu_0 i/4R$, into the page; (c) same as (b)
13. $\mu_0 i\theta$ $(1/b - 1/a)/4\pi$, out of page   **15.** (a) 1.0 mT, out of
the figure; (b) 0.80 mT, out of the figure   **25.** 200 μT, into
page   **27.** (a) it is impossible to have other than $B = 0$
midway between them; (b) 30 A   **29.** 4.3 A, out of page
35. $0.338\mu_0 i^2/a$, toward the center of the square
37. (b) to the right   **39.** (b) 2.3 km/s   **41.** $+5\mu_0 i$

47. (a) $\mu_0 ir/2\pi c^2$; (b) $\mu_0 i/2\pi r$; (c) $\dfrac{\mu_0 i}{2\pi(a^2 - b^2)} \cdot \dfrac{a^2 - r^2}{r}$;

(d) 0   **49.** $3i/8$, into page   **53.** 0.30 mT   **55.** 108 m
61. 0.272 A   **63.** (a) 4; (b) 1/2   **65.** (a) 2.4 A·m²;
(b) 46 cm   **67.** (a) $\mu_0 i(1/a + 1/b)/4$, into page; (b) $\frac{1}{2}i\pi(a^2 + b^2)$,
into page   **69.** (a) 79 μT; (b) 1.1×10^{-6} N·m
71. (b) $(0.060$ **j**$)$ A·m²; (c) $(9.6 \times 10^{-11}$**j**$)$ T, $(-4.8 \times$
10^{-11}**j**$)$ T   **73.** (a) B from sum: 7.069×10^{-5} T; $\mu_0 in =$
5.027×10^{-5} T; 40% difference; (b) B from sum: $1.043 \times$
10^{-4} T; $\mu_0 in = 1.005 \times 10^{-4}$ T; 4% difference; (c) B from
sum: 2.506×10^{-4} T; $\mu_0 in = 2.513 \times 10^{-4}$ T; 0.3%
difference   **75.** (a) $\mathbf{B} = (\mu_0/2\pi)\,[i_1/(x - a) + i_2/x]\mathbf{j}$;
(b) $\mathbf{B} = (\mu_0/2\pi)\,(i_1/a)\,(1 + b/2)\mathbf{j}$

Chapter   31

CP   1. b, then d and e tie, and then a and c tie (zero)   **2.** a
and b tie, then c (zero)   **3.** c and d tie, then a and b tie
4. b, out; c, out; d, into; e, into   **5.** d and e   **6.** (a) 2, 3, 1
(zero); (b) 2, 3, 1   **7.** a and b tie, then c **Q   1.** (a) all tie
(zero); (b) all tie (nonzero); (c) 3, then tie of 1 and 2 (zero)
3. out   **5.** (a) into; (b) counterclockwise; (c) larger
7. (a) leftward; (b) rightward   **9.** c, a, b **11.** (a) 1, 3, 2;
(b) 1 and 3 tie, then 2   **13.** a, tie of b and c   **15.** (a) more;
(b) same; (c) same; (d) same (zero)   **17.** a, 2; b, 4; c, 1; d, 3
EP   1. 57 μWb   **3.** 1.5 mV   **5.** (a) 31 mV; (b) right to
left   **7.** (a) 0.40 V; (b) 20 A   **9.** (b) 58 mA   **11.** 1.2 mV
13. 1.15 μWb   **15.** 51 mV, clockwise when viewed along the
direction of $\mathbf{B}$ **17.** (a) 1.26×10^{-4} T, 0, -1.26×10^{-4} T;
(b) 5.04×10^{-8} V   **19.** (b) no   **21.** 15.5 μC
23. (a) 24 μV; (b) from c to b **25.** (b) design it so that
$Nab = (5/2\pi)$ m²   **27.** (a) 0.598 μV; (b) counterclockwise

29. (a) $\dfrac{\mu_0 ia}{2\pi}\left(\dfrac{2r + b}{2r - b}\right)$; (b) $2\mu_0 iabv/\pi R(4r^2 - b^2)$

31. $A^2 B^2/R\Delta t$ **33.** (a) 48.1 mV; (b) 2.67 mA; (c) 0.128 mW
35. $v_t = mgR/B^2 L^2$ **37.** 268 W   **39.** (a) 240 μV; (b) 0.600

mA; (c) 0.144 μW; (d) 2.88 × 10^{-8} N; (e) same as (c)
41. 1, −1.07 mV; 2, −2.40 mV; 3, 1.33 mV   **43.** at a:
4.4 × 10^7 m/s², to the right; at b: 0; at c: 4.4 × 10^7 m/s², to the
left   **45.** 0.10 μWb   **47.** (a) 800; (b) 2.5 × 10^{-4} H/m
49. (a) $\mu_0 i/W$; (b) $\pi\mu_0 R^2/W$ **51.** (a) decreasing;
(b) 0.68 mH   **53.** (a) 0.10 H/m; (b) 1.3 V/m   **55.** (a) 16 kV;
(b) 3.1 kV; (c) 23 kV   **57.** (b) so that the changing magnetic
field of one does not induce current in the other;
(c) $1/L_{eq} = \sum\limits_{j=1}^{N} (1/L_j)$ **59.** 6.91   **61.** 1.54 s   **63.** (a) 8.45
ns; (b) 7.37 mA   **65.** $(42 + 20t)$ V   **67.** 12.0 A/s
69. (a) $i_1 = i_2 = 3.33$ A; (b) $i_1 = 4.55$ A, $i_2 = 2.73$ A;
(c) $i_1 = 0$, $i_2 = 1.82$ A; (d) $i_1 = i_2 = 0$ **71.** $\mathscr{E}L_1/R(L_1 + L_2)$
73. (a) $i(1 - e^{-Rt/L})$ **75.** $1.23\tau_L$ **77.** (a) 240 W;
(b) 150 W; (c) 390 W   **79.** (a) 97.9 H; (b) 0.196 mJ
81. (a) 10.5 mJ; (b) 14.1 mJ   **83.** (a) 34.2 J/m³; (b) 49.4
mJ   **85.** 1.5 × 10^8 V/m   **87.** $(\mu_0 l/2\pi)\ln(b/a)$ **89.** (a) 1.3
mT; (b) 0.63 J/m³   **91.** (a) 1.0 J/m³; (b) 4.8 × 10^{-15} J/m³
93. (a) 1.67 mH; (b) 6.00 mWb   **95.** 13 H   **99.** magnetic
field exists only within the cross section of solenoid 1

Chapter 32

CP **1.** d, b, c, a (zero)   **2.** (a) 2; (b) 1   **3.** (a) away;
(b) away; (c) less   **4.** (a) toward; (b) toward; (c) less
5. a, c, b, d (zero)   **6.** tie of $b, c,$ and d, then a
Q **1.** (a) a, c, f; (b) bar gh **3.** supplied   **5.** (a) all down;
(b) 1 up, 2 down, 3 zero   **7.** (a) 1 up, 2 up, 3 down;
(b) 1 down, 2 up, 3 zero   **9.** (a) rightward; (b) leftward
11. (a) decreasing; (b) decreasing   **13.** (a) tie of a and b, then
c, d; (b) none (plate lacks circular symmetry, so **B** is not
tangent to a circular loop); (c) none   **15.** 1/4   **EP** **1.** (b)
sign is minus; (c) no, compensating positive flux through open
end near magnet   **3.** 47 μWb, inward   **5.** 55 μT   **7.** (a)
600 MA; (b) yes; (c) no   **9.** (a) 31.0 μT, 0°; (b) 55.9 μT,
73.9°; (c) 62.0 μT, 90°   **11.** 4.6 × 10^{-24} J   **13.** (a) 5.3 ×
10^{11} V/m; (b) 20 mT; (c) 660   **15.** (a) 7; (b) 7; (c) $3h/2\pi$, 0;
(d) $3eh/4\pi m$, 0; (e) $3.5h/2\pi$; (f) 8   **17.** (b) in the direction
of the angular momentum vector   **19.** $\Delta\mu = e^2 r^2 B/4m$
21. 20.8 mJ/T   **23.** yes   **25.** (a) 4 K; (b) 1 K
29. (a) 3.0 μT; (b) 5.6 × 10^{-10} eV   **31.** (a) 8.9 A·m²;
(b) 13 N·m   **35.** (a) 0.14 A; (b) 79 μC   **37.** 2.4 ×
10^{13} V/m·s   **39.** 1.9 pT   **41.** 7.5 × 10^5 V/s
43. 7.2 × 10^{12} V/m·s   **45.** (a) 2.1 × 10^{-8} A, downward;
(b) clockwise   **47.** (a) 0.63 μT; (b) 2.3 × 10^{12} V/m·s
49. (a) 2.0 A; (b) 2.3 × 10^{11} V/m·s; (c) 0.50 A;
(d) 0.63 μT·m   **51.** (a) 7.60 μA; (b) 859 kV·m/s;
(c) 3.39 mm; (d) 5.16 pT

Chapter 33

CP **1.** (a) $T/2$, (b) T, (c) $T/2$, (d) $T/4$ **2.** (a) 5 V;
(b) 150 μJ   **3.** (a) 1; (b) 2   **4.** (a) C, B, A; (b) 1, A;
2, B; 3, S; 4, C; (c) A **5.** (a) increases; (b) decreases
6. (a) 1, lags; 2, leads; 3, in phase; (b) 3 ($\omega_d = \omega$ when
$X_L = X_C$)   **7.** (a) increase (circuit is mainly capacitive;
increase C to decrease X_C to be closer to resonance for

maximum P_{av}); (b) closer   **8.** step-up   **Q** **1.** (a) $T/4$,
(b) $T/4$, (c) $T/2$ (see Fig. 33-2), (d) $T/2$ (see Eq. 31-40)
3. b, a, c **5.** (a) 3, 1, 2; (b) 2, tie of 1 and 3
7. slower   **9.** (a) 1 and 4; (b) 2 and 3   **11.** (a) 3,
then 1 and 2 tie; (b) 2, 1, 3   **13.** (a) negative; (b) lead
15. (a)–(c) rightward, increase   **EP** **1.** 9.14 nF
3. 45.2 mA   **5.** (a) 6.00 μs; (b) 167 kHz; (c) 3.00 μs
7. (a) 89 rad/s; (b) 70 ms; (c) 25 μF   **9.** 38 μH
11. 7.0 × 10^{-4} s   **15.** (a) 3.0 nC; (b) 1.7 mA; (c) 4.5 nJ
17. (a) 3.60 mH; (b) 1.33 kHz; (c) 0.188 ms   **19.** 600, 710,
1100, 1300 Hz   **21.** (a) $Q/\sqrt{3}$; (b) 0.152   **25.** (a) 1.98 μJ;
(b) 5.56 μC; (c) 12.6 mA; (d) −46.9°; (e) +46.9°   **27.** (a) 0;
(b) $2i(t)$ **29.** (a) 356 μs; (b) 2.50 mH; (c) 3.20 mJ
31. 8.66 mΩ **33.** $(L/R)\ln 2$ **35.** (a) $\pi/2$ rad; (b) $q =$
$(I/\omega)\, e^{-Rt/2L} \sin \omega' t$ **39.** (a) 0.0955 A; (b) 0.0119 A
41. (a) 4.60 kHz; (b) 26.6 nF; (c) $X_L = 2.60$ kΩ, $X_C =$
0.650 kΩ **43.** (a) 0.65 kHz; (b) 24 Ω **45.** (a) 39.1 mA;
(b) 0; (c) 33.9 mA   **47.** (a) 6.73 ms; (b) 2.24 ms;
(c) capacitor; (d) 59.0 μF   **49.** (a) $X_C = 0$, $X_L = 86.7$ Ω,
$Z = 182$ Ω, $I = 198$ mA, $\phi = 28.5°$ **51.** (a) $X_C = 37.9$ Ω,
$X_L = 86.7$ Ω, $Z = 167$ Ω, $I = 216$ mA, $\phi = 17.1°$
53. (a) 2.35 mH; (b) they move away from 1.40 kHz
55. 1000V   **57.** (a) 36.0 V; (b) 27.3 V; (c) 17.0 V;
(d) −8.34 V   **59.** (a) 224 rad/s; (b) 6.00 A; (c) 228 rad/s,
219 rad/s; (d) 0.040   **61.** (a) 707 Ω; (b) 32.2 mH;
(c) 21.9 nF   **63.** (a) resonance at $f = 1/2\pi\sqrt{LC} = 85.7$ Hz;
(b) 15.6 μF; (c) 225 mA   **65.** (a) 796 Hz; (b) no change;
(c) decreased; (d) increased   **69.** 141 V   **71.** (a) taking;
(b) supplying   **73.** 0, 9.00 W, 3.14 W, 1.82 W
75. 177 Ω, no   **77.** 7.61 A   **83.** (a) 117 μF; (b) 0;
(c) 90.0 W, 0; (d) 0°, 90°; (e) 1, 0   **85.** (a) 2.59 A;
(b) 38.8 V, 159 V, 224 V, 64.2 V, 75.0 V; (c) 100 W for R,
0 for L and C.   **87.** (a) 2.4 V; (b) 3.2 mA, 0.16 A
89. (a) 1.9 V, 5.9 W; (b) 19 V, 590 W; (c) 0.19 kV, 59 kW
91. (a) $X_C = [(2\pi)(45 \times 10^{-6}$ F$)f]^{-1}$; (c) 17.7 Hz
93. (a) $X_L = (2\pi)(40 \times 10^{-3}$ H$)f$; (c) 796 Hz
95. (b) 61 Hz; (c) 90 Ω and 61 Hz

Chapter 34

CP **1.** (a) (Use Fig. 34-5.) On right side of rectangle, **E** is in
negative y direction; on left side, **E** + d**E** is greater and in
same direction; (b) **E** is downward. On right side, **B** is in
negative z direction; on left side, **B** + d**B** is greater and in
same direction.   **2.** positive direction of x **3.** (a) same;
(b) decrease   **4.** a, d, b, c (zero)   **5.** a **6.** (a) yes; (b) no
Q **1.** (a) positive direction of z; (b) x **3.** (a) same;
(b) increase; (c) decrease   **5.** both 20° clockwise from the y
axis   **7.** two   **9.** b, 30°; c, 60°; d, 60°; e, 30°; f, 60°
11. d, b, a, c **13.** (a) b; (b) blue; (c) c **15.** 1.5
EP **1.** (a) 4.7 × 10^{-3} Hz; (b) 3 min 32 s   **3.** (a) 4.5 × 10^{24}
Hz; (b) 1.0 × 10^4 km or 1.6 Earth radii   **7.** it would steadily
increase; (b) the summed discrepancies between the apparent
time of eclipse and those observed from x; the radius of Earth's
orbit   **9.** 5.0 × 10^{-21} H   **11.** 1.07 pT   **17.** 4.8 × 10^{-29}
W/m²   **19.** 4.51 × 10^{-10} **21.** 89 cm   **23.** 1.2 MW/m²
25. 820 m   **27.** (a) 1.03 kV/m; 3.43 μT   **29.** (a) 1.4 ×

10^{-22} W; (b) 1.1×10^{15} W   **31.** (a) 87 mV/m; (b) 0.30 nT; (c) 13 kW   **33.** 3.3×10^{-8} Pa   **35.** (a) 4.7×10^{-6} Pa; (b) 2.1×10^{10} times smaller   **37.** 5.9×10^{-8} Pa   **39.** (a) 3.97 GW/m^2; (b) 13.2 Pa; (c) 1.67×10^{-11} N; (d) 3.14×10^3 m/s^2 **41.** $I(2 - frac)/c$ **43.** $p_{r\perp} \cos^2 \theta$ **45.** 1.9 mm/s   **47.** (b) 580 nm   **49.** (a) 1.9 V/m; (b) 1.7×10^{-11} Pa   **51.** 1/8   **53.** 3.1%   **55.** 20° or 70°   **57.** 19 W/m^2 **59.** (a) 2 sheets; (b) 5 sheets   **61.** 180°   **63.** 1.26   **65.** 1.07 m   **69.** (a) 0; (b) 20°; (c) still 0 and 20°   **73.** 1.41   **75.** 1.22   **77.** 182 cm   **79.** (a) no; (b) yes; (c) about 43°   **81.** (a) 35.6°; (b) 53.1°   **83.** (b) 23.2°   **85.** (a) 53°; (b) yes   **87.** 55.5°; 55.8°

Chapter 35

CP Kaleidoscope answer: two mirrors that form a V with an angle of 60°   **1.** $0.2d$, $1.8d$, $2.2d$ **2.** (a) real; (b) inverted; (c) same   **3.** (a) e; (b) virtual, same   **4.** virtual, same as object, diverging   **Q 1.** c **3.** (a) a; (b) c **5.** (a) no; (b) yes (fourth is off mirror ed)   **7.** (a) from infinity to the focal point; (b) decrease continually   **9.** d (infinite), tie of a and b, then c **11.** mirror, equal; lens, greater   **13.** (a) all but variation 2; (b) for 1, 3, and 4: right, inverted; for 5 and 6: left, same   **15.** (a) less; (b) less   **EP 1.** (a) virtual; (b) same; (c) same; (d) $D + L$ **3.** 40 cm   **7.** (a) 7; (b) 5; (c) 1 to 3; (d) depends on the position of O and your perspective   **11.** new illumination is 10/9 of the old   **15.** 10.5 cm   **19.** (a) 2.00; (b) none   **23.** 1.14   **25.** (b) separate the lenses by a distance $f_2 - |f_1|$, where f_2 is the focal length of the converging lens   **27.** 45 mm, 90 mm   **29.** (a) +40 cm; (b) at infinity   **33.** (a) 40 cm, real; (b) 80 cm, real; (c) 240 cm, real; (d) −40 cm, virtual; (e) −80 cm, virtual; (f) −240 cm, virtual   **35.** same orientation, virtual, 30 cm to left of second lens, $m = 1$ **37.** (a) final image coincides in location with the object; it is real, inverted, and $m = -1.0$ **39.** (a) coincides in location with the original object and is enlarged 5.0 times; (c) virtual; (d) yes   **45.** $i = \dfrac{(2 - n)r}{2(n - 1)}$, to the right of the right side of the sphere   **47.** 2.1 mm   **49.** (b) when image is at near point   **51.** (b) farsighted   **53.** −125

Chapter 36

CP 1. b (least n), c, a **2.** (a) top; (b) bright intermediate illumination (phase difference is 2.1 wavelengths)   **3.** (a) 3λ, 3; (b) 2.5λ, 2.5   **4.** a and d tie (amplitude of resultant wave is $4E_0$), then b and c tie (amplitude of resultant wave is $2E_0$)   **5.** (a) 1 and 4; (b) 1 and 4   **Q 1.** a, c, b **3.** (a) 300 nm; (b) exactly out of phase   **5.** c **7.** (a) increase; (b) 1λ **9.** down   **11.** (a) maximum; (b) minimum; (c) alternates   **13.** d **15.** (a) 0.5 wavelength; (b) 1 wavelength   **17.** bright   **19.** all   **EP 1.** (a) 5.09×10^{14} Hz; (b) 388 nm; (c) 1.97×10^8 m/s   **5.** 2.1×10^8 m/s   **7.** the time is longer for the pipeline containing air, by about 1.55 ns   **9.** 22°, refraction reduces θ **11.** (a) pulse 2; (b) $0.03L/c$ **13.** (a) 1.70 (or 0.70); (b) 1.70 (or 0.70); (c) 1.30

(or 0.30); (d) brightness is identical, close to fully destructive interference   **15.** (a) 0.833; (b) intermediate, closer to fully constructive interference   **17.** $(2m + 1)\pi$ **19.** 2.25 mm   **21.** 648 nm   **23.** 1.6 mm   **25.** 16   **27.** 0.072 mm   **29.** 8.75λ **31.** 0.03%   **33.** 6.64 μm   **35.** $y = 17 \sin(\omega t + 13°)$ **39.** (a) 1.17 m, 3.00 m, 7.50 m; (b) no   **41.** $I = \frac{1}{9}I_m[1 + 8 \cos^2(\pi d \sin \theta/\lambda)]$, $I_m =$ intensity of central maximum   **43.** $L = (m + \frac{1}{2})\lambda/2$, for $m = 0, 1, 2, \ldots$ **45.** 0.117 μm, 0.352 μm   **47.** $\lambda/5$ **49.** 70.0 nm   **51.** none   **53.** (a) 552 nm; (b) 442 nm   **55.** 338 nm   **59.** $2n_2L \cos \theta_r = (m + \frac{1}{2})\lambda$, for $m = 0, 1, 2, \ldots$, where $\theta_r = \sin^{-1}[(\sin \theta_i)/n_2]$ **61.** intensity is diminished by 88% at 450 nm and by 94% at 650 nm   **63.** (a) dark; (b) blue end   **65.** 1.89 μm   **67.** 1.00025   **69.** (a) 34; (b) 46   **73.** 588 nm   **75.** 1.00030   **77.** $I = I_m \cos^2(2\pi x/\lambda)$

Chapter 37

CP 1. (a) expand; (b) expand   **2.** (a) second side maximum; (b) 2.5   **3.** (a) red; (b) violet   **4.** diminish   **5.** (a) increase; (b) same   **6.** (a) left; (b) less   **Q 1.** (a) contract; (b) contract   **3.** with megaphone (larger opening, less diffraction)   **5.** four   **7.** (a) larger; (b) red   **9.** (a) decrease; (b) same; (c) in place   **11.** (a) A; (b) left; (c) left; (d) right   **EP 1.** 690 nm   **3.** 60.4 μm   **5.** (a) 2.5 mm; (b) 2.2×10^{-4} rad   **7.** (a) 70 cm; (b) 1.0 mm   **9.** 41.2 m from the central axis   **11.** 160°   **15.** (d) 53°, 10°, 5.1°   **19.** (a) 1.3×10^{-4} rad; (b) 10 km   **21.** 50 m   **23.** 30.5 μm   **25.** 1600 km   **27.** (a) 17.1 m; (b) 1.37×10^{-10} **29.** 27 cm   **31.** 4.7 cm   **33.** (a) 0.347°; (b) 0.97°   **35.** (a) red; (b) 130 μm   **37.** five   **41.** $\lambda D/d$ **43.** (a) 5.05 μm; (b) 20.2 μm   **45.** (a) 3.33 μm; (b) 0, $\pm 10.2°$, $\pm 20.7°$, $\pm 32.0°$, $\pm 45.0°$, $\pm 62.2°$ **47.** all wavelengths shorter than 635 nm   **49.** 13,600   **51.** 500 nm   **53.** (a) three; (b) 0.051°   **55.** 523 nm   **61.** 470 nm to 560 nm   **63.** 491   **65.** 3650   **67.** (a) 1.0×10^4 nm; (b) 3.3 mm   **69.** (a) 0.032°/nm, 0.076°/nm, 0.24°/nm; (b) 40,000, 80,000, 120,000   **71.** (a) $\tan \theta$; (b) 0.89   **73.** 0.26 nm   **75.** 6.8°   **77.** (a) 170 pm; (b) 130 pm   **81.** 0.570 nm   **83.** 30.6°, 15.3° (clockwise); 3.08°, 37.8° (counterclockwise)

Chapter 38

CP 1. (a) same (speed of light postulate); (b) no (the start and end of the flight are spatially separated); (c) no (again, because of the spatial separation)   **2.** (a) Sally's; (b) Sally's   **3.** a, negative; b, positive; c, negative   **4.** (a) right; (b) more   **5.** (a) equal; (b) less   **Q 1.** all tie (pulse speed is c)   **3.** (a) C_1; (b) C_1 **5.** (a) 3, 2, 1; (b) 1 and 3 tie, then 2   **7.** (a) negative; (b) positive   **9.** c, then b and d tie, then a **11.** (a) 3, tie of 1 and 2, then 4; (b) 4, tie of 1 and 2, then 3; (c) 1, 4, 2, 3   **13.** greater than f_1 **EP 1.** (a) 3×10^{-18}; (b) 8.2×10^{-8}; (c) 1.1×10^{-6}; (d) 3.7×10^{-5}; (e) 0.10   **3.** $0.75c$ **5.** $0.99c$ **7.** 55 m   **9.** 1.32 m   **11.** 0.63 m   **13.** 6.4 cm   **15.** (a) 26 y; (b) 52 y; (c) 3.7 y   **17.** (b) 0.999 999 15c **19.** (a) $x' = 0$, $t' = 2.29$ s; (b) $x' =$

6.55×10^8 m, $t' = 3.16$ s **21.** (a) 25.8 μs; (b) small flash
23. (a) 1.25; (b) 0.800 μs **25.** 2.40 μs **27.** (a) 0.84c, in
the direction of increasing x; (b) 0.21c, in the direction of
increasing x; the classical predictions are 1.1c and 0.15c
29. (a) 0.35c; (b) 0.62c **31.** 1.2 μs **33.** seven
35. 22.9 MHz **37.** +2.97 nm **39.** (a) $\tau_0/\sqrt{1 - v^2/c^2}$
41. (a) 0.134c; (b) 4.65 keV; (c) 1.1% **43.** (a) 0.9988, 20.6;
(b) 0.145, 1.01; (c) 0.073, 1.0027 **45.** (a) 5.71 GeV,
6.65 GeV, 6.58 GeV/c; (b) 3.11 MeV, 3.62 MeV,
3.59 MeV/c **47.** 18 smu/y **49.** (a) 0.943c; (b) 0.866c
51. (a) 256 kV; (b) 0.746c **53.** $\sqrt{8}mc$ **55.** 6.65×10^6 mi,
or 270 earth circumferences **57.** 110 km **59.** (a) 2.7 $\times$
10^{14} J; (b) 1.8×10^7 kg; (c) 6.0×10^6 **61.** 4.00 u, probably
a helium nucleus **63.** 330 mT
65.

SIGNAL	TIME SENT (h)	TIME REPLY RECEIVED (h)	TIME REPORTED	DISTANCE (m)
1	6.0	400	11.8	2.10×10^{14}
2	12.0	800	23.6	4.19×10^{14}
3	18.0	1200	35.5	6.29×10^{14}
4	24.0	1600	47.3	8.38×10^{14}
5	30.0	2000	59.1	1.05×10^{15}

67. (a) $vt \sin \theta$; (b) $t[1 - (v/c) \cos \theta]$; (c) 3.24c

Chapter 39

CP **1.** b, a, d, c **2.** (a) lithium, sodium, potassium, cesium;
(b) all tie **3.** (a) same; (b)–(d) x rays **4.** (a) proton;
(b) same; (c) proton **5.** same Q **1.** (a) microwave;
(b) x ray; (c) x ray **3.** potassium **5.** Positive charge builds
up on the plate, inhibiting further electron emission.
7. none **9.** (a) greater; (b) less **11.** no essential change
13. (a) decreases by a factor of $1/\sqrt{2}$ (b) decreases by a factor
of 1/2 **15.** extremely small **17.** (a) decreasing;
(b) increasing; (c) same; (d) same **19.** a **21.** (a) zero;
(b) yes EP **3.** 4.14 eV·fs **5.** 5.9 μeV **7.** 1.0×10^{45}
photons/s **9.** 2.047 eV **11.** (a) infrared bulb; (b) 1.4 $\times$
10^{21} photons/s **13.** 4.7×10^{26} photons **15.** (a) 2.96 $\times$
10^{20} photons/s; (b) 48,600 km; (c) 5.89×10^{18} photons/m²·s
17. barium and lithium **19.** 10 eV **21.** 676 km/s
23. (a) 1.3 V; (b) 680 km/s **25.** 233 nm **27.** (a) 6.60 $\times$
10^{-34} J·s; (b) 2.27 eV; (c) 545 nm **29.** 9.68×10^{-20} A
31. (a) 8.57×10^{18} Hz; (b) 35.4 keV; (c) 1.89×10^{-23}
kg·m/s = 35.4 keV/c **33.** (a) 2.7 pm; (b) 6.05 pm
37. (a) 2.43 pm; (b) 1.32 fm; (c) 0.511 MeV; (d) 938 MeV
39. 300% **43.** (a) 41.8 keV; (b) 8.2 keV **45.** 44°
47. 1.12 keV **49.** (a) 1.7×10^{-35} m; (b) de Broglie
wavelength too small **51.** 245 pm **53.** 4.3 μeV
55. (a) 38.8 meV; (b) 146 pm **57.** (a) 73 pm, 3.4 nm;
(b) yes, their average de Broglie wavelength is much smaller
than their average separation **59.** (a) 1.24 keV, 1.50 eV;
(b) 1.24 GeV, 1.24 GeV **61.** 0.062 fm, about 80 times
smaller than a nuclear radius **63.** neutron **65.** 9.70 kV
(relativistic calculation), 9.79 kV (classical calculation)

73. (d) $x = n(\lambda/2)$, where $n = 0, 1, 2, \ldots$ **75.** 2.1 $\times$
10^{-24} kg·m/s **79.** (a) proton: 9.2×10^{-6}; deuteron, 7.6 $\times$
10^{-8}; (b) 3.0 MeV for each; (c) 3.0 MeV for each
81. (a) 10^{104} years (don't hold your breath); (b) 2×10^{-19} s
(the smaller mass of the electron makes an enormous
difference) **83.** $T = 10^{-x}$, where $x = 3.1 \times 10^{39}$, a *very*
small number

Chapter 40

CP **1.** b, a, c **2.** (a) all tie; (b) a, b, c **3.** a, b, c, d
4. (a) $n = 1$; (b) $n = 3$, $n = 2$, $n = 1$ **5.** (a) 5; (b) 7
Q **1.** (a) 1/4; (b) same factor **3.** c
5. (a) $(\sqrt{1/L})\sin(\pi/2L)x$; (b) $(\sqrt{4/L})\sin(2\pi/L)x$;
(c) $(\sqrt{2/L})\sin(\pi/L)x$ **7.** less **9.** (a) wider; (b) deeper
11. $n = 1$, $n = 2$, $n = 3$ **13.** (a) greater; (b) less; (c) less
15. same **17.** (a) $n = 3$; (b) $n = 1$; (c) $n = 5$
EP **1.** multiply it by $\sqrt{2}$ **3.** 850 pm **5.** 0.65 eV
7. meter^{-1} **13.** (a) 5.0%; (b) 10%; (c) 0.95%
15. (a) 19.6%; (b) 60.8%; (c) 19.6% **17.** 13.3 eV
19. (b) $k = (2\pi/h)[2m(E_{pot} - E)]^{1/2}$ **21.** (b) $k = (2\pi/h)(2mE)^{1/2}$ **23.** 2.6 eV **25.** (a) 658 nm;
(b) 366 nm **27.** (a) 12 eV; (b) 6.5×10^{-27} kg·m/s;
(c) 103 nm **31.** (a) 0; (b) 10.2 nm^{-1}; (c) 5.54 nm^{-1}
33. (a) 13.6 eV; (b) 3.40 eV **35.** (a) 13.6 eV;
(b) -27.2 eV **37.** (a) $n = 4$ to $n = 2$; (b) Balmer series
39. (a) 2.6 eV; (b) $n = 4$ to $n = 2$ **41.** $n = 3$ to $n = 1$
43. 43.9% **47.** $n \approx 4348$ **51.** (a) $P_{210} = (r^4/8a^5)e^{-r/a}\cos^2 \theta$; $P_{21+1} = P_{21-1} = 1(r^4/16a^5)e^{-r/a}\sin^2 \theta$

Chapter 41

CP **1.** 7 **2.** (a) decrease; (b)-(c) same **3.** less
4. A, C, B Q **1.** 0, 2, and 3 **3.** $6p$ **5.** (a) 2, 8;
(b) 5, 50 **7.** (a) n; (b) n and l **9.** a, c, e, f
11. (a) unchanged; (b) decrease; (c) decrease **13.** a and b
EP **3.** (a) 32; (b) 2; (c) 18; (d) 8 **5.** (a) 3; (b) 3 **7.** $n = 4$,
$l = 3$, $m_l = -2, -1, 0, 1, 2$ **9.** $l = 4$; $n \geq 5$; $m_s = \pm 1/2$
11. (a) 3; (b) 9; (c) 2; (d) 18; (e) 3 **13.** (a) 3×10^{74};
(b) 6×10^{74}; (c) 6×10^{-38} rad **15.** 54.7° and 125°
17. (a) 58 meV; (b) 14 GHz; (c) 2.1 cm; short radio wave
region **19.** 5.35 cm **21.** 19 mT **25.** argon **27.** (a) 2,
0, 0, $\pm\frac{1}{2}$; (b) $n = 2$, $l = 1$, $m_l = 1, 0$, or -1, $m_s = \pm\frac{1}{2}$
33. (a) 5.7 keV; (b) 87 pm, 14 keV; 220 pm, 5.7 keV
37. (a) 35.4 pm, as for molybdenum; (b) 57 pm; (c) 50 pm
43. (a) 19.7 keV, 17.5 keV; (b) Zr or Nb (Zr better)
45. (a) $(Z - 1)^2/(Z' - 1)^2$; (b) 57.5; (c) 2070
47. (a) 6; (b) 3.2×10^6 years **49.** (a) 2.55 s; (b) 500 ps;
(c) $(4.5 \times 10^{-4})°$ or 1.6″ of arc **51.** 10,000 K
53. 4.4×10^{17} per second **55.** 2.0×10^{16} per second
57. 4.8 km **59.** 1.8 pm **61.** (a) 7.33 μm; (b) 7.07×10^5
W/m²; (c) 2.49×10^{10} W/m² **63.** (a) 4.3 μm; (b) 10 μm;
(c) infared

Chapter 42

CP **1.** (a) larger; (b) same **2.** Cleveland, metal; Troy, none;
Seattle, semiconductor **3.** a, b, and c **4.** b **5.** b
Q **1.** 4 **3.** b and c **5.** (a) anywhere in the lattice; (b) in

any silicon–silicon bond; (c) in a silicon ion core, at a lattice site **7.** b and d **9.** $+4e$ **11.** none **13.** (a) right to left; (b) back bias **15.** a, b, and c **EP 1.** 8.43×10^{28} m^{-3} **5.** (a) $+8.0 \times 10^{-11}$ $\Omega \cdot$m/K; (b) -210 $\Omega \cdot$m/K **9.** (a) 0; (b) 0.096 **13.** 0.91 **15.** (a) 90%; (b) 12%; (c) sodium **17.** (a) 2500 K; (b) 5300 K **19.** (a) 2.7×10^{25} m^{-3}; (b) 8.4×10^{28} m^{-3}; (c) 3100; (d) molecules: 3.3 nm; electrons: 0.23 nm **21.** (a) 1.0, 0.99, 0.50, 0.014, 2.5×10^{-17}; (b) 700 K **25.** (a) 5.9×10^{28} m^{-3}; (b) 5.5 eV; (c) 1390 km/s; (d) 0.52 nm **27.** (b) 1.80×10^{28} m^{-3}eV^{-1} **31.** (a) 19.7 kJ; (b) 197 s **33.** 200°C **35.** (a) 109.5°; (b) 235 pm **37.** (a) 225 nm; (b) ultraviolet **41.** 0.22 μg **43.** (a) 0.744 eV above; (b) 7.13×10^{-7} **45.** (b) 2.5×10^8 **47.** opaque **49.** (a) 5.0×10^{-17} F; (b) about $300e$

Chapter 43

CP 1. ^{90}As and ^{158}Nd **2.** a little more than 75 Bq (elapsed time is a little less than three half-lives) **3.** ^{206}Pb **Q 1.** less **3.** ^{240}U **5.** less **7.** (a) on the $N = Z$ line; (b) positrons; (c) about 120 **9.** no **11.** yes **13.** (a) increase; (b) same **15.** 7 h **17.** d **EP 1.** 15.8 fm **3.** (a) 0.390 MeV; (b) 4.61 MeV **5.** (a) six; (b) eight **9.** (a) 1150 MeV; (b) 4.81 MeV/nucleon, 12.2 MeV/proton **15.** 4×10^{-22} s **17.** $K \approx 30$ MeV **21.** (a) 19.8 MeV, 6.26 MeV, 2.22 MeV; (b) 28.3 MeV; (c) 7.07 MeV **23.** 1.6×10^{25} MeV **25.** 7.92 MeV **27.** 280 d **29.** (a) 7.6×10^{16} s^{-1}; (b) 4.9×10^{16} s^{-1} **31.** (a) 4.8×10^{-18} s^{-1}; (b) 4.6×10^9 y **33.** 5.3×10^{22} **35.** 265 mg **37.** 209 d **39.** 87.8 mg **41.** 730 cm^2 **45.** (a) 3.66×10^7 s^{-1}; (b) $t \geqslant 3.82$ d; (c) 3.66×10^7 s^{-1}; (d) 6.42 ng **47.** Pu: 1.2×10^{-17}, Cm: $e^{-9173} \approx 0$ **49.** (a) 4.25 MeV; (b) -24.1 MeV; (c) 28.3 MeV **51.** $Q_3 = -9.50$ MeV, $Q_4 = 4.66$ MeV, $Q_5 = -1.30$ MeV **53.** 1.21 MeV **55.** 0.782 MeV **59.** (b) 0.961 MeV **61.** 78.4 eV **63.** 1600 y **65.** 1.8 mg **67.** 1.02 mg **69.** (a) 18 mJ; (b) 2.9 mSv = 0.29 rem **71.** (a) 6.3×10^{18}; (b) 2.5×10^{11}; (c) 0.20 J; (d) 2.3 mGy; (e) 30 mSv **73.** 3.87×10^{10} K **75.** (a) 25.4 MeV; (b) 12.8 MeV; (c) 25.0 MeV

77. (a) 3.85 MeV, 7.95 MeV; (b) 3.98 MeV, 7.33 MeV **79.** (a) 5.8 MeV; (b) 11 MeV

Chapter 44

CP 1. c and d **2.** (a) no; (b) yes; (c) no **3.** e **Q 1.** a **3.** b **5.** (a) ^{93}Sr; (b) ^{140}I; (c) ^{155}Nd **7.** c **9.** a **11.** c **EP 1.** (a) 2.6×10^{24}; (b) 8.2×10^{13} J; (c) 2.6×10^4 y **3.** 3.1×10^{10} s^{-1} **7.** $+5.00$ MeV **9.** (a) 16 fissions/d; (b) 4.3×10^8 **11.** (a) 10; (b) 226 MeV **13.** (a) 252 MeV; (b) typical fission energy is 200 MeV **15.** 461 kg **17.** yes **19.** (a) 1.2 MeV; (b) 3.2 kg **21.** (a) 44 kton **25.** 1.6×10^{16} **27.** (b) 1.0, 0.89, 0.28, 0.019; (c) 8 **29.** (a) 75 kW; (b) 5800 kg **33.** (a) 30 MeV; (b) 6 MeV **35.** (a) 170 kV **37.** 1.41 MeV **41.** (a) 3.1×10^{31} protons/m^3; (b) 1.2×10^6 times **43.** (a) 4.0×10^{27} MeV; (b) 5.1×10^{26} MeV **45.** (a) 1.83×10^{38} s^{-1}; (b) 8.25×10^{28} s^{-1} **49.** (a) 6.3×10^{14} J/kg; (b) 6.2×10^{11} kg/s; (c) 4.3×10^9 kg/s; (d) 15×10^9 y **51.** (a) 24.9 MeV; (b) 8.65 megatons TNT **53.** $K_\alpha = 3.52$ MeV, $K_n = 14.1$ MeV

Chapter 45

CP 1. (a) the muon family; (b) a particle; (c) $L_\mu = +1$ **2.** b and e **3.** c **Q 1.** d **3.** the π^+ pion whose track curves downward at the left **5.** a, b, c, d **7.** c, f **9.** 1d, 2e, 3a, 4b, 5c **11.** 1b, 2c, 3d, 4e, 5a **13.** (a) 0; (b) $+1$; (c) -1; (d) $+1$; (e) -1 **EP 1.** 6.03×10^{-29} kg **3.** 2.4×10^{-43} **5.** 1.08×10^{42} J **7.** 2.7 cm/s **9.** (a) 1.90×10^{-18} kg$\cdot$m/s; (b) 9.90 m **13.** (a) L_μ, L_e, angular momentum; (b) charge; (c) energy, L_μ **15.** $Q = 0$, $B = -1$, $S = 0$ **17.** (a) energy; (b) strangeness; (c) charge **19.** 338 MeV **23.** (a) $\mathrm{u\bar{u}d}$; (b) $\mathrm{\bar{u}dd}$ **25.** (a) sud; (b) uss **29.** Σ^0, 7530 km/s **31.** 669 nm **33.** (b) 0.934; (c) 1.15×10^{10} ly **35.** (a) 256 μeV; (b) 4.84 mm **37.** (a) 122 m/s; (b) 246 y **39.** (a) 2.6 K; (b) 29 nm **41.** (a) $0.785c$; (b) $0.993c$; (c) C2; (d) C1; (e) 51 ns; (f) 40 ns **43.** (a) 4.7×10^4; (b) 4.3 mm; (c) 24 nm

Index

Page references followed by lowercase roman t indicate material in tables. References followed by lowercase italic *n* indicate material in footnotes.